DIFFERENTIAL AND
INTEGRAL CALCULUS

DIFFERENTIAL AND INTEGRAL CALCULUS

BY

EDMUND LANDAU

PROFESSOR OF MATHEMATICS

GÖTTINGEN UNIVERSITY

TRANSLATED FROM THE GERMAN BY

MELVIN HAUSNER

AND

MARTIN DAVIS

CHELSEA PUBLISHING COMPANY

NEW YORK

Second Edition, 1960

Printed in the United States of America

TO MY BELOVED MOTHER
JOHANNA LANDAU,
née JACOBY

TRANSLATORS PREFACE

We wish to thank Mr. F. Steinhardt for his generous help in the preparation of this translation of Edmund Landau's *Einführung in die Differentialrechnung und Integralrechnung.*

PREFACE TO THE FIRST (GERMAN) EDITION

Over a period of 32 years I have lectured on analysis, among other subjects, at various universities; in 1930 I published a book *Grundlagen der Analysis* [English translation, *Foundations of Analysis,* Chelsea Publishing Company, New York] which received tolerant and even some friendly reviews, and in which I gave a complete development—along classical lines—of the arithmetical laws for whole, rational, irrational, and complex numbers (i.e. of the foundation on which the differential and integral calculus must build and which is "familiar" to the student from his high school days) ;

and now I take the next step.

Having taught for such a length of time, I now feel ready at last to publish my lectures on the differential and integral calculus.

There are a great many books on this subject. A reader whose main interest lies in the applications of the calculus and who can do without a complete presentation of the concepts and theorems of the subject, should not make this book his choice. The reader who wishes to practice on a great number of examples should supplement this book with a collection of problems, although I do, as a rule, give an example for every suitable theorem unless the theorem occurs again in a specialized form among subsequent applications.

I have not included any geometric applications in this text. The reason therefor is not that I am not a geometer; I am familiar, to be sure, with the geometry involved. But the exposition of the axioms and of the elements of geometry— I know them well and like to give courses on them—requires a separate volume which would have to precede the present one. In my lecture courses on the calculus, the geometric applications do, of course, make up a considerable portion of the material that is covered. But I do not wish to wait any longer to make generally available an account, rigorous and complete in every particular, of that which I have considered in my courses to be the most suitable method of treating the differential and integral calculus.

I need hardly mention that not a single one of all the theorems in this book is new, and that at most one half of one theorem is due to myself. My task, not an easy one, was merely that of selecting among the many known facts those which I prefer to communicate to the student at the beginning of his studies, of arranging the selected facts in a suitable sequence, and above all, of bringing out into the open the definitions and theorems which are often implicitly assumed and which serve as the mortar when the whole structure is being built up with all the right floors in the right places.

Some mathematicians may think it unorthodox to give as the second theorem after the definition of the derivative, Weierstrass' theorem on the existence of functions which are continuous everywhere but differentiable nowhere. To them I would say that while there are very good mathematicians who have never learned any proof of that theorem, it can do the beginner no harm to learn the simplest proof to date right from his textbook, and it may serve as a useful illustration which will enhance his understanding of the concept of derivative.

I do not follow any particular one of my courses on the calculus; I have, rather, taken apart the contents of the most recent of them and put them together again differently. I hope that, in the result, I have cut a suitable path for the beginner in traversing which he can learn, of the elements of the differential and integral calculus (including infinite series), everything he will need in the course of his further contacts with mathematics or with physics, and in his subsequent studies of the best literature on the more advanced parts of the integral calculus, on the applications of the differential and integral calculus, and on the rest of the field of analysis.

Groningen, February 9, 1934.

EDMUND LANDAU

TABLE OF CONTENTS

PART ONE

DIFFERENTIAL CALCULUS

PART TWO

INTEGRAL CALCULUS

5

INTRODUCTION

This book presupposes a familiarity only with the basic rules of arithmetic; in fact, except in Chap. 20, § 1 (which will be used only in Chap. 20, § 2, Chap. 23, and Chap. 24), only with the arithmetic of real numbers.

Thus, we shall use without further justification such theorems as

1) $$a(b + c) = ab + ac.$$

2) $$(ab)c = a(cb).$$

3) If
$$ab = 0$$
then
$$a = 0 \quad \text{or} \quad b = 0.$$

4) If
$$a > b, \quad b \geqq c$$
then
$$a > c.$$

5) $$\left| \sum_{\nu=1}^{n} x_\nu \right| \leqq \sum_{\nu=1}^{n} |x_\nu|.$$

(We use the familiar notation $|x|$, where x is real, to stand for the number x if $x \geqq 0$ and for the number $-x$ if $x < 0$.)

6) $$\left| \prod_{\nu=1}^{n} x_\nu \right| = \prod_{\nu=1}^{n} |x_\nu|.$$

7) In every set (*scilicet* non-empty; the expression *set of numbers* is always so intended) of positive integers, there exists a least.

This theorem is important for the reason that, in order to prove any assertion formulated for all integers $n \geqq 1$, it allows one to state: It suffices to prove the assertion for $n = 1$ and to show that if it holds for n then it holds for $n + 1$ ("proceeding from n to $n + 1$").

In fact, the assertion then holds generally; for otherwise, consider the least number m of the (non-empty) set which consists of those n for which the assertion does not hold. Then m is neither 1 (for the assertion holds for 1), nor > 1 (since, holding for $m - 1$, it would have to hold for m). Contradiction.

In exactly the same way, Theorem 7) yields the following: Let $k > 1$ be an integer; an assertion formulated for the integers n which satisfy $1 \leq n \leq k$ is true if it is true for $n = 1$, and if for each n such that $1 \leq n < k$ its truth for $n + 1$ follows from its truth for n.

Indeed, assume to the contrary that m is the smallest n satisfying $1 \leq n \leq k$ for which the assertion does not hold; then m is neither 1 (since the assertion holds for 1) nor > 1 (since, holding for $m - 1$, the assertion would have to hold for m). Contradiction.

We now give five examples employing these applications of Theorem 7), all of which will be used later. In all of these examples $n \geq 1$ is an integer, v is an integer, and l is an integer.

I) If

$$x_v < y_v \text{ for } 1 \leq v \leq n$$

then

$$\sum_{v=1}^{n} x_v < \sum_{v=1}^{n} y_v.$$

For, this is clear for $n = 1$; for $n = 2$ it is an elementary result (see F.o.A.). On the basis of these special cases the theorem for $n + 1$ follows from the theorem for n since

$$\sum_{v=1}^{n+1} x_v = \sum_{v=1}^{n} x_v + x_{n+1} < \sum_{v=1}^{n} y_v + y_{n+1} = \sum_{v=1}^{n+1} y_v.$$

II) Under the hypothesis of I) it follows, if in addition the $x_v \geq 0$, that

$$\prod_{v=1}^{n} x_v < \prod_{v=1}^{n} y_v.$$

For, this is clear for $n = 1$; for $n = 2$ it is an elementary result (see F.o.A.). $n + 1$ follows from n (the meaning of this abbreviated terminology, of which we will make frequent use, is clear) since

$$\prod_{v=1}^{n+1} x_v = \prod_{v=1}^{n} x_v \cdot x_{n+1} < \prod_{v=1}^{n} y_v \cdot y_{n+1} = \prod_{v=1}^{n+1} y_v.$$

III) In particular, if

$$0 \leq x < y$$

then

$$x^n < y^n.$$

For, in II) let all the $x_v = x$ and all the $y_v = y$.

It should be added that in the hypothesis, statement, and proof of I), II), and III), $<$ may be replaced by $\leq$. The converse of III) follows directly: If

$$x \geq 0, \ y \geq 0, \text{ and } x^n < y^n,$$

then

$$x < y.$$

IV) If x_ν is defined for $l \leq \nu \leq l + n - 1$, then there exists an integer μ such that

$$l \leq \mu \leq l + n - 1, \quad x_\nu \leq x_\mu \text{ for } l \leq \nu \leq l + n - 1.$$

x_μ is the so-called largest of the numbers x_ν; **notation:** $\underset{l \leq \nu \leq l+n-1}{\text{Max}} x_\nu$ or, e.g. $\text{Max}(a, b, c)$ if $l = 1$, $n = 3$, $x_1 = a$, $x_2 = b$, $x_3 = c$. Max is to be read *maximum*.

For, $n = 1$ is clear; $n = 2$ is an elementary result (see F.o.A.). To proceed from n to $n + 1$, choose an integer ϱ such that

$$l \leq \varrho \leq l + n - 1, \quad x_\nu \leq x_\varrho \text{ for } l \leq \nu \leq l + n - 1,$$

and choose $\mu = \varrho$ or $= l + n$ such that

$$x_\mu = \text{Max } (x_\varrho, x_{l+n}).$$

Then

$$l \leq \mu \leq l + n,$$

$$x_\nu \left\{ \begin{matrix} \leq x_\varrho \\ = x_{l+n} \end{matrix} \right\} \leq x_\mu \text{ for } \left\{ \begin{matrix} l \leq \nu \leq l + n - 1, \\ \nu = l + n. \end{matrix} \right.$$

V) Under the hypothesis of IV), there exists an integer μ such that

$$l \leq \mu \leq l + n - 1, \quad x_\nu \geq x_\mu \text{ for } l \leq \nu \leq l + n - 1.$$

x_μ is the so-called smallest of the numbers x_ν, **notation:** $\underset{l \leq \nu \leq l+n-1}{\text{Min}} x_\nu$ or, e.g. $\text{Min}(a, b, c)$. Min is to be read *minimum*.

For, let

$$\underset{l \leq \nu \leq l+n-1}{\text{Max}} (-x_\nu) = -x_\mu;$$

then x_μ is as required.

8) (The deepest and most important of the fundamental properties of the real numbers.) Let there be given any division of all the real numbers into two classes, having the following properties:

a) Neither class is empty.

b) Every number of the first class is smaller than every number of the second class. (In other words, if

$$a < b$$

and if a lies in the second class, then b lies in the second class.)

Then there exists a unique real number ξ such that every $\eta < \xi$ belongs to the first class and every $\eta > \xi$ belongs to the second class.

9) For each $x \geq 0$, there is exactly one $y \geq 0$ such that

$$y^2 = x.$$

This y is denoted by $\sqrt{x}$.

As an exercise in the use of Theorem 8), I reproduce the standard proof of 9) here, proving, in the process, the following more general theorem (of which the special case $n = 2$ is 9)):

For every $x \geq 0$ and every integer $n \geq 1$, there exists precisely one $y \geq 0$ for which

$$y^n = x.$$

However, in what follows I shall only use the special case $n = 2$, since the case of arbitrary integral $n \geq 1$ will automatically drop into our lap in Chap. 2.

Proof: 1) For

$$0 \leq y_1 < y_2$$

we have by III) that

$$y_1{}^n < y_2{}^n,$$

so that at most one of the numbers $y_1{}^n$ and $y_2{}^n$ can be $= x$. Hence, there exists at most one y having the desired property.

2) For $x = 0$, the requirement is fulfilled by $y = 0$. Hence, let $x > 0$, so that it remains to be shown that there exists a $y > 0$ (since $y = 0$ need not be considered) for which

$$y^n = x.$$

We place η in

Class I, if $\eta > 0$ and $\eta^n < x$, or if $\eta \leq 0$; and in
Class II, if $\eta > 0$ and $\eta^n \geq x$.

Then every real number η belongs to exactly one of these classes. The positive number

$$\eta = \tfrac{1}{2} \operatorname{Min} (1, x)$$

ies in class I, since

$$\eta < 1, \; \eta < x,$$
$$\eta^{n-1} \leq 1^{n-1} = 1,$$
$$\eta^n = \eta^{n-1} \cdot \eta \leq 1 \cdot \eta = \eta < x.$$

The positive number

$$\eta = \operatorname{Max} (1, x)$$

lies in class II, since

$$\eta^n = \eta^{n-1} \cdot \eta \geq 1 \cdot \eta = \eta \geq x.$$

If η is in class II, and $\zeta > \eta$, then

$$\zeta > \eta > 0,$$
$$\zeta^n > \eta^n \geq x,$$

so that ζ is in class II.

Therefore there exists a real number y such that every $\eta < y$ belongs to class I, and every $\eta > y$ belongs to class II. Since there is a positive number in class I, it follows that

$$y > 0.$$

We shall show of this y that it satisfies

$$y^n = x.$$

Let 0^0 always be understood as meaning 1, so that for all c,

$$c^0 = 1.$$

(For, this holds for all c different from 0 by definition, even in elementary mathematics.)

For all a, b, we have

$$(a - b) \sum_{\nu=0}^{n-1} a^\nu b^{n-1-\nu} = a \sum_{\nu=0}^{n-1} a^\nu b^{n-1-\nu} - b \sum_{\nu=0}^{n-1} a^\nu b^{n-1-\nu}$$

$$= \sum_{\nu=0}^{n-1} a^{\nu+1} b^{n-1-\nu} - \sum_{\nu=0}^{n-1} a^\nu b^{n-\nu} = \sum_{\nu=1}^{n} a^\nu b^{n-\nu} - \sum_{\nu=0}^{n-1} a^\nu b^{n-\nu} = a^n - b^n.$$

Hence, for all h (setting $a = 1 - h$, $b = 1$),

$$(1 - h)^n = 1 - h \sum_{\nu=0}^{n-1} (1 - h)^\nu,$$

so that for $0 < h < 1$,

$$(1 - h)^n \geqq 1 - h \sum_{\nu=0}^{n-1} 1 = 1 - nh,$$

so that if moreover $0 < h < \dfrac{1}{n}$ (hence $1 - nh > 0$),

$$\frac{1}{(1 - h)^n} \leqq \frac{1}{1 - nh},$$

$$\left(\frac{y}{1 - h}\right)^n = \frac{y^n}{(1 - h)^n} \leqq \frac{y^n}{1 - nh},$$

and furthermore

$$(y(1 - h))^n = y^n(1 - h)^n \geqq y^n(1 - nh).$$

Now, if we had

$$y^n < x,$$

then it would follow that, for

$$0 < h < \frac{1}{n}\left(1 - \frac{y^n}{x}\right)$$

$\Bigg($ since in that case

$$h < \frac{1}{n},$$

$$1 - nh > \frac{y^n}{x}\Bigg)$$

$$\left(\frac{y}{1 - h}\right)^n < \frac{y^n}{\dfrac{y^n}{x}} = x,$$

so that $\dfrac{y}{1-h}$ would be in class I, and yet $> y$.

If we had

$$y^n > x,$$

then it would follow that for

$$0 < h < \frac{1}{n}\left(1 - \frac{x}{y^n}\right)$$

$\Bigg($ since in that case

$$h < \frac{1}{n},$$

$$1 - nh > \frac{x}{y^n}\Bigg),$$

$$\big(y(1-h)\big)^n > y^n \frac{x}{y^n} = x,$$

so that $y(1-h)$ would be in class II, and yet $< y$.

Therefore,

$$y^n = x.$$

The remainder of this introduction is properly a part of the secondary school curriculum, and may be omitted by the reader who is familiar with the material involved. It was necessary that I include these matters (as well as the five illustrations in connection with 7)) since they will be employed in what follows and are not treated in my book *The Foundations of Analysis* [referred to in the sequel as "F.o.A."], in which not even the number 3 is defined.

The material involved concerns

§ 1. The subdivision of all of the integers into residue classes with respect to a "divisor" n.

§ 2. The representation of the positive integers in the decimal system — a good preparation for the development of real numbers into decimal fractions in Chap. 12. I do not wish to pretend that the reader knows this from his secondary school work. For, I could just as well have assumed as known the concepts of limit and of infinite series, whose treatment occupies the greater part of those portions of this book which do not concern the calculus proper.

§ 3. The difference between finite and infinite sets of numbers and the concept of the number of elements in a finite set.

§ 1. Residue Classes

Theorem 1: *To every real number x, there corresponds precisely one integer n for which*

$$n \leqq x < n + 1.$$

Proof: 1) There is at most one such n. For if n_1 and n_2 are two such, then

$$n_1 \leqq x < n_2 + 1, \quad n_2 \leqq x < n_1 + 1,$$

so that

$$n_1 \leqq n_2, \quad n_2 \leqq n_1,$$

and hence

$$n_1 = n_2.$$

2) There is an integer $g > x$; for if $x \leqq 0$, $g = 1$ is such an integer, while if $x > 0$, there is (a fact known to the reader) a rational number $y > x$ and an integer $g > y$.

If this is applied to $-x$ instead of to x, then we determine an integer $k > -x$, and thus an integer $l = -k < x$. The set of integers m (of necessity positive) for which $l + m > x$, is not empty (since it contains $m = g - l$). Therefore there is a least such m, and for this least m, $n = l + m - 1$ is as required.

Definition 1: *The n of Theorem 1 is called $[x]$.*

To be read: the greatest integer in x, or bracket x.

Theorem 2: $\qquad\qquad x - 1 < [x] \leqq x.$

Proof: By Theorem 1 and Definition 1,

$$[x] \leqq x < [x] + 1.$$

Theorem 3: *If a and n are integers, $n > 0$, then there exists precisely one pair of integers q, r for which*

$$a = qn + r, \qquad 0 \leqq r < n.$$

Proof: It is being asserted that there exists precisely one q for which

$$qn \leqq a < qn + n = (q + 1)n,$$

i.e. for which

$$q \leqq \frac{a}{n} < q + 1,$$

and by Theorem 1 and Definition 1, this relation is satisfied by precisely the number

$$q = \left[\frac{a}{n} \right].$$

Definition 2: $\qquad\qquad 2 = 1 + 1.$

If we choose some fixed integer $n > 0$, then the totality of all integers a is decomposed into "residue classes with respect to n," determined by the value of the r, with $0 \leqq r < n$, given by Theorem 3. None of these classes is empty. For,

$$r = 0.n + r.$$

In the case $n = 2$, there are two such classes, and they have special names.

Definition 3: *a is called even if*

$$a = 2q, q \text{ integral};$$

a is called odd if

$$a = 2q + 1, q \text{ integral.}$$

Examples: -2, 0, and 2 are even; -1 and 1 are odd.

§ 2. The Decimal System

Definition 4: $3 = 2 + 1, \quad 4 = 3 + 1, \quad 5 = 4 + 1,$
$6 = 5 + 1, \quad 7 = 6 + 1, \quad 8 = 7 + 1, \ 9 = 8 + 1, \ 10 = 9 + 1.$

Theorem 4: *Each of the inequalities*
$$0 \leq r < 10$$
and
$$0 \leq r \leq 9$$
holds for
$$r = 0, \ 1, \ 2, \ 3, \ 4, \ 5, \ 6, \ 7, \ 8, \ 9$$
and for no other integers r.

Proof: Obvious.

Theorem 5: 1) *Each integer $a > 0$ is of the form*
$$a = \sum_{\nu=0}^{n} x_\nu 10^\nu,$$
where
$$\text{the } x_\nu \text{ are integers,}$$
$$0 \leq x_\nu \leq 9,$$
$$x_n > 0.$$

2) *And indeed, n and the x_ν are uniquely determined.*

Proof: 1) $\quad 10^a > 10^a - 1 = (10 - 1) \sum_{\nu=0}^{a-1} 10^\nu > \sum_{\nu=0}^{a-1} 1 = a.$

Hence, there exists an integer $m > 0$ for which
$$10^m > a.$$
Let $n + 1$ be the least such m. Then
$$n \geq 0, \quad 10^n \leq a < 10^{n+1}.$$

For integral ν for which $0 \leqq \nu \leqq n$, we set

$$x_\nu = \left[\frac{a}{10^\nu}\right] - 10 \left[\frac{a}{10^{\nu+1}}\right].$$

Then,

$$x_\nu \text{ is integral,}$$

$$x_n = \left[\frac{a}{10^n}\right] - 10 \left[\frac{a}{10^{n+1}}\right] = \left[\frac{a}{10^n}\right] > 0,$$

and for $0 \leqq \nu \leqq n$:

$$-1 = \left(\frac{a}{10^\nu} - 1\right) - 10 \frac{a}{10^{\nu+1}} < x_\nu < \frac{a}{10^\nu} - 10 \left(\frac{a}{10^{\nu+1}} - 1\right) = 10,$$

so that

$$0 \leqq x_\nu \leqq 9.$$

Furthermore

$$\sum_{\nu=0}^{n} x_\nu 10^\nu = \sum_{\nu=0}^{n} \left(10^\nu \left[\frac{a}{10^\nu}\right] - 10^{\nu+1} \left[\frac{a}{10^{\nu+1}}\right]\right)$$

$$= \sum_{\nu=0}^{n} 10^\nu \left[\frac{a}{10^\nu}\right] - \sum_{\nu=0}^{n} 10^{\nu+1} \left[\frac{a}{10^{\nu+1}}\right] = \sum_{\nu=0}^{n} 10^\nu \left[\frac{a}{10^\nu}\right] - \sum_{\nu=1}^{n+1} 10^\nu \left[\frac{a}{10^\nu}\right]$$

$$= [a] - 10^{n+1} \left[\frac{a}{10^{n+1}}\right] = a.$$

2) If

$$a = \sum_{\nu=0}^{n} x_\nu 10^\nu = \sum_{\nu=0}^{N} X_\nu 10^\nu,$$

where n and the x_ν, and N and the X_ν, satisfy the conditions enumerated under 1) of the present theorem, then

$$n = N, \quad x_\nu = X_\nu \quad \text{for } 0 \leqq \nu \leqq n;$$

for otherwise we should have

$$0 = a - a = \sum_{\nu=0}^{s} e_\nu 10^\nu, \; s > 0, \; e_\nu \text{ is integral}, \; e_s \neq 0, \; |e_\nu| \leqq 9,$$

so that

$$10^s \leqq |e_s 10^s| = \left|- \sum_{\nu=0}^{s-1} e_\nu 10^\nu\right| \leqq \sum_{\nu=0}^{s-1} 9 \cdot 10^\nu = 9 \frac{10^s - 1}{10 - 1} = 10^s - 1 < 10^s.$$

Definition 5: *The representation*

$$\sum_{\nu=0}^{n} x_\nu 10^\nu$$

of Theorem 5 is written so that the "digits" (i.e. numbers of the sequence $0, 1, 2, 3, 4, 5, 6, 7, 8, 9$) $\mathfrak{x}_\nu$ *are placed one after another, ordered according to decreasing ν* (the so-called decimal notation for a).

Definition 5 is in agreement with our old notation for $a = 1, 2, 3, 4, 5, 6, 7, 8, 9, 10$.

Example: $\qquad 4 \cdot 10^0 + 0 \cdot 10 + 3 \cdot 10^2 = 304.$

The possibility of confusion with products is eliminated by always placing a dot between factors which are numbers (not letters). For example, the calculation

$$13 \cdot 13 = (3 + 10)(3 + 10) = 3 \cdot 3 + 3 \cdot 10 + 10 \cdot 3 + 10^2$$
$$= 9 + 6 \cdot 10 + 10^2 = 169$$

is unambiguous.

§ 3. Finite and Infinite Sets of Numbers

Definition 6: *A set of numbers $\mathfrak{M}$ is called finite if there exists an integer $m > 0$ such that the numbers of $\mathfrak{M}$ can be mapped one-to-one onto the positive integers $\leqq m$.*

Theorem 6: *If $\mathfrak{M}$ is a finite set of numbers, then there is only one m in the sense of Definition 6.*

Proof: If both m_1 and m_2 have this property, then the positive integers $\leqq m_1$ may be mapped one-to-one onto the positive integers $\leqq m_2$. But it is a familiar fact that this implies that

$$m_1 = m_2.$$

Definition 7: *If $\mathfrak{M}$ is a finite set of numbers, then the number m which is uniquely determined by Theorem 6 is called the cardinal number, or cardinality, of $\mathfrak{M}$. One also says that $\mathfrak{M}$ consists of m numbers, or that $\mathfrak{M}$ contains m numbers.*

Theorem 7: *Let $\mathfrak{M}$ be a set consisting of m numbers, $\mathfrak{N}$ a set consisting of n numbers, and let $\mathfrak{M}$ and $\mathfrak{N}$ have no numbers in common. Then the union of $\mathfrak{M}$ and $\mathfrak{N}$ (that is, the set which consists of all numbers which belong either to $\mathfrak{M}$ or to $\mathfrak{N}$) is a finite set of numbers, and it contains $m + n$ numbers.*

Proof: The numbers of $\mathfrak{M}$ may be denoted by

$$a_q, 1 \leqq q \leqq m, q \text{ integral},$$

those of $\mathfrak{N}$ by

$$b_r, 1 \leqq r \leqq n, r \text{ integral}.$$

If we set

$$a_q = b_{q-m} \text{ for } m + 1 \leqq q \leqq m + n, q \text{ integral},$$

then the numbers of the union of $\mathfrak{M}$ and $\mathfrak{N}$ are

$$a_q, 1 \leqq q \leqq m + n, q \text{ integral}.$$

Theorem 8: *If $k > 0$ is an integer, $\mathfrak{M}_\nu$ a finite set of numbers for $1 \leqq \nu \leqq k$ and ν integral, and if no number belongs to more than one of the $\mathfrak{M}_\nu$, then the union of all the $\mathfrak{M}_\nu$ is a finite set.*

Proof: $k = 1$ is clear. To proceed from k to $k + 1$: The union of the $\mathfrak{M}_\nu$ for $1 \leqq \nu \leqq k$ is finite, and so, by Theorem 7, is the union of this union and $\mathfrak{M}_{k+1}$.

Theorem 9: *If* $\mathfrak{M}$ *is a set consisting of* m *numbers, and if every number of a certain set* $\mathfrak{N}$ *of numbers belongs to* $\mathfrak{M}$ *(that is, if* $\mathfrak{N}$ *is a "subset" of* $\mathfrak{M}$*), then* $\mathfrak{N}$ *is finite, and consists of at most* m *numbers.*

Proof: 1) If $m = 1$, then $\mathfrak{N}$ is identical with $\mathfrak{M}$, and so consists of exactly one number.

2) To proceed from m to $m + 1$: Let $\mathfrak{M}$ be mapped onto the positive integers $\leq m + 1$. Thus the numbers of $\mathfrak{N}$ are mapped onto a subset of these integers.

If, first, $m + 1$ does not belong to the subset, then $\mathfrak{N}$ is mapped onto a subset of the positive integers $\leq m$, and so is finite. Moreover, the number of elements of $\mathfrak{N}$ is $\leq m < m + 1$.

If, on the other hand, $m + 1$ does belong to this subset, then either $\mathfrak{N}$ consists of only one number (so that, since $1 < m + 1$, we are through), or the set obtained by removing the "image" of $m + 1$ from $\mathfrak{N}$ is mapped one-to-one onto a subset of the positive integers $\leq m$, so that it is finite and consists of at most m numbers, whence, by Theorem 7, $\mathfrak{N}$ is itself finite and consists of at most $m + 1$ numbers.

Theorem 10: *There exists a set of numbers which is not finite. In particular, the set of positive integers is not finite.*

Proof: If the set $\mathfrak{M}$ of positive integers were finite, and if m were its cardinality, then the set $\mathfrak{N}$ of positive integers $\leq m + 1$, being a subset of $\mathfrak{M}$, would consist by Theorem 9 of at most m numbers, whereas it actually consists of $m + 1$ numbers.

Definition 8: *A set of numbers is called infinite if it is not finite. One also says that it consists of infinitely many numbers.*

Examples: 1) If a is real, then the set of integers $n > a$ is infinite. For, if $k = [a]$, then the set of numbers n concerned is the set of all $n = k + l, l \geq 1$ integral.

2) The set of even $n > a$ and the set of odd $n > a$ are also infinite. For, we are concerned in the one case with the set of numbers n of the form $n = 2q$, $q > \dfrac{a}{2}$ and integral, and in the other case with the set of numbers n such that $n = 2q + 1$, $q > \dfrac{a - 1}{2}$ and integral.

PART ONE

DIFFERENTIAL
CALCULUS

CHAPTER I

LIMITS FOR $n = \infty$

Introduction

In this chapter n, m, N, m_1, m_2, k, v, and N always serve to denote integers. As I have already stated, all numbers are to be real in Chapters 1–19, and from Chapter 20, § 2 to the end of the book (Chap. 31).

If one says that the sequence of numbers

$$1, \tfrac{1}{2}, \tfrac{1}{3}, \tfrac{1}{4}, \ldots$$

approaches 0 as a limit, this statement has no proper sense as yet, for it has not been stated which numbers are given nor in what order they are given. Most readers will probaby assume that $\tfrac{1}{4}$ is to be followed by the number $\tfrac{1}{5}$ and that, more generally, we wish to say the following:

Let

(1) $$s_n = \frac{1}{n} \quad \text{for } n \geq 1;$$

then the sequence s_n approaches 0; it has the limit 0. Indeed, this will accord with the definitions we shall lay down. However, why shall we wish to say that this sequence approaches 0? Why shall we not say, for any $s \neq 0$, that it approaches s? Why shall we associate with every sequence s_n, defined for $n \geq 1$, either no number or precisely one number as its limit? In which case none, and in which case one?

Continuing to consider the above example, we note that 0 is not a number of the sequence, since for every $n \geq 1$ we have

$$s_n > 0,$$

and therefore

$$s_n \neq 0.$$

But ultimately (i.e., from some number of the sequence on) s_n differs by little from 0. What do we mean by little?

Let any $\delta > 0$ whatsoever be given. Then, setting

$$s = 0,$$

for every $n > \dfrac{1}{\delta}$ we have

$$\left| \, s_n - s \, \right| = \left| \dfrac{1}{n} - 0 \right| = \dfrac{1}{n} < \delta \, .$$

Thus there is associated with δ an m (depending on δ), namely

$$m = \left[\dfrac{1}{\delta} \right] + 1 \qquad \left(> \dfrac{1}{\delta} \right),$$

such that

$$\left| \, s_n - s \, \right| < \delta \quad \text{for all} \quad n \geqq m.$$

On the other hand, it would not suffice merely to note that infinitely often (i.e. for infinitely many n),

$$\left| \, s_n - s \, \right| < \delta.$$

For, for every $\delta > 0$, the sequence

$$(2) \qquad s_n = \begin{cases} 1 - \dfrac{1}{n} & \text{for odd} \quad n \geqq 1, \\[2ex] \dfrac{1}{n} & \text{for even} \quad n \geqq 1 \end{cases}$$

satisfies the condition

$$\left| \, s_n - 0 \, \right| < \delta \text{ for infinitely many } n,$$

namely, for all even $n \geqq \left[\dfrac{1}{\delta} \right] + 1$ (as well as for certain other n, e.g. in the case $\delta = \tfrac{5}{6}$ for $n = 1$, $n = 3$, and $n = 5$). However, it is not true that for every $\delta > 0$ there is an m for which

$$\left| \, s_n - 0 \, \right| < \delta \text{ for } n \geqq m.$$

Thus, for $\delta = \tfrac{5}{6}$, there is no such m, since for odd $n > 5$,

$$\left| \, s_n - 0 \, \right| = \left| 1 - \dfrac{1}{n} \right| \geqq \tfrac{6}{7} > \tfrac{5}{6}.$$

On the other hand, the requirement

$$s_n \neq 0 \text{ for } n > 1$$

of example (1) is unessential. For if we consider the sequence

$$(3) \qquad s_n = 0 \text{ for } n > 1,$$

then for every $\delta > 0$, there is of course an m (and indeed one which may be chosen independently of δ, namely $= 1$) such that

$$\left| \, s_n - 0 \, \right| = 0 < \delta \text{ for } n \geqq m.$$

And if we consider the sequence

(4)
$$s_n = \begin{cases} 0 \ \text{ for odd } n \geqq 1, \\ \dfrac{1}{n} \ \text{ for even } n \geqq 1 \end{cases}$$

(infinitely many of whose terms are zero, and infinitely many of whose terms are non-zero), then

$$| \, s_n - 0 \, | \leqq \frac{1}{n} < \delta \ \text{ for } \ n \geqq \left[\frac{1}{\delta} \right] + 1.$$

The fact that, in example (1),

$$s_n \geqq 0$$

holds from some point on (indeed from the beginning on) is not essential. For in the example

(5)
$$s_n = \frac{(-1)^n}{n} \quad \text{ for } \ n \leqq 1$$

we have, for every $\delta > 0$,

$$| \, s_n - 0 \, | = \left| \frac{(-1)^n}{n} \right| = \frac{1}{n} < \delta \ \text{ for } n \geqq \left[\frac{1}{\delta} \right] + 1.$$

The s_n of each of the five examples just considered are defined for all $n \geqq 1$. However, this too is not essential. All that is required is the existence of an s such that for every $\delta > 0$ there is an m for which

$$| \, s_n - s \, | < \delta \ \text{ for } n \geqq m.$$

Thus, s_n must certainly be defined for all sufficiently large n (i.e. for all $n \geqq N$, or as we shall say, ultimately). We shall thus say that the sequence

(6)
$$s_n = 1 + \frac{1}{n-4} \quad \text{ for } \ n \geqq 3$$

approaches 1, in spite of the fact that s_4 is undefined. For, if we set

$$s = 1$$

and if $\delta > 0$ is given, then, for $n > 4 + \left[\frac{1}{\delta} \right] + 1 \left(> 4 + \frac{1}{\delta} \right)$,

$$| \, s_n - s \, | = \left| \frac{1}{n-4} \right| = \frac{1}{n-4} < \delta.$$

Thus I have verified that the desired property is possessed by the number $s = 0$ in examples (1), (3), (4), and (5); by the number $s = 1$ in example (6); and is not possessed by the number $s = 0$ in example (2).

We shall now convince ourselves that the desired property is not possessed by any $s \neq 0$ in examples (1), (3), (4), and (5); nor by any $s \neq 1$ in example (6); nor by any s whatsoever in example (2).

If some $s \neq 0$ had the desired property in example (1), then, setting $\delta = \dfrac{|s|}{2}$ and choosing m suitably, we should have for $n \geqq m$ that

$$\left| \frac{1}{n} - s \right| = |\, s_n - s\,| < \frac{|s|}{2},$$

so that

$$\frac{1}{n} = \left| s + \left(\frac{1}{n} - s \right) \right| \geqq |\, s\, | - \left| \frac{1}{n} - s \right| > |\, s\, | - \frac{|s|}{2} = \frac{|s|}{2},$$

which, for

$$n \geqq \frac{2}{|\, s\, |},$$

is certainly false.

In example (2), we have

$$s_n \begin{cases} \geqq \frac{2}{3} & \text{for odd } n \geqq 3, \\ \leqq \frac{1}{2} & \text{for even } n \geqq 1. \end{cases}$$

For every $s \leqq \frac{7}{12}$, we thus have, for infinitely many n,

$$s_n - s \geqq \frac{2}{3} - \frac{7}{12} = \frac{1}{12},$$

$$|\, s_n - s\, | \geqq \frac{1}{12},$$

so that there is no suitable m associated with $\delta = \frac{1}{12}$. For every $s > \frac{7}{12}$, we have, for infinitely many n,

$$s_n - s < \frac{1}{2} - \frac{7}{12} = - \frac{1}{12},$$

$$|\, s_n - s\, | > \frac{1}{12},$$

so that there is no suitable m associated with $\delta = \frac{1}{12}$.

In example (3), we have for every $s \neq 0$ that

$$|\, s_n - s\, | = |\, s\, |,$$

so that there is no m associated with $\delta = |\, s\, |$.

In example (4), we have for every $s \neq 0$ the equality

$$|\, s_n - s\, | = |\, s\, |$$

holds for infinitely many n, so that there is no m associated with $\delta = |\, s\, |$.

In example (5), we have for $s \neq 0$ that

$$|\, s_n - s\, | = \left| \frac{(-1)^n}{n} - s \right| \geqq |\, s\, | - \frac{1}{n},$$

so that, for $n \geqq \dfrac{2}{|s|}$,

$$|s_n - s| \geqq \dfrac{|s|}{2} .$$

Hence there is no m associated with $\delta = \dfrac{|s|}{2}$.

In example (6), if $s \neq 1$ and $n \geqq 4 + \dfrac{2}{|1 - s|}$, then

$$|s_n - s| = \left|(1 - s) + \dfrac{1}{n - 4}\right| \geqq |1 - s| - \dfrac{1}{n - 4} \geqq \dfrac{|1 - s|}{2},$$

so that there is no m associated with $\delta = \dfrac{|1 - s|}{2}$.

And now, we can finally proceed from examples to a general definition (Definition 9). However, we shall first have to prove Theorem 11, which states that limits, when they exist, are unique.

Theorem 11: *Let* N *be given, and let* s_n *be defined for all* $n \geqq$ N *(i.e. for all sufficiently large* n, *i.e. ultimately). Then there is either no number, or exactly one number* s, *with the following property:*

For every $\delta > 0$ *we have, for all sufficiently large* n,

$$| s_n - s | < \delta.$$

In other words, with each $\delta > 0$ there is associated an m for which

$$| s_n - s | < \delta \text{ for } n \geqq m.$$

More concisely, for every $\delta > 0$ we have that, ultimately,

$$| s_n - s | < \delta.$$

Proof: Suppose that

$$S \neq T$$

where both S and T fulfill what is required of s. Then we set

$$\delta = \frac{| S - T |}{2} \qquad (> 0).$$

Then there would be an m_1 such that

$$| s_n - S | < \delta \text{ for } n \geqq m_1$$

and an m_2 such that

$$| s_n - T | < \delta \text{ for } n \geqq m_2.$$

Thus, we should have for $n \geqq \text{Max}(m_1, m_2)$ that

$$| S - T | = |(s_n - T) - (s_n - S) |$$
$$\leqq | s_n - T | + | s_n - S | < \delta + \delta = 2\delta = | S - T |.$$

Definition 9: *If* s_n *is ultimately defined, and if there exists an* s *in the sense of Theorem 11, then we say that* s_n *(the sequence* s_n*) has ("as* $n \to \infty$*") the limit* s, *or approaches* s *("as* $n \to \infty$*"), and we write*

$$\lim_{n=\infty} s_n = s,$$

or, more briefly,

$$s_n \to s.$$

∞ is to be read: *infinity*; lim is to be read: *limit*.

Of course, any letter that stands for integers may be used instead of n. (Similar remarks hold for almost all other definitions.)

Examples: 1) $\qquad \lim\limits_{k=\infty} \left(1 + \dfrac{1}{k-4}\right) = 1.$

2) $\qquad\qquad\qquad \lim\limits_{n=\infty} c = c;$

for we always have

$$|c - c| = 0.$$

3) If

$$s_n = (-1)^n, \ n \geq 0$$

then

$$\lim\limits_{n=\infty} s_n$$

does not exist. For if $s \leq 0$, then we have for infinitely many n that

$$s_n - s = 1 - s \geq 1,$$

$$|s_n - s| \geq 1,$$

and if $s > 0$, then for infinitely many n we have

$$s_n - s = -1 - s < -1,$$

$$|s_n - s| > 1.$$

4) If

$$0 < \vartheta < 1$$

then

$$\lim\limits_{n=\infty} \vartheta^n = 0.$$

For if $p > 0$ and $n \geq 1$, then

$$(1 + p)^n > (1 + p)^n - 1 = p \sum_{\nu=0}^{n-1} (1 + p)^\nu \geq p \sum_{\nu=0}^{n-1} 1 = pn.$$

If we set

$$\frac{1}{\vartheta} - 1 = p,$$

then

$$p > \frac{1}{1} - 1 = 0,$$

so that, for $n \geq 1$,

$$0 < \vartheta^n = \left(\frac{1}{1+p}\right)^n = \frac{1}{(1+p)^n} < \frac{1}{pn}.$$

Hence, given any $\delta > 0$, then for $n \geq \dfrac{1}{p\delta}$ (i.e., ultimately) we have

$$\left| \vartheta^n - 0 \right| = \left| \vartheta^n \right| < \delta.$$

5) If $\left| \vartheta \right| < 1$, then

$$\lim_{k = \infty} \sum_{n=0}^{k} \vartheta^n = \dfrac{1}{1 - \vartheta}.$$

For if $k \geq 0$, then

$$(1 - \vartheta) \sum_{n=0}^{k} \vartheta^n = 1 - \vartheta^{k+1}.$$

This last equality actually holds for all ϑ. Hence if $\vartheta \neq 1$, then

$$\sum_{n=0}^{k} \vartheta^n = \dfrac{1}{1 - \vartheta} - \dfrac{\vartheta^{k+1}}{1 - \vartheta},$$

$$\left| \sum_{n=0}^{k} \vartheta^n - \dfrac{1}{1 - \vartheta} \right| = \left| -\dfrac{\vartheta^{k+1}}{1 - \vartheta} \right| = \left| \dfrac{\vartheta}{1 - \vartheta} \right| \left| \vartheta \right|^k.$$

If $\vartheta = 0$, then

$$\sum_{n=0}^{k} \vartheta^n = 1 \rightarrow 1 = \dfrac{1}{1 - \vartheta}.$$

If $0 < \left| \vartheta \right| < 1$, then, by example 4) (with $\left| \dfrac{1 - \vartheta}{\vartheta} \right| \delta$ instead of our usual δ), we may associate with $\delta > 0$ an m such that

$$\left| \vartheta \right|^k < \left| \dfrac{1 - \vartheta}{\vartheta} \right| \delta \quad \text{for } k \geq m.$$

But then, for $k \geq m$ we have

$$\left| \sum_{n=0}^{k} \vartheta^n - \dfrac{1}{1 - \vartheta} \right| < \left| \dfrac{\vartheta}{1 - \vartheta} \right| \left| \dfrac{1 - \vartheta}{\vartheta} \right| \delta = \delta.$$

Theorem 12: *We have*

$$s_n \rightarrow s$$

if and only if

$$s_n - s \rightarrow 0.$$

Proof: Both state that for every $\delta > 0$, we have that, ultimately,

$$\left| s_n - s \right| < \delta.$$

Theorem 13: *Let s_n be defined for $n \geq N$, and let*

$$\lim_{n = \infty} s_n = s.$$

Let n_ν, $\nu \geq N$, be an increasing sequence of integers with $n_\nu \geq N$. Then

$$\lim_{\nu = \infty} s_{n_\nu} = s.$$

Proof: Let $\delta > 0$ be given. Then, for suitable $k \geq N$,

$$|s_n - s| < \delta \text{ for } n \geq k.$$

Now for suitable $m \geq N$,

$$n_\nu \geq k \text{ for } \nu \geq m.$$

Hence for $\nu \geq m$ we have

$$|s_{n_\nu} - s| < \delta.$$

Examples: 1) If

$$\lim_{n = \infty} s_n = s$$

then

$$\lim_{n = \infty} s_{n-1} = s$$

and

$$\lim_{n = \infty} s_{n+1} = s.$$

For, let s_n be defined for $n \geq N$. Then the $n_\nu = \nu - 1$ with $\nu \geq N + 1$, and also the $n_\nu = \nu + 1$ with $\nu \geq N - 1$, satisfy the hypotheses of Theorem 13.

2) If

(1)
$$\lim_{n = \infty} s_n = s$$

then

(2)
$$\lim_{n = \infty} s_{2n} = s$$

and

(3)
$$\lim_{n = \infty} s_{2n+1} = s.$$

For, let s_n be defined for $n \geq N$. Then the $n_\nu = 2\nu$ with $\nu \geq \dfrac{N}{2}$, and also the $n_\nu = 2\nu + 1$ with $\nu \geq \dfrac{N-1}{2}$, satisfy the hypotheses of Theorem 13, so that

$$\lim_{\nu = \infty} s_{2\nu} = s,$$

$$\lim_{\nu = \infty} s_{2\nu+1} = s.$$

Hence, (2) and (3) follow from (1).

Conversely, (1) follows from (2) and (3) (taken together). For, by (2) and (3), we have that for every $\delta > 0$,

$$|s_n - s| < \delta$$

holds for all large even numbers and for all large odd numbers, and hence for all large n.

Theorem 14: *If*

$$s_n \to s, \; t_n \to t,$$

then

$$s_n + t_n \to s + t.$$

For short:

$$\lim_{n=\infty} (s_n + t_n) = \lim_{n=\infty} s_n + \lim_{n=\infty} t_n,$$

if the right-hand side is meaningful.

Proof: Let $\delta > 0$ be given. Ultimately,

(1)
$$|s_n - s| < \frac{\delta}{2};$$

and ultimately,

(2)
$$\left| t_n - t \right| < \frac{\delta}{2}.$$

Hence, both (1) and (2) hold ultimately, so that

$$|(s_n + t_n) - (s + t)| = |(s_n - s) + (t_n - t)|$$
$$\leqq |s_n - s| + |t_n - t| < \frac{\delta}{2} + \frac{\delta}{2} = \delta.$$

Example: If $|\vartheta| < 1$ then

$$\lim_{n=\infty} \left(\vartheta^n + 1 + \frac{1}{n-4} \right) = \lim_{n=\infty} \vartheta^n + \lim_{n=\infty} \left(1 + \frac{1}{n-4} \right) = 0 + 1 = 1.$$

Theorem 15: *If $k > 0$, and if each of the k sequences*

$$s_n^{(\nu)}, \; 1 \leqq \nu \leqq k,$$

has a limit, then the sequence

$$\sum_{\nu=1}^{k} s_n^{(\nu)}$$

has a limit; and indeed, if

$$s_n^{(\nu)} \to s^{(\nu)} \; for \; 1 \leqq \nu \leqq k,$$

then

$$\sum_{\nu=1}^{k} s_n^{(\nu)} \to \sum_{\nu=1}^{k} s^{(\nu)}.$$

For short:

$$\lim_{n=\infty} \sum_{\nu=1}^{k} s_n^{(\nu)} = \sum_{\nu=1}^{k} \lim_{n=\infty} s_n^{(\nu)},$$

if the right-hand side is meaningful.

Proof: 1) If $k = 1$, then

$$\sum_{\nu=1}^{k} s_n^{(\nu)} = s_n^{(1)} \to s^{(1)} = \sum_{\nu=1}^{k} s^{(\nu)}.$$

2) $k + 1$ follows from k by Theorem 14, since

$$\sum_{\nu=1}^{k+1} s_n^{(\nu)} = \sum_{\nu=1}^{k} s_n^{(\nu)} + s_n^{(k+1)} \to \sum_{\nu=1}^{k} s^{(\nu)} + s^{(k+1)} = \sum_{\nu=1}^{k+1} s^{(\nu)}.$$

Theorem 16: *If*

$$s_n \to s, \quad t_n \to t,$$

then

$$s_n t_n \to st.$$

Proof: s_n and t_n are defined ultimately. Thus, ultimately,

$$s_n t_n - st = s_n(t_n - t) + t(s_n - s).$$

Let $\delta > 0$ be given. Then we have that ultimately both

$$|s_n - s| < \frac{\delta}{2(|t| + 1)}$$

and

$$|t_n - t| < \frac{\delta}{2|s| + \delta},$$

so that

$$|s_n| = |s + (s_n - s)| \leqq |s| + |s_n - s| < |s| + \frac{\delta}{2},$$

$$|s_n t_n - st| \leqq |s_n||t_n - t| + |t||s_n - s|$$

$$< \left(|s| + \frac{\delta}{2}\right)\frac{\delta}{2|s| + \delta} + |t|\frac{\delta}{2(|t| + 1)} < \frac{\delta}{2} + \frac{\delta}{2} = \delta.$$

Example:

$$\lim_{n=\infty} \left(\left(1 + \frac{(-1)^n}{n}\right)\left(1 + \frac{1}{n-4}\right)\right)$$

$$= \lim_{n=\infty}\left(1 + \frac{(-1)^n}{n}\right)\lim_{n=\infty}\left(1 + \frac{1}{n-4}\right) = 1 \cdot 1 = 1.$$

Theorem 17: *If $k > 0$, and if*

$$s_n^{(\nu)} \to s^{(\nu)} \text{ for } 1 \leqq \nu \leqq k,$$

then

$$\prod_{\nu=1}^{k} s_n^{(\nu)} \to \prod_{\nu=1}^{k} s^{(\nu)}.$$

Proof: 1) If $k = 1$, then

$$\prod_{\nu=1}^{k} s_n^{(\nu)} = s_n^{(1)} \to s^{(1)} = \prod_{\nu=1}^{k} s^{(\nu)}.$$

2) $k + 1$ follows from k by Theorem 16, since

$$\prod_{\nu=1}^{k+1} s_n^{(\nu)} = \prod_{\nu=1}^{k} s_n^{(\nu)} \cdot s_n^{(k+1)} \to \prod_{\nu=1}^{k} s^{(\nu)} \cdot s^{(k+1)} = \prod_{\nu=1}^{k+1} s^{(\nu)}.$$

Theorem 18: *If $k > 0$ and*

$$s_n \to s,$$

then

$$s_n^{\ k} \to s^k.$$

Proof: Theorem 17, with

$$s_n^{(\nu)} = s_n \quad \text{for } 1 \leq \nu \leq k.$$

Example: $\lim\limits_{n=\infty} \left(1 + \dfrac{1}{n-4}\right)^k = \left(\lim\limits_{n=\infty} \left(1 + \dfrac{1}{n-4}\right)\right)^k = 1^k = 1.$

Theorem 19: *If*

$$s_n \to s, \quad t_n \to t,$$

then

$$s_n - t_n \to s - t.$$

Proof: By example 2 to Definition 9, and by Theorem 16,

$$-t_n = (-1)t_n \to (-1)t = -t,$$

so that by Theorem 14,

$$s_n - t_n = s_n + (-t_n) \to s + (-t) = s - t.$$

Theorem 20: *If*

$$s_n \to s,$$
$$s \neq 0,$$

then

$$\frac{1}{s_n} \to \frac{1}{s}.$$

Proof: For every $\delta > 0$,

$$|s_n - s| < \text{Min}\left(\frac{\delta s^2}{2}, \frac{|s|}{2}\right)$$

ultimately holds, so that

$$|s_n| = |s + (s_n - s)| \geq |s| - |s_n - s| > |s| - \frac{|s|}{2} = \frac{|s|}{2},$$

$$\left|\frac{1}{s_n} - \frac{1}{s}\right| = \frac{|s_n - s|}{|s_n||s|} \leq \frac{2}{s^2}|s_n - s| < \frac{2}{s^2}\frac{\delta s^2}{2} = \delta.$$

Example: $\lim\limits_{n=\infty} \dfrac{1}{1 + \dfrac{(-1)^n}{n}} = \dfrac{1}{\lim\limits_{n=\infty}\left(1 + \dfrac{(-1)^n}{n}\right)} = \dfrac{1}{1} = 1.$

Theorem 21: *If*

$$s_n \to s, \quad t_n \to t,$$

$$t \neq 0,$$

then

$$\frac{s_n}{t_n} \to \frac{s}{t}.$$

Proof: By Theorems 16 and 20,

$$\frac{s_n}{t_n} = s_n \frac{1}{t_n} \to s \frac{1}{t} = \frac{s}{t}.$$

Example: $\lim\limits_{n=\infty} \dfrac{\dfrac{1}{n-4}}{1 + \dfrac{(-1)^n}{n}} = \dfrac{0}{1} = 0.$

Theorem 22: *If*

$$s_n \to s, \quad t_n \to t,$$

and if

$$s_n \leqq t_n$$

ultimately holds, then

$$s \leqq t.$$

Proof: By Theorem 19,

$$t_n - s_n \to t - s.$$

Hence for every $\delta > 0$, we ultimately have

$$0 \leqq t_n - s_n < t - s + \delta,$$

$$s - t \quad < \delta.$$

Thus

$$s - t \leqq 0$$

(since otherwise, $\delta = s - t$ would yield a contradiction), and so

$$s \leqq t.$$

Example: If

$$t_n \to t, \quad t_n \geqq c,$$

then

$$t \geqq c.$$

Theorem 23: $$s_n \to 0$$

if and only if

$$|s_n| \to 0.$$

Proof: Since

$$||s_n|| = |s_n|,$$

both statements mean that for every $\delta > 0$ we ultimately have

$$|s_n| < \delta.$$

Theorem 24: *If*

$$t_n \to 0$$

and if

$$|s_n| \leqq t_n$$

ultimately holds, then

$$s_n \to 0.$$

Proof: Let $\delta > 0$ be given. Then ultimately,

$$|t_n| < \delta,$$

so that, ultimately

$$|s_n| < \delta.$$

Theorem 25: *Let*

$$s_n \to 0.$$

Let t_n be defined for $n \geqq k$, and let there be a g, independent of n, such that

$$|t_n| < g \text{ for } n \geqq k.$$

Then

$$s_n t_n \to 0.$$

Proof: Let $\delta > 0$ be given. Ultimately,

$$|s_n| < \frac{\delta}{g},$$

so that, ultimately

$$|s_n t_n| < \frac{\delta}{g} g = \delta.$$

Theorem 26: *If s_n is defined for $n \geqq N$, and if*

$$\lim_{n = \infty} s_n$$

exists, then there exists a g, independent of n, such that

$$|s_n| < g \text{ for } n \geqq N.$$

Proof: Let

$$\lim_{n = \infty} s_n = s.$$

There exists an $m > N$ such that for $n \geqq m$

$$| s_n - s | < 1,$$

so that

$$| s_n | = | s + (s_n - s) | \leqq | s | + | s_n - s | < | s | + 1.$$

Hence

$$g = | s | + 1 + \underset{N \leqq n \leqq m-1}{\text{Max}} | s_n |$$

satisfies the requirements.

Theorem 27: *Let s_n be defined for $n \geqq N$. Moreover, let*

$$s_n \leqq s_{n+1}.$$

Let there be a g, independent of n, such that for $n \geqq N$

$$s_n \leqq g.$$

1) *Then*

$$\lim_{n = \infty} s_n$$

exists.

2) *If this limit is called s, then*

$$s_N \leqq s \leqq g.$$

Preliminary Remarks: I) Hitherto everything has been quite simple. However, Theorem 27, 1) is deep.

II) The result is no longer true if the assumption

$$s_n \leqq s_{n+1}$$

is removed. For, if we consider the sequence

$$s_n = (-1)^n \text{ for } n \geqq 0,$$

then, although

$$s_n \leqq 1,$$

the limit

$$\lim_{n = \infty} s_n$$

does not exist.

Proof: 1) We divide all numbers α into two classes as follows: α is in

Class I   if at least one $s_n > \alpha$,
Class II   if all $s_n \leqq \alpha$.

Then every α belongs to exactly one of these classes.
Class I is not empty. For, since

$$s_N > s_N - 1,$$

it contains $s_N - 1$.

Class II is not empty since it contains g.

If α is in class II, and if $\beta > \alpha$, then for every $n \geqq N$,

$$s_n \leqq \alpha < \beta,$$

so that β is in class II.

Hence there exists an s such that every $\alpha < s$ belongs to class I, and every $\alpha > s$ belongs to class II.

We shall show that

$$s_n \to s$$

for this s.

Let $\delta > 0$ be given. Then, since $s + \dfrac{\delta}{2}$ is in class II,

$$s_n \leqq s + \frac{\delta}{2} < s + \delta.$$

$s - \delta$ is in class I. Hence for some $m \geqq N$,

$$s_m > s - \delta.$$

For $n \geqq m$ (as is clear by 7) of the introduction)

$$s_m \leqq s_n,$$

so that

$$s - \delta < s_n < s + \delta,$$
$$\left| s_n - s \right| < \delta.$$

Hence

$$s_n \to s.$$

2) For all $n \geqq N$,

$$s_N \leqq s_n \leqq g,$$

so that, by Theorem 22,

$$s_N \leqq \lim_{n=\infty} s_n = s \leqq g.$$

Example: $\qquad \lim\limits_{n=\infty} \sum\limits_{\nu=1}^{n} \dfrac{1}{\nu^2}$

exists. For if

$$s_n = \sum_{\nu=1}^{n} \frac{1}{\nu^2} \text{ for } n \geqq 1,$$

then

$$s_n < s_{n+1}$$

and

$$s_n < 1 + \sum_{\nu=2}^{n+1} \frac{1}{\nu^2} < 1 + \sum_{\nu=2}^{n+1} \frac{1}{(\nu-1)\nu} = 1 + \sum_{\nu=2}^{n+1} \left(\frac{1}{\nu-1} - \frac{1}{\nu} \right)$$

$$= 1 + \sum_{\nu=2}^{n+1} \frac{1}{\nu-1} - \sum_{\nu=2}^{n+1} \frac{1}{\nu} = 1 + \sum_{\nu=1}^{n} \frac{1}{\nu} - \sum_{\nu=2}^{n+1} \frac{1}{\nu} = 1 + 1 - \frac{1}{n+1} < 2.$$

CHAPTER 2

LOGARITHMS, POWERS, AND ROOTS

In this chapter, n and m denote positive integers and k is an abbreviation for 2^n.

Theorem 28: *If $x > 0$, then for each n,*

$$y^k = x, \quad y > 0$$

has exactly one solution.

Proof: 1) If $0 < y_1 < y_2$, then

$$y_1{}^k < y_2{}^k;$$

hence there is at most one solution.

2) There exists at least one solution. For, we first note that

$$y = \sqrt{x}$$

satisfies our equation with $n = 1$, since

$$\sqrt{x} > 0, \quad (\sqrt{x})^{2^1} = (\sqrt{x})^2 = x.$$

$n + 1$ follows from n. For, if we choose z such that

$$z^{2^n} = x, \quad z > 0,$$

and set

$$y = \sqrt{z},$$

then

$$y > 0,$$
$$y^{2^{n+1}} = (y^2)^{2^n} = z^{2^n} = x.$$

Definition 10: *The y of Theorem 28 is called $\sqrt[k]{x}$.*
To be read: The k-th root of x.

Example: $\sqrt[k]{1} = 1.$

Theorem 29: *If $x > 0$ and $y > 0$, then*

$$\sqrt[k]{xy} = \sqrt[k]{x}\,\sqrt[k]{y}.$$

Proof:

$$\sqrt[k]{x}\,\sqrt[k]{y} > 0,$$

$$\left(\sqrt[k]{x}\,\sqrt[k]{y}\right)^k = \left(\sqrt[k]{x}\right)^k\left(\sqrt[k]{y}\right)^k = xy.$$

Example $\left(y = \dfrac{1}{x}\right)$: If $x > 0$, then

$$\sqrt[k]{x}\,\sqrt[k]{\frac{1}{x}} = 1,$$

so that

$$\sqrt[k]{\frac{1}{x}} = \frac{1}{\sqrt[k]{x}}.$$

Theorem 30: *If $x > 0$, then*

$$\lim_{n=\infty}\sqrt[k]{x} = 1.$$

Proof: 1) If $x > 1$, then

$$\left(\sqrt[k]{x}\right)^k = x > 1,$$

so that

$$\sqrt[k]{x} > 1.$$

Given $\delta > 0$, then (cf. example 4 to Definition 9)

$$(1 + \delta)^k > k\delta,$$

so that, ultimately,

$$(1 + \delta)^k > x = \left(\sqrt[k]{x}\right)^k,$$

$$1 < \sqrt[k]{x} < 1 + \delta,$$

$$\left|\sqrt[k]{x} - 1\right| < \delta.$$

Thus

$$\lim_{n=\infty}\sqrt[k]{x} = 1.$$

2) If $x = 1$, then

$$\sqrt[k]{x} = 1 \to 1.$$

3) If $0 < x < 1$, then by 1),

$$\sqrt[k]{\frac{1}{x}} \to 1,$$

so that, by the example to Theorem 29,

$$\frac{1}{\sqrt[k]{x}} \to 1,$$

and hence, by Theorem 20,

$$\sqrt[k]{x} \to 1.$$

Definition 11 (to be borne in mind a short while only—namely until the proof of Theorem 37): *For $x > 0$, we set*

$$a(n, x) = k\left(\sqrt[k]{x} - 1\right).$$

Theorem 31: *If $x > 0$, then*

$$\lim_{n=\infty} a(n, x)$$

exists.

Proof: 1) Let $x > 1$. If we set

$$y = \sqrt[2k]{x},$$

then

$$y > 1,$$
$$x = y^{2k} = (y^2)^k,$$
$$\sqrt[k]{x} = y^2,$$
$$a(n, x) = k(y^2 - 1) = k(y + 1)(y - 1) > k \cdot 2(y - 1) = 2k\left(\sqrt[2k]{x} - 1\right)$$
$$= a(n + 1, x).$$

Hence, by Theorem 27, 1) (with $g = 0$), the sequence of negative numbers $- a(n, x)$ has a limit. Thus, by Theorem 16, so does the sequence $a(n, x)$.

2) Let $x = 1$. Then

$$a(n, x) = 0 \to 0.$$

3) Let $0 < x < 1$. By 1),

$$\lim_{n=\infty} a\left(n, \frac{1}{x}\right)$$

exists. By the example to Theorem 29, we have

$$a(n, x) = (-1)k\left(\sqrt[k]{\frac{1}{x}} - 1\right)\sqrt[k]{x} = (-1)\, a\left(n, \frac{1}{x}\right)\sqrt[k]{x}.$$

From this, by Theorems 17 and 30, our assertion follows.

Definition 12: $\qquad \log x = \lim_{n=\infty} a(n, x)$ *for $x > 0$.*

To be read: Logarithm of x.

Theorem 32: $$\log 1 = 0.$$

Proof: $$a(n,\ 1) = 0 \to 0.$$

Theorem 33: $\log (xy) = \log x + \log y$ *for* $x > 0,\ y > 0$.

Proof: By Theorem 29,

$$k\left(\sqrt[k]{xy} - 1\right) = k\left(\sqrt[k]{x} - 1\right)\sqrt[k]{y} + k\left(\sqrt[k]{y} - 1\right),$$

so that, by Definition 12 and Theorem 30,

$$\log (xy) = \lim_{n=\infty} k\left(\sqrt[k]{xy} - 1\right) = \lim_{n=\infty} k\left(\sqrt[k]{x} - 1\right) \lim_{n=\infty} \sqrt[k]{y} + \lim_{n=\infty} k\left(\sqrt[k]{y} - 1\right)$$

$$= \log x \cdot 1 + \log y = \log x + \log y.$$

Theorem 34: $\log \dfrac{x}{y} = \log x - \log y$ *for* $x > 0,\ y > 0$.

Proof: By Theorem 33,

$$\log x = \log \left(\frac{x}{y}\, y\right) = \log \frac{x}{y} + \log y.$$

Theorem 35: $\log \prod\limits_{\nu=1}^{m} x_\nu = \sum\limits_{\nu=1}^{m} \log x_\nu$ *for positive* x_ν.

Proof: $m = 1$ is obvious. $m + 1$ from m by Theorem 33, since

$$\log \prod_{\nu=1}^{m+1} x_\nu = \log \left(\prod_{\nu=1}^{m} x_\nu \cdot x_{m+1}\right) = \log \prod_{\nu=1}^{m} x_\nu + \log x_{m+1}$$

$$= \sum_{\nu=1}^{m} \log x_\nu + \log x_{m+1} = \sum_{\nu=1}^{m+1} \log x_\nu.$$

Theorem 36: *For* $a > 0$ *and integral* x, *we have*

$$\log (a^x) = x \log a.$$

Proof: 1) If $x > 0$, then this follows from Theorem 35 with $m = x, x_\nu = a$.
2) If $x = 0$, then by Theorem 32,

$$\log (a^x) = \log 1 = 0 = x \log a.$$

3) If $x < 0$, then by Theorems 34 and 32 and 1),

$$\log (a^x) = \log \frac{1}{a^{-x}} = \log 1 - \log (a^{-x}) = -(-x \log a) = x \log a.$$

Theorem 37: $$\log x \leqq x - 1 \ \textit{for} \ x > 0.$$

Proof: If $y > 0$, then

$$\sum_{\nu=0}^{k-1} y^\nu \left\{\begin{matrix} \leqq \\ \geqq \end{matrix}\right\} \sum_{\nu=0}^{k-1} 1 = k, \ \text{for} \ \left\{\begin{matrix} y \leqq 1, \\ y \geqq 1. \end{matrix}\right.$$

Thus if $y > 0$, then in any case, we have

$$y^k - 1 = (y - 1) \sum_{v=0}^{k-1} y^v \geq k(y - 1).$$

Setting $y = \sqrt[k]{x}$, we obtain

$$x - 1 \geq k\left(\sqrt[k]{x} - 1\right) = a(n, x).$$

Hence, by Theorem 22,

$$x - 1 \geq \lim_{n = \infty} a(n, x) = \log x.$$

Theorem 38: $\qquad \log x \geq 1 - \dfrac{1}{x} \quad for \ x > 0.$

Proof: By Theorem 37 (with $\dfrac{1}{x}$ for x), we have

$$\log x = - \log \frac{1}{x} \geq - \left(\frac{1}{x} - 1\right) = 1 - \frac{1}{x}.$$

Theorem 39: $\qquad \log x \begin{cases} > 0 \ for \ x > 1, \\ = 0 \ for \ x = 1, \\ < 0 \ for \ 0 < x < 1. \end{cases}$

Proof: Theorems 38, 32, and 37.

Theorem 40: $\qquad \log x < \log y \ for \ 0 < x < y.$

Proof: $\qquad 0 < \dfrac{x}{y} < 1,$

so that, by Theorems 34 and 39,

$$\log x - \log y = \log \frac{x}{y} < 0.$$

Theorem 41: *For every* x,

$$\log y = x$$

has exactly one solution y.

Proof: W.l.g. (i.e., without loss of generality—this abbreviation will be used frequently), let $x > 0$; for, if $x = 0$, the only solution is $y = 1$, and in case $x < 0$ the given equation is equivalent to

$$\log \frac{1}{y} = - x.$$

1) By Theorem 40, there is at most one solution.
2) We place a in

Class $\ $ I $\ $ if $a \leq 0$ or if $\log a \leq x$,
Class $\ $ II $\ $ if $\log a > x$.

Then each α belongs to exactly one of these classes.

Class I contains the positive number $a = 1$. For, by Theorem 32,

$$\log 1 = 0 \leq x.$$

Class II contains $a = 2^m$ if $m > \dfrac{x}{\log 2}$. For, by Theorem 36, we have in this case

$$\log (2^m) = m \log 2 > x.$$

If α is in class II, and $\beta > \alpha$, then

$$\beta > \alpha > 0,$$

$$\log \beta > \log \alpha > x,$$

so that β belongs to class II.

Hence there exists a $y > 0$ such that every $\alpha < y$ belongs to I and every $a > y$ to II. I assert that

$$\log y = x.$$

If we had

$$\log y < x,$$

then, setting

$$h = x - \log y \qquad (> 0),$$

we would have by Theorem 37 that

$$\log \big((1 + h)y\big) = \log (1 + h) + \log y \leq h + \log y = x,$$

so that $(1 + h)y$ would be in class I, and yet $> y$.

If we had

$$\log y > x,$$

then, setting

$$h = \frac{\log y - x}{2} \qquad (> 0),$$

we would have by Theorem 37 that

$$\log \frac{y}{1 + h} = \log y - \log (1 + h) \geq \log y - h > \log y - (\log y - x) = x,$$

so that $\dfrac{y}{1 + h}$ would be in class II, and yet $< y$.

Definition 13: *e is the solution of*

$$\log y = 1.$$

The letter e may now no longer be used to denote anything other than this positive universal constant.

Definition 14: *For each x, e^x is the solution of*

$$\log y = x.$$

To be read: e to the x-th power, or simply e to the x. Nomenclature: A power with exponent x and base e.

Definition 14 had to be preceded by Theorem 36 for $a = e$, since the definition of a power with integral exponent and positive base is an elementary matter (cf. F.o.A.), and it is precisely by Theorem 36 that we have, for integral x (with the original meaning of e^x), that

$$\log (e^x) = x \log e = x \cdot 1 = x.$$

Theorem 42: $\qquad\qquad e^x > 0.$

Proof: By Definition 14, e^x has a logarithm, and so is > 0.

Theorem 43: *If $x < y$, then $e^x < e^y$.*

Proof: $\qquad\qquad \log e^x = x < y = \log e^y$

and Theorem 40.

Theorem 44: *The equation*

$$e^x = y$$

has exactly one solution for each $y > 0$.

Proof: By Definition 14,

$$e^x = y$$

means the same as

$$\log y = x.$$

Theorem 45: *For $a > 0$ and integral x,*

$$e^{x \log a} = a^x.$$

Proof: By Theorem 36,

$$\log (a^x) = x \log a.$$

Definition 15: $\qquad a^x = e^{x \log a}$ *for $a > 0$.*

To be read: a to the x-th power, or simply a to the x. Nomenclature: A power with exponent x and base a.

This definition had to be preceded by Theorem 45. It should also be observed that this definition, for $a = e$, agrees with Definition 14. For,

$$e^{x \log e} = e^{x \cdot 1} = e^x.$$

Theorem 46: $\qquad\qquad 1^x = 1.$

Proof: $\qquad\qquad 1^x = e^{x \log 1} = e^0 = 1.$

Theorem 47: *If $a > 0$ then $a^x > 0$.*

Proof: Definition 15 and Theorem 42.

Theorem 48: $\log(a^x) = x \log a$ *for* $a > 0$.

Proof: Definitions 14 and 15.

Theorem 49: $a^x \begin{cases} < a^y \ for \ a > 1, \\ = a^y \ for \ a = 1, \\ > a^y \ for \ 0 < a < 1, \end{cases}$ *if* $x < y$.

Proof: For $a > 1$, we have by Theorem 43 that

$$a^x = e^{x \log a} < e^{y \log a} = a^y.$$

For $a = 1$,

$$a^x = 1 = a^y.$$

For $0 < a < 1$ we have by Theorem 43 that
$$a^x = e^{x \log a} > e^{y \log a} = a^y.$$

Theorem 50: $a^x a^y = a^{x+y}$ *for* $a > 0$.

Proof: $\log(a^x a^y) = \log(a^x) + \log(a^y) = x \log a + y \log a$
$$= (x + y) \log a = \log(a^{x+y}).$$

Theorem 51: $\dfrac{a^x}{a^y} = a^{x-y}$ *for* $a > 0$.

Proof: By Theorem 50, we have
$$a^y a^{x-y} = a^{y+(x-y)} = a^x.$$

Theorem 52: $a^x a^{-x} = 1$ *for* $a > 0$.

Proof: By Theorem 50, we have
$$a^x a^{-x} = a^{x+(-x)} = a^0 = 1.$$

Theorem 53: $\prod\limits_{\nu=1}^{m} a^{x_\nu} = a^{\sum\limits_{\nu=1}^{m} x_\nu}$ *for* $a > 0$.

Proof: By Theorem 35, we have
$$\log \prod_{\nu=1}^{m} a^{x_\nu} = \sum_{\nu=1}^{m} \log a^{x_\nu} = \sum_{\nu=1}^{m} x_\nu \log a = \left(\sum_{\nu=1}^{m} x_\nu \right) \log a = \log \left(a^{\sum\limits_{\nu=1}^{m} x_\nu} \right).$$

Theorem 54: $(ab)^x = a^x b^x$ *for* $a > 0$, $b > 0$.

Proof: $(ab)^x = e^{x \log(ab)} = e^{x(\log a + \log b)} = e^{x \log a} e^{x \log b} = a^x b^x$.

Theorem 55: $\qquad (a^x)^y = a^{xy}$ for $a > 0$.

Proof: $\qquad (a^x)^y = e^{y \log (a^x)} = e^{yx \log a} = a^{yx} = a^{xy}$.

Theorem 56: If $0 < a < 1$ or if $a > 1$, then a^y takes on each value $x > 0$ exactly once, namely for

$$y = \frac{\log x}{\log a}.$$

Proof: $\qquad a^y = x$

is equivalent to

$$e^{y \log a} = e^{\log x},$$

and so to

$$y \log a = \log x.$$

Definition 16: If $x > 0$, $a > 0$, and $a \neq 1$, then $\log_{(10)} x$ denotes the solution y of

$$a^y = x.$$

That is,

$$\log_{(a)} x = \frac{\log x}{\log a}.$$

To be read: The logarithm of x to the base a.

Definition 17: $\log_{(10)} x$ (for $x > 0$) is called the Briggs (or common) logarithm of x.

It is "known" to the reader from secondary school.

Theorem 57: $\qquad \log_{(e)} x = \log x$ for $x > 0$.

Proof: $\qquad \dfrac{\log x}{\log e} = \log x$.

Theorem 58: $\log_{(a)} (xy) = \log_{(a)} x + \log_{(a)} y$ for $x > 0$, $y > 0$, $a > 0$, $a \neq 1$.

Proof: $\qquad \dfrac{\log (xy)}{\log a} = \dfrac{\log x + \log y}{\log a} = \dfrac{\log x}{\log a} + \dfrac{\log y}{\log a}$.

Theorem 59: $\log_{(a)} \left(\dfrac{x}{y} \right) = \log_{(a)} x - \log_{(a)} y$ for $x > 0$, $y > 0$, $a > 0$, $a \neq 1$.

Proof: By Theorem 58, we have

$$\log_{(a)} x = \log_{(a)} \left(\frac{x}{y} y \right) = \log_{(a)} \left(\frac{x}{y} \right) + \log_{(a)} y.$$

Theorem 60: *If* $x \geq 0$, *then for every* m,

$$y^m = x, \quad y \geq 0$$

has exactly one solution.

Proof: 1) For $x = 0$, it is clear that $y = 0$ is a solution, and indeed the only solution.

2) For $x > 0$, the positive number

$$y = x^{\frac{1}{m}}$$

satisfies our equation, since by Theorem 55, we have

$$\left(x^{\frac{1}{m}}\right)^m = x^{\frac{1}{m} \cdot m} = x^1 = x.$$

Conversely, for $x > 0$ it follows from

$$y^m = x, \quad y \geq 0$$

and Theorem 55 (since $y = 0$ need not be considered) that

$$x^{\frac{1}{m}} = (y^m)^{\frac{1}{m}} = y^{m \cdot \frac{1}{m}} = y^1 = y.$$

Definition 18: *The* y *of Theorem 60 is called* $\sqrt[m]{x}$.
To be read: The m-th root of x.
Definition 18 agrees, for $x > 0$, $m = 2^n$, with Definition 10.

Theorem 61: $\qquad\qquad \sqrt[1]{x} = x \; for \; x \geq 0.$

Proof: $\qquad\qquad\qquad x^1 = x.$

Theorem 62: $\qquad\qquad \sqrt[2]{x} = \sqrt{x} \; for \; x \geq 0.$

Proof: $\qquad\qquad\qquad \sqrt{x} \geq 0,$

$$\left(\sqrt{x}\right)^2 = x.$$

CHAPTER 3

FUNCTIONS AND CONTINUITY

Introduction

We first wish to illustrate, by examples, the following concept: y "depends" on x or, y is a "function" of x. We shall then give a formal definition of this concept. We shall next seek to grasp, by means of examples, the following concept: y "depends continuously" on x or, y is a "continuous function" of x. We shall then give a formal definition of this concept.

1) The formula

$$y = x^2$$

assigns exactly one y to each x. For example, if $x = 1$ then $y = 1$, if $x = -1$ then $y = 1$, and if $x = \sqrt{2}$ then $y = 2$.

Thus y is determined by x. Of course, there is nothing to prevent different values of x from being assigned to the same y.

2) If c is fixed ("constant"), then

$$y = c$$

assigns exactly one y to each x. Of course, there is nothing to prevent all values of x from being assigned to the same y.

3)
$$y = \log x$$

assigns exactly one y to each $x > 0$ (and no y to any $x \leqq 0$).

4)
$$y = \sqrt{x}$$

assigns exactly one y to each $x \geqq 0$ (and no y to any $x < 0$).

5)
$$y = \frac{x}{x}$$

assigns exactly one y to each $x \neq 0$ (namely, $y = 1$), and no y to $x = 0$.

6) If a, b, and c are fixed ("constants"), then

$$y = a + bx + cx^2$$

is defined for all x.

7) If

$$y = 3 \text{ for } x > 2, \text{ and}$$
$$y \text{ is not defined for } x \leq 2,$$

then exactly one y is assigned to each $x > 2$, and no y to any $x \leq 2$.

8) If

$$y = \begin{cases} 0 & \text{for } x \geq 0, \\ -1 & \text{for } x < 0, \end{cases}$$

then exactly one y is assigned to each x. This example shows that it is not required that y be defined by a single formula.

9)
$$y = \begin{cases} 0 \text{ for rational } x, \\ 1 \text{ for irrational } x. \end{cases}$$

10) (contains 1), 2), and 6) as special cases.) Let $n \geq 0$ be integral, let a_ν be given for integral ν with $0 \leq \nu \leq n$, and let

$$y = \sum_{\nu=0}^{n} a_\nu x^\nu$$

(for all x).

11)
$$y = |x| \text{ for all } x.$$

12)
$$y = \begin{cases} 1 \text{ for } x = 0, \\ \prod_{\nu=1}^{x} \nu \text{ for integral } x > 0. \end{cases}$$

13)
$$y = e^x \text{ for all } x.$$

14)
$$y = \sqrt[n]{x} \text{ for } x \geq 0 \text{ if } n \text{ is an integer } > 0.$$

We have now had sufficient preparation for the understanding of

Definition 19: *Let $\mathfrak{M}$ be a set of numbers. Let exactly one number y be assigned to each x of $\mathfrak{M}$. We then call y a function of x and write, say,*

$$y = f(x).$$

x is called the independent, y the dependent variable. (We may, of course, use any letters instead of x, y, and f.)

Definition 20: *A function of the type given in example* 10) *is called an entire rational function or a polynomial.*

Definition 21: *The function of example* 12) *is called $x!$.*
To be read: x factorial. $x!$ is thus defined only for integral $x \geq 0$.
The following are important examples of sets of numbers:

If

$$a < b,$$

the set of x for which

1) $a \leq x \leq b,$
2) $a < x < b,$
3) $a < x \leq b,$
4) $a \leq x < b;$

for every b the set of x for which
5) $$x \leq b,$$
6) $$x < b;$$
for every a the set of x for which
7) $$x \geq a,$$
8) $$x > a.$$

Further examples are the sets consisting of
9) all x,
10) all rational x,
11) all irrational x,
12) a single number $x = a$.

We now come to the examples which precede the definition of continuity. Continuity is a property which a function either has or does not have at any given x.

1) The function
$$y = 2 \text{ for } x \leq 1,$$
$$y = x \text{ for } x > 1,$$
does not have the property at $x = 1$, but does have it for all other x.

2) The function
$$y = 1 \text{ for } 0 \leq x \leq 1,$$
$$y = x \text{ for } x > 1,$$
has the property for all $x > 0$, but for no $x \leq 0$.

3) The function
$$y = 1 \text{ for rational } x,$$
$$y = 0 \text{ for irrational } x$$
does not have the property for any x.

4) The function
$$y = x! \text{ for integral } x \geq 0$$
does not have the property for any x.

5) The function
$$y = x^2 \text{ for all } x$$
has the property for all x.

What is the property with which we are concerned if $x = \xi$ is any arbitrary number?

First of all, $f(x)$ must be defined at $x = \xi$ and indeed in an entire "neighborhood" of ξ; i. e. there must exist an $a < \xi$ and a $\beta > \xi$ such that $f(x)$ is defined for $a < x < \beta$.

(This already enables us to settle example 4) in the negative. Similarly for the $x \leq 0$ in example 2)).

Crudely speaking, the property is the following: If x is near ξ, then $f(x)$ is near $f(\xi)$.

What is the precise meaning of this? Set

$$f(\xi) = \eta.$$

Let δ be any positive number. We then require that, in a whole neighborhood of ξ, we have both

(1)
$$f(x) < f(\xi) + \delta$$

and

(2)
$$f(x) > f(\xi) - \delta.$$

Taken together, these inequalities mean that

$$|f(x) - f(\xi)| < \delta.$$

By a "neighborhood" we mean

$$\alpha < x < \beta,$$

where $\alpha < \xi < \beta$. (Incidentally, $x = \xi$ needs no investigation, since (1) and (2) automatically hold there.) But it is quite equivalent to require a neighborhood of the form

$$\xi - \varepsilon < x < \xi + \varepsilon$$

where $\varepsilon > 0$, i. e. to speak of the x for which

$$|x - \xi| < \varepsilon.$$

For, if $\alpha < \xi < \beta$, then all x for which

$$|x - \xi| < \varepsilon = \text{Min} \; (\beta - \xi, \; \xi - \alpha)$$

belong to $\alpha < x < \beta$, since for such x we have

$$\alpha = \xi - (\xi - \alpha) \leqq \xi - \varepsilon < x < \xi + \varepsilon \leqq \xi + (\beta - \xi) = \beta.$$

In example 1), we have

$$f(1) = 2.$$

If $\delta = \frac{1}{2}$, it would be required that

$$\tfrac{3}{2} = f(1) - \tfrac{1}{2} < f(x) < f(1) + \tfrac{1}{2} = \tfrac{5}{2}$$

in some neighborhood of 1. But if $1 < x < \frac{3}{2}$, then

$$f(x) = x < \frac{3}{2},$$

so that there is no $\beta > \xi = 1$ such that

$$\tfrac{3}{2} < f(x) \quad \text{for} \quad 1 < x < \beta.$$

Therefore, $f(x)$ does not have the desired property at $\xi = 1$. It has the property at every $\xi < 1$. For, if $x \leqq 1$, then

$$f(x) - f(\xi) = 2 - 2 = 0.$$

Thus for suitable α, β for which $\alpha < \xi < \beta$, we have

$$|f(x) - f(\xi)| = 0 \quad \text{for} \quad \alpha < x < \beta.$$

$f(x)$ also has the desired property for all $\xi > 1$. For if $x > 1$, we have

$$| f(x) - f(\xi) | = | x - \xi |.$$

If $\delta > 0$ is given, then for

$$| x - \xi | < \text{Min} \ (\xi - 1, \delta),$$

we have, since

$$x = \xi + (x - \xi) > \xi - (\xi - 1) = 1,$$
$$| f(x) - f(\xi) | < \delta.$$

In example 2), if $\xi = 1$, then

$$f(x) - f(\xi) = \begin{cases} 0 & \text{for } 0 \le x \le \xi, \\ x - \xi & \text{for } x > \xi, \end{cases}$$

so that, for all $x \ge 0$,

$$| f(x) - f(\xi) | \le | x - \xi |,$$

and hence, for every $\delta > 0$,

$$| f(x) - f(\xi) | < \delta \text{ for } | x - \xi | < \text{Min} \ (1, \delta).$$

If $0 < \xi < 1$, then

$$f(x) - f(\xi) = 0 \quad \text{for} \quad 0 \le x \le 1,$$

and therefore for $| x - \xi | < \text{Min}(\xi, 1 - \xi)$. If $\xi > 1$, then

$$f(x) - f(\xi) = x - \xi \quad \text{for} \quad x > 1.$$

Thus if $| x - \xi | < \text{Min}(\xi - 1, \delta)$, then

$$| f(x) - f(\xi) | = | x - \xi | < \delta.$$

As for example 3), we remark that if $a < b$ then there is a rational x between a and b, i.e. one such that

$$a < x < b.$$

The reader who knows this fact through his elementary work (cf. F.o.A.) only for $a > 0$, may also obtain it for $a = 0$ by choosing a rational x between $\frac{b}{2}$ and b, and for $a < 0$ by choosing a rational $y = - x$ between $\text{Max}(- b, 0)$ and $- a$.

Then if $a < b$ there is also an irrational x between a and b. For let us choose a rational r such that

$$a < r < b,$$

and a positive integer n such that

$$n > \frac{\sqrt{2}}{b - r}.$$

Then $r + \dfrac{\sqrt{2}}{n}$ is irrational (for otherwise $\sqrt{2}$ would be rational), and

$$a < r + \frac{\sqrt{2}}{n} < b.$$

Thus for every ξ, and for every $\varepsilon > 0$, there is an x such that

$$\xi - \varepsilon < x < \xi + \varepsilon, \quad |f(x) - f(\xi)| = 1,$$

so that for $\delta = 1$, there is no ε of the desired sort.

In example 5), for each ξ, and for every $\delta > 0$, we have that if

$$|x - \xi| < \mathrm{Min}\left(1, \frac{\delta}{1 + 2|\xi|}\right),$$

then

$$|x + \xi| = |(x - \xi) + 2\xi| \leq |x - \xi| + 2|\xi| < 1 + 2|\xi|,$$

so that

$$|f(x) - f(\xi)| = |x^2 - \xi^2| = |x + \xi| \, |x - \xi| \leq (1 + 2|\xi|)|x - \xi| < \delta.$$

We have now had sufficient preparation to understand

Definition 22: $f(x)$ *is said to be continuous at* (for) $x = \xi$ *if for every* $\delta > 0$ *there exists an* $\varepsilon > 0$ (independent of x) *such that*

$$|f(x) - f(\xi)| < \delta \quad for \quad |x - \xi| < \varepsilon.$$

(It would be equivalent to require that this hold for $0 < |x - \xi| < \varepsilon$.)

In other words: If for every $\delta > 0$ there exists an $\varepsilon > 0$ (independent of h) such that

$$|f(\xi + h) - f(\xi)| < \delta \quad for \quad |h| < \varepsilon$$

(or—as above—only for $0 < |h| < \varepsilon$).

Theorem 63: *If*
$$a < \xi < b$$
and
$$f(x) = c \ \text{for} \ a < x < b$$
(where c is independent of x), *then $f(x)$ is continuous at ξ.*

Proof: For every $\delta > 0$ and for $|h| < \mathrm{Min}(b - \xi, \xi - a)$, we have
$$a < \xi + h < b,$$
$$|f(\xi + h) - f(\xi)| = |c - c| = 0 < \delta.$$

Theorem 64: *If*
$$a < \xi < b$$
and
$$f(x) = x \ \text{for} \ a < x < b,$$
then $f(x)$ is continuous at ξ.

Proof: If $|x - \xi| < \mathrm{Min}(\delta, b - \xi, \xi - a)$, then
$$a < x < b,$$
$$|f(x) - f(\xi)| = |x - \xi| < \delta.$$

Theorem 65: *Let $f(x)$ and $g(x)$ be continuous at ξ. Then $f(x) + g(x)$ is continuous at ξ.*

Proof: For every $\delta > 0$ there is an $\varepsilon_1 > 0$ and an $\varepsilon_2 > 0$ such that
$$|f(\xi + h) - f(\xi)| < \frac{\delta}{2} \ \text{for} \ |h| < \varepsilon_1,$$
$$|g(\xi + h) - g(\xi)| < \frac{\delta}{2} \ \text{for} \ |h| < \varepsilon_2.$$

Hence for $|h| < \mathrm{Min}(\varepsilon_1, \varepsilon_2)$, we have
$$|(f(\xi + h) + g(\xi + h)) - (f(\xi) + g(\xi))|$$
$$= |(f(\xi + h) - f(\xi)) + (g(\xi + h) - g(\xi))|$$
$$\leq |f(\xi + h) - f(\xi)| + |g(\xi + h) - g(\xi)| < \frac{\delta}{2} + \frac{\delta}{2} = \delta.$$

Example: $c + x$ is continuous everywhere, by Theorems 63, 64 and 65.

Theorem 66: *If $m \geq 1$ is integral, and if $f_n(x)$ is continuous at ξ for every integer n such that $1 \leq n \leq m$, then $\sum\limits_{n=1}^{m} f_n(x)$ is continuous at ξ.*

Proof: $m = 1$ is obvious. To proceed from m to $m + 1$:

$$\sum_{n=1}^{m+1} f_n(x) = \sum_{n=1}^{m} f_n(x) + f_{m+1}(x)$$

and Theorem 65.

Theorem 67: *If $f(x)$ is continuous at ξ, then $cf(x)$ is continuous at ξ.*

Proof: For every $\delta > 0$ there is an $\varepsilon > 0$ such that if $|h| < \varepsilon$, we have

$$| f(\xi + h) - f(\xi) | < \frac{\delta}{|c| + 1},$$

so that

$$| cf(\xi + h) - cf(\xi) | = | c(f(\xi + h) - f(\xi)) |$$
$$= | c | | f(\xi + h) - f(\xi) | < (| c | + 1) \frac{\delta}{|c| + 1} = \delta.$$

Theorem 68: *Let $f(x)$ and $g(x)$ be continuous at ξ. Then $f(x) - g(x)$ is continuous at ξ.*

Proof: $f(x) - g(x) = f(x) + (-1) g(x)$ and Theorems 67, 65.

Theorem 69: *Let $f(x)$ and $g(x)$ be continuous at ξ. Then $f(x)g(x)$ is continuous at ξ.*

Proof: Let $\delta > 0$ be given. Choose an $\varepsilon > 0$ such that if $|h| < \varepsilon$, then

$$| f(\xi + h) - f(\xi) | < \mathrm{Min} \left(1, \frac{\delta}{3(1 + | g(\xi) |)} \right)$$

and

$$| g(\xi + h) - g(\xi) | < \frac{\delta}{3(1 + | f(\xi) |)}.$$

Then if $|h| < \varepsilon$, we have

$$| f(\xi + h)g(\xi + h) - f(\xi)g(\xi) |$$
$$= | (f(\xi+h) - f(\xi)) (g(\xi+h) - g(\xi)) + f(\xi)(g(\xi+h) - g(\xi)) + g(\xi)(f(\xi+h) - f(\xi)) |$$
$$\leq | f(\xi+h) - f(\xi) | | g(\xi+h) - g(\xi) | + | f(\xi) | | g(\xi+h) - g(\xi) | + | g(\xi) | | f(\xi+h) - f(\xi) |$$
$$< 1 \cdot \frac{\delta}{3} + | f(\xi) | \frac{\delta}{3(1 + | f(\xi) |)} + | g(\xi) | \frac{\delta}{3(1 + | g(\xi) |)} < \frac{\delta}{3} + \frac{\delta}{3} + \frac{\delta}{3} = \delta.$$

Theorem 70: *If $m \geq 1$ is integral, and if $f_n(x)$ is continuous at ξ for each integer n such that $1 \leq n \leq m$, then $\prod\limits_{n=1}^{m} f_n(x)$ is continuous at ξ.*

Proof: $m = 1$ is obvious. To proceed from m to $m + 1$:

$$\prod_{n=1}^{m+1} f_n(x) = \prod_{n=1}^{m} f_n(x) \cdot f_{m+1}(x)$$

and Theorem 69.

Theorem 71: If $f(x)$ *is continuous at* ξ, *and if* m *is an integer* $\geqq 1$, *then* $f^m(x)$ *is continuous at* ξ.

($f^m(x)$ is a more convenient notation for $(f(x))^m$.)

Proof: Theorem 70, with

$$f_n(x) = f(x) \text{ for } 1 \leqq n \leqq m.$$

Examples: 1) For integral $m \geqq 1$, x^m is continuous everywhere by Theorems 64 and 71.

2) Thus every polynomial $\sum\limits_{\nu=0}^{n} a_\nu x^\nu$ is continuous everywhere. For, $a_\nu x^\nu$ is continuous everywhere for $\nu = 0$ by Theorem 63, and for $0 < \nu \leqq n$ by Example 1) and Theorem 67. Thus the polynomial itself is continuous everywhere by Theorem 66.

Theorem 72: If $f(x)$ *is continuous at* ξ *and if*

$$f(\xi) > 0,$$

then there is a $p > 0$ *and a* $q > 0$ *such that*

$$f(\xi + h) > p \quad \text{for} \quad |h| < q.$$

Proof: Choose $q > 0$ such that

$$|f(\xi + h) - f(\xi)| < \tfrac{1}{2} f(\xi) \text{ for } |h| < q.$$

Then if $|h| < q$, we have

$$f(\xi+h) = f(\xi) + (f(\xi+h) - f(\xi)) > f(\xi) - \tfrac{1}{2}f(\xi) = \tfrac{1}{2}f(\xi) = p.$$

Theorem 73: If $f(x)$ *is continuous at* ξ *and if*

$$f(\xi) < 0,$$

then there is a $p > 0$ *and a* $q > 0$ *such that*

$$f(\xi + h) < -p \text{ for } |h| < q.$$

Proof: Theorem 72 with $-f(x)$ for $f(x)$. In fact, $-f(x)$ is continuous at ξ by Theorem 67.

Theorem 74: If $f(x)$ *is continuous at* ξ *and if*

$$f(\xi) \neq 0,$$

then $\dfrac{1}{f(x)}$ *is continuous at* ξ.

Proof: By Theorem 72 or 73, choose $p > 0$ and $q > 0$ such that
$$|f(\xi + h)| > p \text{ for } |h| < q.$$

Then if $|h| < q$, we have

$$\left| \frac{1}{f(\xi + h)} - \frac{1}{f(\xi)} \right| = \left| \frac{f(\xi) - f(\xi + h)}{f(\xi + h)f(\xi)} \right| = \frac{|f(\xi + h) - f(\xi)|}{|f(\xi + h)| \, |f(\xi)|}$$

$$\leqq \frac{1}{p \, |f(\xi)|} |f(\xi + h) - f(\xi)|.$$

For every $\delta > 0$ there is an ε with $0 < \varepsilon \leqq q$ such that, for $|h| < \varepsilon$,

$$|f(\xi + h) - f(\xi)| < \delta p |f(\xi)|,$$

which implies

$$\left| \frac{1}{f(\xi + h)} - \frac{1}{f(\xi)} \right| < \frac{1}{p |f(\xi)|} \delta p |f(\xi)| = \delta.$$

Example: $\dfrac{1}{x}$ is continuous at every $\xi \neq 0$.

Theorem 75: *Let $f(x)$ and $g(x)$ be continuous at ξ. Let*

$$g(\xi) \neq 0.$$

Then $\dfrac{f(x)}{g(x)}$ is continuous at ξ.

Proof: By Theorem 74, $\dfrac{1}{g(x)}$ is continuous at ξ. Therefore, by Theorem 69, so is

$$f(x) \frac{1}{g(x)} = \frac{f(x)}{g(x)}.$$

Example: Let $f(x)$ and $g(x)$ be polynomials, and let

$$g(\xi) \neq 0.$$

Then $\dfrac{f(x)}{g(x)}$ is continuous at ξ. For example, $\dfrac{1 + x^3}{1 + x^2}$ is continuous at all ξ, and

$\dfrac{1 - x^3}{1 - x}$ at all $\xi \neq 1$.

Theorem 76: *If $f(x)$ is continuous at ξ, then $|f(x)|$ is continuous at ξ.*

Proof: For every $\delta > 0$ there is an $\varepsilon > 0$ such that

$$|f(\xi + h) - f(\xi)| < \delta \text{ for } |h| < \varepsilon.$$

Therefore if $|h| < \varepsilon$, we have

$$\left| |f(\xi + h)| - |f(\xi)| \right| \leqq |f(\xi + h) - f(\xi)| < \delta.$$

Example: $|x|$ is continuous everywhere.

Theorem 77: *Let $g(x)$ be continuous at ξ, $g(\xi) = \eta$, and let $f(x)$ be continuous at η. Then $f(g(x))$ is continuous at ξ.*

Proof: Let $\delta > 0$ be given. Choose $\zeta > 0$ such that

$$|f(\eta + k) - f(\eta)| < \delta \text{ for } |k| < \zeta,$$

and then $\varepsilon > 0$ such that

$$|g(\xi + h) - g(\xi)| < \zeta \text{ for } |h| < \varepsilon.$$

Then if $|h| < \varepsilon$ and if we set

$$k = g(\xi + h) - g(\xi),$$

we have

$$|k| < \zeta,$$

so that

$$|f(g(\xi + h)) - f(g(\xi))| = |f(\eta + k) - f(\eta)| < \delta.$$

Example: $|1 + x - x^2|$ is continuous at every ξ, by Theorem 77 with

$$f(x) = |x|, \quad g(x) = 1 + x - x^2.$$

Theorem 78: $\log x$ *is continuous at every* $\xi > 0$.
Proof: Let $\delta > 0$ be given. Then

$$\alpha = \xi e^{-\delta} < \xi < \xi e^{\delta} = \beta.$$

And if

$$\alpha < x < \beta$$

then

$$\log \xi - \delta = \log \alpha < \log x < \log \beta = \log \xi + \delta,$$

$$|\log x - \log \xi| < \delta.$$

Theorem 79: e^x *is continuous at every* ξ.
Proof: Let $\delta > 0$ be given and, w. l. g., let it be $< e^{\xi}$. Then

$$\alpha = \log (e^{\xi} - \delta) < \log e^{\xi} = \xi < \log (e^{\xi} + \delta) = \beta.$$

And if

$$\alpha < x < \beta$$

then

$$e^{\xi} - \delta = e^{\alpha} < e^x < e^{\beta} = e^{\xi} + \delta,$$

$$|e^x - e^{\xi}| < \delta.$$

Theorem 80: *If* $a > 0$, *then* a^x *is continuous at every* $x = \xi$.
Proof: Theorem 77, with

$$f(x) = e^x, \quad g(x) = x \log a.$$

Theorem 81: *For all* n, x^n *is continuous at every* $x = \xi > 0$.
Proof: Theorem 77, with

$$f(x) = e^x, \quad g(x) = n \log x.$$

Example: $\sqrt{x}$ is continuous for every $\xi > 0$.
As might be expected, this example can also be dealt with directly. For $h \geqq -\xi$, we have

$$\sqrt{\xi + h} - \sqrt{\xi} = \frac{(\sqrt{\xi + h})^2 - (\sqrt{\xi})^2}{\sqrt{\xi + h} + \sqrt{\xi}} = \frac{h}{\sqrt{\xi + h} + \sqrt{\xi}},$$

so that for $h \geqq -\xi$, $|h| < \delta \sqrt{\xi}$ we have

$$\left|\sqrt{\xi + h} - \sqrt{\xi}\right| \leqq \frac{|h|}{\sqrt{\xi}} < \delta.$$

Theorem 82: *If n is an integer, then*

$$[x + n] = [x] + n.$$

([x] was defined in Definition 1.)

Proof: $[x] + n \leq x + n < ([x] + 1) + n = ([x] + n) + 1.$

Definition 23 (only a temporary one until we reach Theorem 86, and also for Theorem 100):

$$\{x\} = \text{Min} \, (x - [x], \, 1 - x + [x]).$$

Thus $\{ x \}$ is the "distance" of x to its "nearest" integer. If $x - \frac{1}{2}$ is integral, then there are two integers (namely $x - \frac{1}{2}$ and $x + \frac{1}{2}$) which have the smallest possible distance from x.

Theorem 83: *If n is an integer, then*

$$\{x + n\} = \{x\}.$$

Proof: By Definition 23 and Theorem 82, we have

$$\{x + n\} = \text{Min} \, (x + n - [x + n], \; 1 - x - n + [x + n])$$
$$= \text{Min} \, (x - [x], \; 1 - x + [x]) = \{x\}.$$

Theorem 84: $\qquad 0 \leq \{x\} \leq \frac{1}{2}.$

Proof: 1) By Theorem 2, we have

$$x - [x] \geq 0, \quad 1 - x + [x] > 0,$$

so that

$$\{x\} \geq 0.$$

2) $\qquad 2\{x\} = \{x\} + \{x\} \leq (x - [x]) + (1 - x + [x]) = 1,$

$$\{x\} \leq \frac{1}{2}.$$

Theorem 85: $\qquad | \, \{x\} - \{y\} \, | \leq | \, x - y \, |.$

Proof: Since both sides remain unchanged upon interchanging x and y, let, w. l. g.,

$$\{x\} \geq \{y\}.$$

There exists an integer n such that

$$| \, y - n \, | = \{y\}.$$

This implies that

$$\{x\} \leq | \, x - n \, | = | \, (x - y) + (y - n) \, | \leq | \, x - y \, | + | \, y - n \, |$$
$$= | \, x - y \, | + \{y\},$$
$$0 \leq \{x\} - \{y\} \leq | \, x - y \, |,$$
$$| \, \{x\} - \{y\} \, | \leq | \, x - y \, |.$$

Theorem 86: $\{ x \}$ *is continuous everywhere.*

Proof: Let $\delta > 0$. For every ξ and for $| \, h \, | < \delta$ we have, by Theorem 85,

$$| \, \{\xi + h\} - \{\xi\} \, | \leq | \, (\xi + h) - \xi \, | = | \, h \, | < \delta.$$

CHAPTER 4

LIMITS AT $x = \xi$

Introduction

1) The function

$$f(x) = \frac{x^2 - 9}{x - 3}$$

is defined only for $x \neq 3$. We shall say that it has a limit, namely 6, at $x = 3$. Why? For those x which are near 3 **but not equal to 3,** $f(x)$ is near 6. For if $x \neq 3$, then

$$f(x) = x + 3,$$

and $x + 3$ equals 6 at $x = 3$ and is continuous there.

It may appear like mere sophistry not to consider the function $x + 3$ in the first place, instead of $\frac{x^2 - 9}{x - 3}$. However, the fact that there was a denominator which could be cancelled in the neighborhood of $x = 3$, except at $x = 3$ itself, is a coincidence. In the next example, no such coincidence occurs.

2) The function

$$f(x) = \frac{\log(1 + x)}{x}$$

is defined for all $x > -1$ with the exception of 0. We shall find that the situation here at $x = 0$ and for the number 1 is entirely similar to that in example 1) at $x = 3$ and for the number 6.

For $x > -1$, we have, by Theorems 37 and 38,

$$\frac{x}{1 + x} \leq \log(1 + x) \leq x,$$

so that for $x > 0$,

$$\frac{1}{1 + x} \leq \frac{\log(1 + x)}{x} \leq 1,$$

$$-\frac{x}{1+x} \leqq \frac{\log\,(1+x)}{x} - 1 \leqq 0,$$

and, for $-1 < x < 0$,

$$\frac{1}{1+x} \geqq \frac{\log\,(1+x)}{x} \geqq 1,$$

$$-\frac{x}{1+x} \geqq \frac{\log\,(1+x)}{x} - 1 \geqq 0.$$

Thus if $0 < |x| < \frac{1}{2}$, then

$$\left|\frac{\log\,(1+x)}{x} - 1\right| \leqq \frac{|x|}{1+x} < 2\,|x|,$$

so that for any $\delta > 0$, if $0 < |x| < \mathrm{Min}\left(\frac{1}{2}, \frac{\delta}{2}\right)$, then

$$\left|\frac{\log\,(1+x)}{x} - 1\right| < \delta.$$

3)
$$f(x) = \frac{1}{x}$$

is defined for $x \neq 0$. No number η has the desired property at the critical value 0. For, if there were an $\varepsilon > 0$ such that

$$\left|\frac{1}{x} - \eta\right| < 1 \text{ for } 0 < |x| < \varepsilon,$$

then we should have

$$\frac{1}{x} = \left(\frac{1}{x} - \eta\right) + \eta < 1 + |\eta|,$$

for $0 < x < \varepsilon$, which is not the case for

$$x = \mathrm{Min}\left(\frac{\varepsilon}{2}, \frac{1}{1+|\eta|}\right).$$

4) Let

$$f(x) = \begin{cases} 0 \text{ for } x \neq 5, \\ 1 \text{ for } x = 5. \end{cases}$$

0 has the desired property for the critical value 5. Indeed, $|f(x)-0|$ is even equal to 0 for all $x \neq 5$.

Before we proceed to define the concept of limit, we shall prove a theorem which states that limits, when they exist, are unique.

Theorem 87. *Let $a < \xi < b$. Let $f(x)$ be defined for $a < x < \xi$ and for $\xi < x < b$. Then there is at most one number η such that*

$$F(x) = \begin{cases} f(x) & \text{for } a < x < \xi \text{ and } \xi < x < b, \\ \eta & \text{for } x = \xi \end{cases}$$

is continuous at ξ.

Proof: Let η_1 and η_2 be two such numbers. Let $F_1(x)$ and $F_2(x)$ be the corresponding functions $F(x)$. We need only show that

$$g(x) = F_1(x) - F_2(x)$$

is equal to zero at $x = \xi$.

By Theorem 68, $g(x)$ is continuous at $x = \xi$. If we had

$$g(\xi) \neq 0,$$

then for a suitable h we should have, by Theorems 72 and 73,

$$0 < h < \text{Min } (\xi - a, b - \xi), \; g(\xi + h) \neq 0,$$

while, for $a < x < b, x \neq \xi$, we have

$$g(x) = f(x) - f(x) = 0.$$

Definition 24: *Let $a < \xi < b$. Let $f(x)$ be defined for $a < x < \xi$ and for $\xi < x < b$. If there exists an η in the sense of Theorem 87, then we write*

$$\lim_{x = \xi} f(x) = \eta$$

(lim is to be read "limit"), *or more concisely*

$$f(x) \to \eta,$$

and we say that $f(x)$ has the limit η at ξ, or that $f(x)$ approaches η at $x = \xi$ (or as $x \to \xi$).

An equivalent condition (which makes no use of the previous chapter) is that for every $\delta > 0$ there exists an $\varepsilon > 0$ such that

$$|f(\xi + h) - \eta| < \delta \; \text{ for } \; 0 < |h| < \varepsilon,$$

or (equivalently)

$$|f(x) - \eta| < \delta \; \text{ for } \; 0 < |x - \xi| < \varepsilon.$$

This wording of the definition shows that the concept $\lim\limits_{x=\xi} f(x)$, given in Definition 24, is independent of the particular choice of a and b.

Examples (see above): 1) $\lim\limits_{x=3} \dfrac{x^2 - 9}{x - 3} = 6.$

2) $\qquad\qquad \lim\limits_{x=0} \dfrac{\log (1 + x)}{x} = 1,$

and therefore, evidently,

$$\lim\limits_{x=1} \frac{\log x}{x - 1} = 1.$$

Theorem 88: $f(x)$ *is continuous at* ξ *if and only if* $\lim\limits_{x=\xi} f(x)$ *exists and is* $= f(\xi)$.

Proof: Obvious.

For the remainder of this chapter, all limits will be taken at some fixed ξ.

Theorem 89: *If*

$$f(x) \to \eta, \quad g(x) \to \zeta,$$

then

$$f(x) + g(x) \to \eta + \zeta.$$

Proof: For a suitable $p > 0$, $f(x) + g(x)$ is defined for $0 < |x - \varepsilon| < p$. If we define

$$F(x) = \begin{cases} f(x) & \text{for } 0 < |x - \xi| < p, \\ \eta & \text{for } x = \xi, \end{cases}$$

$$G(x) = \begin{cases} g(x) & \text{for } 0 < |x - \xi| < p, \\ \zeta & \text{for } x = \xi, \end{cases}$$

$$\Phi(x) = F(x) + G(x) \text{ for } |x - \xi| < p,$$

then

$$\Phi(x) = \begin{cases} f(x) + g(x) & \text{for } 0 < |x - \xi| < p, \\ \eta + \zeta & \text{for } x = \xi. \end{cases}$$

$F(x)$ and $G(x)$ are continuous at ξ. Therefore, by Theorem 65, so is $\Phi(x)$. Thus we have

$$\Phi(x) \to \eta + \zeta,$$
$$f(x) + g(x) \to \eta + \zeta.$$

Example: $\quad \lim\limits_{x=0} \left(\dfrac{x^2 - 9}{x - 3} + \dfrac{\log (1 + x)}{x} \right) = 3 + 1 = 4.$

Theorem 90: *If*
$$f(x) \to \eta, \quad g(x) \to \zeta,$$
then
$$f(x) - g(x) \to \eta - \zeta.$$

Proof: Like that of Theorem 89, except with
$$\Phi(x) = F(x) - G(x)$$
and Theorem 68.

Theorem 91: *If*
$$f(x) \to \eta, \quad g(x) \to \zeta,$$
then
$$f(x)g(x) \to \eta\zeta.$$

Proof: Like that of Theorem 89, except with
$$\Phi(x) = F(x)\, G(x)$$
and Theorem 69.

Example: $\lim\limits_{x=3} \left((x+4)\dfrac{x^2-9}{x-3} \right) = \lim\limits_{x=3} (x+4) \cdot \lim\limits_{x=3}\dfrac{x^2-9}{x-3} = 7 \cdot 6 = 42.$

Theorem 92: *If*
$$f(x) \to \eta, \quad g(x) \to \zeta, \quad \zeta \neq 0,$$
then
$$\frac{f(x)}{g(x)} \to \frac{\eta}{\zeta}.$$

Proof: Like that of Theorem 89, except with
$$\Phi(x) = \frac{F(x)}{G(x)}$$
and Theorem 75. Of course, p is to be chosen so small that
$$g(x) \neq 0 \text{ for } 0 < |x - \xi| < p.$$

Example: $\lim\limits_{x=0} \dfrac{\log(1+x)}{x(2+x)} = \dfrac{\lim\limits_{x=0}\dfrac{\log(1+x)}{x}}{\lim\limits_{x=0}(2+x)} = \dfrac{1}{2}.$

Theorem 93: *If m is an integer ≥ 1, and if*
$$f_n(x) \to \eta_n \text{ for } 1 \leq n \leq m, n \text{ integral},$$
then
$$\sum_{n=1}^{m} f_n(x) \to \sum_{n=1}^{m} \eta_n.$$

Proof: $m = 1$: Obvious. To proceed from m to $m + 1$:

$$\sum_{n=1}^{m+1} f_n(x) = \sum_{n=1}^{m} f_n(x) + f_{m+1}(x) \to \sum_{n=1}^{m} \eta_n + \eta_{m+1} = \sum_{n=1}^{m+1} \eta_n.$$

Theorem 94: *If m is an integer $\geqq 1$, and if*

$$f_n(x) \to \eta_n \quad \text{for} \quad 1 \leqq n \leqq m, n \text{ integral},$$

then

$$\prod_{n=1}^{m} f_n(x) \to \prod_{n=1}^{m} \eta_n.$$

Proof: $m = 1$: Obvious. To proceed from m to $m + 1$:

$$\prod_{n=1}^{m+1} f_n(x) = \prod_{n=1}^{m} f_n(x) \cdot f_{m+1}(x) \to \prod_{n=1}^{m} \eta_n \cdot \eta_{m+1} = \prod_{n=1}^{m+1} \eta_n.$$

Theorem 95: *If*

$$f(x) \to \eta$$

then, for integral $m \geqq 1$,

$$f^m(x) \to \eta^m.$$

Proof: Theorem 94, with

$$f_n(x) = f(x) \quad \text{for} \quad 1 \leqq n \leqq m.$$

Theorem 96: *If*

$$f(x) \to \eta$$

then

$$|f(x)| \to |\eta|.$$

Proof: Like that of Theorem 89, except without using $g(x)$ and $G(x)$, and with

$$\Phi(x) = |F(x)|$$

and Theorem 76.

Theorem 97: *Let*

$$\lim_{x=\xi} f(x) = 0,$$

$$\varepsilon > 0,$$

$$|g(x)| \leqq |f(x)| \quad \text{for} \quad 0 < |x - \xi| < \varepsilon.$$

Then

$$\lim_{x=\xi} g(x) = 0.$$

Proof: Let $\delta > 0$ be given. There exists a ζ with $0 < \zeta \leqq \varepsilon$ such that, for $0 < |x - \xi| < \zeta$,

$$|f(x)| < \delta,$$

so that

$$|g(x)| < \delta.$$

And now the reader is perhaps waiting for the analogue of Theorem 77 in the following form:
"If

$$\lim_{x=\xi} g(x) = \eta,$$

$$\lim_{x=\eta} f(x) = c$$

then

$$\lim_{x=\xi} f(g(x)) = c."$$

The attempt to prove this by the method of proof of Theorem 89, using Theorem 77, will prove unsuccessful. For, the proposition is false.

Counter-example: $\xi = 0, \eta = 0, c = 0,$

$$f(x) = \begin{cases} 0 & \text{for } x \neq 0, \\ 1 & \text{for } x = 0, \end{cases}$$

$$g(x) = 0 \quad \text{for all } x.$$

Here we have

$$\lim_{x=0} g(x) = \lim_{x=0} 0 = 0,$$

$$\lim_{x=0} f(x) = \lim_{x=0} 0 = 0,$$

$$f(g(x)) = 1 \quad \text{for all } x,$$

$$\lim_{x=0} f(g(x)) = 1,$$

$$1 \neq 0.$$

An even gorier one is the following
Counter-example: $\xi = 0, \quad \eta = 0, \quad c = 0,$

$$f(x) \begin{cases} = 0 & \text{for } x \neq 0, \\ \text{undefined} & \text{for } x = 0, \end{cases}$$

$$g(x) = 0 \quad \text{for all } x.$$

We have

$$\lim_{x=0} g(x) = 0,$$

$$\lim_{x=0} f(x) = 0,$$

$$f(g(x)) \quad \text{undefined for all } x.$$

A weaker, but correct substitute is
Theorem 98: *For a suitable $p > 0$, let*

$$g(x) \neq \eta \quad \text{for} \quad 0 < |x - \xi| < p.$$

Then if

$$\lim_{x=\xi} g(x) = \eta,$$

$$\lim_{x=\eta} f(x) = c,$$

we have

$$\lim_{x=\xi} f(g(x)) = c.$$

Proof: Choose a $q > 0$ such that $f(x)$ is defined for $0 < |x - \eta| < q$. Then choose an r such that $0 < r < p$ and such that for $0 < |x - \xi| < r$, we have

$$|g(x) - \eta| < q,$$

and therefore

$$0 < |g(x) - \eta| < q.$$

Set

$$F(x) = \begin{cases} f(x) & \text{for } 0 < |x - \eta| < q, \\ c & \text{for } x = \eta, \end{cases}$$

$$G(x) = \begin{cases} g(x) & \text{for } 0 < |x - \xi| < r, \\ \eta & \text{for } x = \xi. \end{cases}$$

Then $F(x)$ is continuous at η and $G(x)$ is continuous at ξ. Therefore, by Theorem 77, $F(G(x))$ is continuous at ξ. Thus,

$$\lim_{x=\xi} F(G(x)) = F(G(\xi)) = F(\eta) = c.$$

If $0 < |x - \xi| < r$, we have

$$G(x) = g(x),$$

$$F(G(x)) = F(g(x)) = f(g(x)).$$

Thus,

$$\lim_{x=\xi} f(g(x)) = c.$$

CHAPTER 5

DEFINITION OF THE DERIVATIVE

Introduction

Let $f(x)$ be defined in a neighborhood of $x = \xi$, i. e. for $|x - \xi| < p$ with some suitable $p > 0$. If $0 < |h| < p$, then $f(\xi + h) - f(\xi)$ is the increment of the function $f(x)$ as x changes from $x = \xi$ to $x + h$. This increment is either > 0, $= 0$, or < 0. But the increment h of the variable x is thought of as either > 0 or < 0 (not $= 0$ since we shall soon divide by h). The quotient ("difference quotient") $\dfrac{f(\xi + h) - f(\xi)}{h}$ consequently represents $\dfrac{\text{increment of } f(x)}{\text{increment of } x}$. This may have a $\lim\limits_{h=0}$.

Examples: 1) If
$$f(x) = x^2,$$
then, for every ξ and for every $h \neq 0$,
$$\frac{f(\xi + h) - f(\xi)}{h} = \frac{(\xi + h)^2 - \xi^2}{h} = \frac{2\xi h + h^2}{h} = 2\xi + h.$$
And since
$$\lim_{h=0} (2\xi + h) = 2\xi,$$
we have
$$\lim_{h=0} \frac{f(\xi + h) - f(\xi)}{h} = 2\xi.$$

2) If
$$f(x) = \begin{cases} x^2 & \text{for rational } x, \\ 0 & \text{for irrational } x, \end{cases}$$
then for $\xi = 0$, $h \neq 0$, we have
$$\frac{f(\xi + h) - f(\xi)}{h} = \frac{f(h)}{h} = \begin{cases} h & \text{for rational } h, \\ 0 & \text{for irrational } h. \end{cases}$$

Thus in any case,

$$\left| \frac{f(\xi + h) - f(\xi)}{h} \right| \leq |h|,$$

so that we have

$$\lim_{h=0} \frac{f(\xi + h) - f(\xi)}{h} = 0.$$

But,

$$(1) \qquad \lim_{h=0} \frac{f(\xi + h) - f(\xi)}{h}$$

does not exist for any $\xi \neq 0$. For if ξ is rational, then for every $p > 0$ there exists an irrational $\xi + h$ such that $0 < h < p$, and for this h we have

$$(2) \qquad \frac{f(\xi + h) - f(\xi)}{h} = -\frac{\xi^2}{h}.$$

On the other hand, if ξ is irrational then for every $p > 0$ there exists a rational $\xi + h$ such that $0 < h < p$, and for this h we have

$$(3) \qquad \frac{f(\xi + h) - f(\xi)}{h} = \frac{(\xi + h)^2}{h}.$$

These remarks exclude the existence of the limit (1) in either case. For, suppose it did exist and were $= t$. Then for a suitable $\varepsilon > 0$ and for $0 < |h| < \varepsilon$, we would have

$$\left| \frac{f(\xi + h) - f(\xi)}{h} - t \right| < 1,$$

so that

$$\left| \frac{f(\xi + h) - f(\xi)}{h} \right| < |t| + 1.$$

But for a suitable choice of $p < \varepsilon$, the absolute value of the right-hand sides of (2) and (3) can be made larger than $|t| + 1$ for all h with $0 < h < p$.

3) If

$$f(x) = |x|$$

(an everywhere continuous function), then for $\xi = 0$ and $h \neq 0$, we have

$$\frac{f(\xi + h) - f(\xi)}{h} = \frac{|h|}{h} = \begin{cases} 1 & \text{for } h > 0, \\ -1 & \text{for } h < 0, \end{cases}$$

so that $\lim_{h=0}$ does not exist. On the other hand, if $\xi > 0$ and $0 < |h| < \xi$, then

$$\frac{f(\xi + h) - f(\xi)}{h} = \frac{(\xi + h) - \xi}{h} = 1,$$

so that the limit exists and is $= 1$ for $\xi > 0$. And if $\xi < 0$ and $0 < |h| < -\xi$, then

$$\frac{f(\xi + h) - f(\xi)}{h} = \frac{-(\xi + h) - (-\xi)}{h} = -1,$$

so that the limit exists and is -1 for $\xi < 0$.

Definition 25: $f(x)$ *is differentiable at* $x = \xi$ *if*

$$\lim_{h=0} \frac{f(\xi + h) - f(\xi)}{h}$$

exists. This limit is then called the derivative of $f(x)$ *at* $x = \xi$*, and is denoted by* $f'(\xi)$.

If $y = f(x)$*, then we also write* $f'(x)$. For, the derivative, where it exists, is a function of ξ. And this independent variable may also be called x. *We also write* $\frac{dy}{dx}$ *or* $\frac{df(x)}{dx}$ *or* $\frac{d}{dx} f(x)$ *and,* when there is no possibility of confusion, $(f(x))'$ *or* y'.

(Such confusion might be possible in cases such as the following: What is the meaning of

$$(xz)'?$$

Does it mean

$$\lim_{h=0} \frac{(x+h)z - xz}{h} \qquad (= z),$$

or

$$\lim_{h=0} \frac{x(z+h) - xz}{h} \qquad (= x)?$$

The first limit will be unambiguously designated by $\frac{d(xz)}{dx}$, the second by $\frac{d(xz)}{dz}$. However, we may employ the expression $(x z)'$ with a clear conscience whenever the meaning is unambiguous from the context.

In other words (without making use of the previous chapter): $f(x)$ is differentiable at $x = \xi$ and has the derivative t there if for every $\delta > 0$ there exists an $\varepsilon > 0$ such that

$$\left| \frac{f(\xi + h) - f(\xi)}{h} - t \right| < \delta \text{ for } 0 < |h| < \varepsilon.$$

Expressed in still another way,

$$f'(\xi) = \lim_{x=\xi} \frac{f(x) - f(\xi)}{x - \xi},$$

if this limit exists; i. e. if there is a t (the limit) such that for every $\delta > 0$ there is an $\varepsilon > 0$ for which

$$\left| \frac{f(x) - f(\xi)}{x - \xi} - t \right| < \delta \text{ for } 0 < | x - \xi | < \varepsilon.$$

Theorem 99: *If $f(x)$ is differentiable at $x = \xi$, then $f(x)$ is continuous there.*

Proof: As $h \to 0$, we have

$$\frac{f(\xi + h) - f(\xi)}{h} \to t,$$

so that, by Theorem 91,

$$f(\xi + h) - f(\xi) = \frac{f(\xi + h) - f(\xi)}{h} h \to t \cdot 0 = 0.$$

The third example of the introduction to this chapter shows that continuity does not imply differentiability. In that example, $f(x)$ was continuous everywhere and $f'(x)$ did not exist for one value of x, but did for all other values of x. One might think, and it was indeed thought for a long time, that an everywhere-continuous function must be differentiable somewhere. The following theorem of Weierstrass shows that this is not so. We shall prove it, using a recent example of Van der Waerden's.

Theorem 100: *There exists an everywhere-continuous, nowhere-differentiable function.*

Proof: 1) By Theorems 86, 77 (with $f(x) = \{ x \}$, $g(x) = 4^n x$), and 67 $\left(\text{with } c = \dfrac{1}{4^n} \right)$,

$$f_n(x) = \frac{\{4^n x\}}{4^n}$$

is continuous everywhere for every integer $n \geq 0$. By Theorem 84, we have

$$0 \leq f_n(x) \leq \frac{1}{2 \cdot 4^n} < \frac{1}{4^n}.$$

2) Setting

$$F_m(x) = \sum_{n=0}^{m} f_n(x)$$

for integral $m \geq 0$, we have

$$0 \leq F_m(x) \leq F_{m+1}(x).$$

Since

$$F_m(x) < \sum_{n=0}^{m} \frac{1}{4^n} = \frac{1 - \dfrac{1}{4^{m+1}}}{1 - \frac{1}{4}} < \tfrac{4}{3},$$

Theorem 27 yields, for any fixed x, the existence of

$$\lim_{m=\infty} F_m(x) = f(x).$$

We shall prove all of the above for this function $f(x)$.

3) We first prove that $f(x)$ is continuous for every ξ.

For integral m, k, with $m > k \geqq 0$, and every x, we have

$$0 \leqq F_m(x) - F_k(x) = \sum_{n=k+1}^{m} f_n(x) < \sum_{n=k+1}^{m} \frac{1}{4^n} = \frac{\dfrac{1}{4^{k+1}} - \dfrac{1}{4^{m+1}}}{1 - \frac{1}{4}}$$

$$< \frac{4}{3} \frac{1}{4^{k+1}} < \frac{1}{4^k}.$$

Let $\delta > 0$ be given. We choose an integer $k \geqq 0$ such that

$$\frac{1}{4^k} < \frac{\delta}{3}.$$

Then for every x and for integral $m > k$,

$$0 \leqq F_m(x) - F_k(x) < \frac{\delta}{3},$$

so that $(m \to \infty)$, by Theorem 22,

$$0 \leqq f(x) - F_k(x) \leqq \frac{\delta}{3}.$$

Hence for every ξ and every h, we have

$$|f(\xi + h) - F_k(\xi + h)| \leqq \frac{\delta}{3}$$

and

$$|f(\xi) - F_k(\xi)| \leqq \frac{\delta}{3}.$$

Now let ξ be fixed. By Theorem 66, $F_k(x)$ is continuous at ξ. Thus for suitable $\varepsilon > 0$, and for $|h| < \varepsilon$, we have

$$|F_k(\xi + h) - F_k(\xi)| < \frac{\delta}{3},$$

so that

$$|f(\xi + h) - f(\xi)|$$
$$= |(f(\xi + h) - F_k(\xi + h)) - (f(\xi) - F_k(\xi)) + (F_k(\xi + h) - F_k(\xi))|$$
$$\leqq |f(\xi + h) - F_k(\xi + h)| + |f(\xi) - F_k(\xi)| + |F_k(\xi + h) - F_k(\xi)|$$
$$< \frac{\delta}{3} + \frac{\delta}{3} + \frac{\delta}{3} = \delta.$$

4) Finally, we show that $f(x)$ is not differentiable at any ξ. If we had

$$f'(\xi) = t$$

for some value ξ, then for suitable $\varepsilon > 0$ we would have

$$\left| \frac{f(x) - f(\xi)}{x - \xi} - t \right| < \tfrac{1}{2} \ \text{for} \ 0 < |x - \xi| < \varepsilon.$$

For every sequence ξ_k, $k \geq 1$ for which

$$\xi_k \neq \xi, \ \xi_k \to \xi,$$

there would exist a k_0 such that for $k \geq k_0$ we would have

$$\left| \frac{f(\xi_k) - f(\xi)}{\xi_k - \xi} - t \right| < \tfrac{1}{2},$$

and therefore also

$$\left| \frac{f(\xi_{k+1}) - f(\xi)}{\xi_{k+1} - \xi} - t \right| < \tfrac{1}{2},$$

so that

$$\left| \frac{f(\xi_k) - f(\xi)}{\xi_k - \xi} - \frac{f(\xi_{k+1}) - f(\xi)}{\xi_{k+1} - \xi} \right| < 1.$$

Thus to obtain a contradiction, it suffices to produce a sequence ξ_k, $k \geq 1$ and integral, with

$$\xi_k \neq \xi, \quad \xi_k \to \xi$$

such that

$$\frac{f(\xi_k) - f(\xi)}{\xi_k - \xi}$$

is an integer for all k, and in fact is even if k is even and odd if k is odd. For then we should have, for all k, that

$$\left| \frac{f(\xi_k) - f(\xi)}{\xi_k - \xi} - \frac{f(\xi_{k+1}) - f(\xi)}{\xi_{k+1} - \xi} \right| \geq 1.$$

And this can and will be done.
For integral $k \geq 1$, we set

$$\xi_k = \begin{cases} \xi + 4^{-k}, & \text{if } [4^k \xi] \text{ is even,} \\ \xi - 4^{-k}, & \text{if } [4^k \xi] \text{ is odd.} \end{cases}$$

Evidently, we have

$$\xi_k \neq \xi,$$

$$|\xi_k - \xi| = 4^{-k} \to 0,$$

$$\xi_k \to \xi.$$

If n is an integer $\geq k$, then

$$4^n \xi_k = 4^n \xi \pm 4^{n-k} = 4^n \xi + \text{ an integer,}$$

so that by Theorem 83,

$$\{4^n \xi_k\} = \{4^n \xi\},$$

$$f_n(\xi_k) = f_n(\xi).$$

Thus, for integers m, k, with $m \geq k \geq 1$,

$$F_m(\xi_k) - F_m(\xi) = \sum_{n=0}^{m} (f_n(\xi_k) - f_n(\xi)) = \sum_{n=0}^{k-1} (f_n(\xi_k) - f_n(\xi)),$$

so that, for integers $k \geq 1$,

$$(1) \qquad f(\xi_k) - f(\xi) = \sum_{n=0}^{k-1} (f_n(\xi_k) - f_n(\xi)).$$

If n is an integer such that $0 \leq n \leq k-1$, then

$$2 \cdot 4^{-k} = 2^{1-2k} \leq 2^{1-2(n+1)} = 2^{-2n-1}.$$

Thus

$$4^{-k} \leq 2^{-2n-1} - 4^{-k}.$$

Setting

$$a = [2^{2n+1} \xi],$$

we have

$$a \leq 2^{2n+1} \xi < a + 1,$$

$$(2) \qquad 2^{-2n-1} a \leq \xi < 2^{-2n-1}(a+1).$$

I assert that we have (for our k which is $\geq n+1$)

$$(3) \qquad 2^{-2n-1} a \leq \xi_k < 2^{-2n-1}(a+1),$$

and distinguish three cases for the purpose of the proof.

   I) If

$$2^{-2n-1} a + 4^{-k} \leq \xi < 2^{-2n-1}(a+1) - 4^{-k},$$

then (3) follows, since

$$|\xi_k - \xi| = 4^{-k}.$$

   II) If

$$2^{-2n-1} a \leq \xi < 2^{-2n-1} a + 4^{-k},$$

then

$$2^{2k-2n-1} a \leq 4^k \xi < 2^{2k-2n-1} a + 1,$$

$$[4^k \xi] = 2^{2k-2n-1} a = \text{ an even number,}$$

$$\xi_k = \xi + 4^{-k},$$

$$2^{-2n-1} a < \xi_k < 2^{-2n-1} a + 2 \cdot 4^{-k} \leq 2^{-2n-1}(a+1).$$

III) If

$$2^{-2n-1}(a + 1) - 4^{-k} \leqq \xi < 2^{-2n-1}(a + 1),$$

then

$$2^{2k-2n-1}(a + 1) - 1 \leqq 4^k\xi < 2^{2k-2n-1}(a + 1),$$

$$[4^k\xi] = 2^{2k-2n-1}(a + 1) - 1 = \text{an odd integer},$$

$$\xi_k = \xi - 4^{-k},$$

$$2^{-2n-1}a \leqq 2^{-2n-1}(a + 1) - 2 \cdot 4^{-k} \leqq \xi_k < 2^{-2n-1}(a + 1).$$

Thus (3) always holds.
If a is even, then it follows from (2) and (3), setting

$$\frac{a}{2} = b,$$

that

$$b \leqq 4^n\xi < b + \tfrac{1}{2},$$

$$b \leqq 4^n\xi_k < b + \tfrac{1}{2},$$

$$\{4^n\xi\} = 4^n\xi - b,$$

$$\{4^n\xi_k\} = 4^n\xi_k - b,$$

$$f_n(\xi) = \xi - \frac{b}{4^n},$$

$$f_n(\xi_k) = \xi_k - \frac{b}{4^n},$$

$$(4) \qquad f_n(\xi_k) - f_n(\xi) = \xi_k - \xi.$$

If a is odd, then it follows from (2) and (3), setting

$$\frac{a + 1}{2} = b,$$

that

$$b - \tfrac{1}{2} \leqq 4^n\xi < b,$$

$$b - \tfrac{1}{2} \leqq 4^n\xi_k < b,$$

$$\{4^n\xi\} = b - 4^n\xi,$$

$$\{4^n\xi_k\} = b - 4^n\xi_k,$$

$$f_n(\xi) = \frac{b}{4^n} - \xi,$$

$$f_n(\xi_k) = \frac{b}{4^n} - \xi_k,$$

$$(5) \qquad f_n(\xi_k) - f_n(\xi) = -(\xi_k - \xi).$$

If $0 \leqq n \leqq k - 1$, we have by (4) and (5) that, in either case,

$$\frac{f_n(\xi_k) - f_n(\xi)}{\xi_k - \xi} = \pm 1.$$

Thus if $k \geqq 1$, we have by (1) that

$$\frac{f(\xi_k) - f(\xi)}{\xi_k - \xi} = \sum_{n=0}^{k-1} (\pm 1) = \sum_{n=0}^{k-1} (1 + \text{even number})$$
$$= k + \text{even number},$$

and so is even for even k, and odd for odd k.

CHAPTER 6

GENERAL THEOREMS ON THE
CALCULATION OF DERIVATIVES

Introduction

The purpose of this chapter is, on the one hand, to investigate the most important of the functions with which we are familiar (e.g. $x^n, \log x, e^x$) as to whether, where, and with what result, they are differentiable, and on the other hand, given several differentiable functions, to investigate the same questions for their sum, product, etc. This alone would not, however, get us very far. The most difficult but also the most important theorem of this chapter, namely Theorem 101 (the so-called chain rule), with which we shall begin this chapter (although several later results will be obtained directly, without its use) enables us to differentiate "composite" functions $f(g(x))$ (e.g. $\log(1 + x^4)$) provided we can differentiate $f(x)$ and $g(x)$ (in this example, $\log x$ and $1 + x^4$).

Theorem 101: *Let*

$$g(\xi) = \eta, \quad g'(\xi) = t, \quad f'(\eta) = \tau.$$

Then $f(g(x))$ is differentiable at ξ, and its derivative is τt.
For short:

$$\frac{d}{dx} f(g(x)) = f'(g(x))g'(x).$$

Even shorter:

$$\frac{dz}{dx} = \frac{dz}{dy} \frac{dy}{dx}.$$

Proof:
$$\lim_{k=0} \frac{f(\eta + k) - f(\eta)}{k} = \tau.$$

Hence there exists a $p > 0$ such that if we set

$$\varphi(k) = \begin{cases} \dfrac{f(\eta + k) - f(\eta)}{k} & \text{for } 0 < |k| < p, \\[2mm] \tau & \text{for } k = 0, \end{cases}$$

then $\varphi(k)$ is continuous at $k = 0$.
If $|k| < p$, then

$$f(\eta + k) - f(\eta) = k\,\varphi(k).$$

If we set

$$k = g(\xi + h) - g(\xi),$$

then $k = k(h)$ is continuous and equal to 0 at $h = 0$. Hence there exists a $q > 0$ such that

$$|k| < p \text{ for } |h| < q.$$

If $0 < |h| < q$, then

$$\frac{f(g(\xi + h)) - f(g(\xi))}{h} = \frac{f(\eta + k) - f(\eta)}{h} = \frac{k(h)}{h} \varphi(k(h)).$$

Now we have

$$\lim_{h=0} \frac{k(h)}{h} = t.$$

By Theorem 77, $\varphi(k(h))$ is continuous at $h = 0$, so that

$$\lim_{h=0} \varphi(k(h)) = \varphi(k(0)) = \varphi(0) = \tau.$$

Hence we have (Theorem 91)

$$\lim_{h=0} \frac{f(g(\xi + h)) - f(g(\xi))}{h} = t\tau = \tau t.$$

Theorem 102: *Everywhere, we have*

$$\frac{dc}{dx} = 0.$$

Proof: If

$$f(x) = c,$$

then for every ξ we have for $h \neq 0$ that

$$\frac{f(\xi + h) - f(\xi)}{h} = \frac{c - c}{h} = 0 \to 0.$$

Theorem 103: *For integral $n > 0$ and for all x, we have*

$$\frac{dx^n}{dx} = nx^{n-1}.$$

Proof: If

$$f(x) = x^n,$$

then for every ξ we have for $h \neq 0$ that

$$\frac{f(\xi + h) - f(\xi)}{h} = \frac{(\xi + h)^n - \xi^n}{h} = \sum_{\nu=0}^{n-1} (\xi + h)^\nu \xi^{n-1-\nu}$$

$$\to \sum_{\nu=0}^{n-1} \xi^\nu \xi^{n-1-\nu} = \sum_{\nu=0}^{n-1} \xi^{n-1} = n\xi^{n-1}.$$

Theorem 104: $\quad \dfrac{d \log x}{dx} = \dfrac{1}{x}$ *for $x > 0$.*

Proof: By example 2) to Definition 24, we have

$$\lim_{h=0} \frac{\log(1 + h)}{h} = 1.$$

If $x > 0$, then by Theorem 98 (with

$$g(h) = \frac{h}{x}, \quad \eta = 0, \quad \xi = 0, \quad f(h) = \frac{\log(1 + h)}{h}, \quad c = 1),$$

$$\lim_{h=0} \frac{\log\left(1 + \dfrac{h}{x}\right)}{\dfrac{h}{x}} = 1,$$

so that (Theorem 92)

$$\lim_{h=0} \frac{\log\left(1 + \dfrac{h}{x}\right)}{h} = \frac{1}{x},$$

$$\lim_{h=0} \frac{\log\,(x+h) - \log x}{h} = \frac{1}{x}.$$

Theorem 105: $\dfrac{d \log\,(-x)}{dx} = \dfrac{1}{x}$ for $x < 0$.

Proof: By Theorems 101 (with

$$f(x) = \log x, \quad g(x) = -x)$$

and 104, we have

$$\frac{d \log\,(-x)}{dx} = \frac{1}{-x}\,(-x)' = -\frac{1}{x}\,(-1) = \frac{1}{x}.$$

Theorem 106: *Everywhere, we have*

$$\frac{de^x}{dx} = e^x.$$

Proof: By example 2) to Definition 24, we have

$$\lim_{x=1} \frac{\log x}{x-1} = 1,$$

so that, by Theorem 92,

$$\lim_{x=1} \frac{x-1}{\log x} = 1.$$

Since

$$e^x \neq 1 \quad \text{for} \quad x \neq 0,$$

we have, by Theorem 98 (with

$$g(x) = e^x, \quad \eta = 1, \quad \xi = 0, \quad f(x) = \frac{x-1}{\log x}, \quad c = 1),$$

$$\lim_{x=0} \frac{e^x - 1}{x} = 1.$$

Since

$$\frac{e^{\xi+h} - e^\xi}{h} = e^\xi \frac{e^h - 1}{h} \quad \text{for } h \neq 0,$$

we have, for every ξ,

$$\lim_{h=0} \frac{e^{\xi+h} - e^\xi}{h} = e^\xi.$$

Theorem 107: $\left(cf(x)\right)' = cf'(x),$

if the right-hand side is meaningful.

Proof: Suppose $f'(\xi)$ exists. Then for suitable $p > 0$ and $0 < |h| < p$, we have

$$\frac{cf(\xi + h) - cf(\xi)}{h} = c\,\frac{f(\xi + h) - f(\xi)}{h} \to cf'(\xi).$$

Theorem 108: *For every $a > 0$ and for all x we have*

$$\frac{da^x}{dx} = a^x \log a.$$

Proof: By Theorems 101 (with

$$f(x) = e^x, \quad g(x) = x \log a),$$

106, 107, and 103 (with $n = 1$), we have

$$(a^x)' = (e^{x \log a})' = e^{x \log a} \log a = a^x \log a.$$

Theorem 109: *If $x > 0$, then we have for any n that*

$$\frac{dx^n}{dx} = nx^{n-1}.$$

Proof: By Theorems 101 (with

$$f(x) = e^x, \quad g(x) = n \log x),$$

106, 107, and 104, we have

$$(x^n)' = (e^{n \log x})' = e^{n \log x}\,\frac{n}{x} = x^n\,\frac{n}{x} = nx^{n-1}.$$

Example: If $x > 0$, then

$$\frac{d\sqrt{x}}{dx} = \frac{1}{2\sqrt{x}}.$$

Theorem 110: $(f(x) + g(x))' = f'(x) + g'(x)$,

if the right-hand side is meaningful (i.e. if $f'(x)$ and $g'(x)$ exist).
Proof: Suppose $f'(\xi)$ and $g'(\xi)$ exist. Then for suitable $p > 0$, we have for $0 < |h| < p$ that

$$\frac{\left(f(\xi + h) + g(\xi + h)\right) - \left(f(\xi) + g(\xi)\right)}{h}$$

$$= \frac{f(\xi + h) - f(\xi)}{h} + \frac{g(\xi + h) - g(\xi)}{h} \to f'(\xi) + g'(\xi).$$

Example: $(1 + x^4)' = 4x^3$,

so that, by Theorems 101 and 109, (for all x)

$$\frac{d\sqrt{1 + x^4}}{dx} = \frac{1}{2\sqrt{1 + x^4}}\,4x^3 = \frac{2x^3}{\sqrt{1 + x^4}}.$$

Theorem 111: $\qquad \left(\sum\limits_{n=1}^{m} f_n(x) \right)' = \sum\limits_{n=1}^{m} f_n'(x),$

if the right-hand side is meaningful.

Proof: $m = 1$ is obvious. To proceed from m to $m + 1$:

$$\sum_{n=1}^{m+1} f_n'(x) = \sum_{n=1}^{m} f_n'(x) + f_{m+1}'(x) = \left(\sum_{n=1}^{m} f_n(x) \right)' + f_{m+1}'(x)$$

$$= \left(\sum_{n=1}^{m} f_n(x) + f_{m+1}(x) \right)' = \left(\sum_{n=1}^{m+1} f_n(x) \right)'.$$

Theorem 112: *If m is a positive integer, then for all x*

$$\left(\sum_{n=0}^{m} a_n x^n \right)' = \sum_{n=1}^{m} n a_n x^{n-1}.$$

Proof: $\qquad\qquad\qquad a_0' = 0$ (Theorem 102),

$\qquad\qquad (x^n)' = n x^{n-1}$ for $n > 0$ (Theorem 103),

so that

$\qquad\qquad (a_n x^n)' = n a_n x^{n-1}$ for $n > 0$ (Theorem 107),

and Theorem 111.

Theorem 113: $\qquad (f(x) - g(x))' = f'(x) - g'(x),$

if the right-hand side is meaningful.

Proof: $f'(x) - g'(x) = f'(x) + (-1)g'(x) = f'(x) + ((-1)g(x))'$
$\qquad = f'(x) + (-g(x))' = (f(x) + (-g(x)))' = (f(x) - g(x))'.$

Theorem 114: $\qquad (f(x)g(x))' = f(x)g'(x) + f'(x)g(x),$

if the right-hand side is meaningful.

Proof: Suppose $f'(\xi)$ and $g'(\xi)$ exist. Then there is a $p > 0$ such that, for $0 < |h| < p,$

$$\frac{f(\xi+h)g(\xi+h) - f(\xi)g(\xi)}{h} = f(\xi+h)\frac{g(\xi+h)-g(\xi)}{h} + g(\xi)\frac{f(\xi+h)-f(\xi)}{h}$$

$$\to f(\xi)g'(\xi) + g(\xi)f'(\xi),$$

by Theorem 99.

Theorem 115: *We have for integral $m \geqq 2$ that*

$$\left(\prod_{n=1}^{m} f_n(x) \right)' = \sum_{n=1}^{m} f_n'(x) \prod_{\substack{\nu=1 \\ except\ \nu=n}}^{m} f_\nu(x),$$

if the right-hand side is meaningful.

(The meaning of $\prod\limits_{\substack{\nu=1 \\ except\ \nu=n}}^{m}$ is quite clear; it is a product of $m - 1$ factors.)

Proof: The case $m = 2$ is Theorem 114. To proceed from m to $m + 1$: By Theorem 114, we have

$$\left(\prod_{n=1}^{m+1} f_n(x) \right)' = \left(\prod_{n=1}^{m} f_n(x) \cdot f_{m+1}(x) \right)'$$

$$= \prod_{n=1}^{m} f_n(x) \cdot f'_{m+1}(x) + \sum_{n=1}^{m} f'_n(x) \prod_{\substack{\nu=1 \\ \text{except } \nu=n}}^{m} f_\nu(x) \cdot f_{m+1}(x)$$

$$= \sum_{\nu=1}^{m+1} f'_n(x) \prod_{\substack{\nu=1 \\ \text{except } \nu=n}}^{m+1} f_\nu(x).$$

Theorem 116: *For integral* $m \geq 1$,

$$\frac{df^m(x)}{dx} = m f^{m-1}(x) f'(x),$$

if the right-hand side is meaningful.

Proof: $m = 1$ is obvious; $m > 1$ follows from Theorem 115 with

$$f_n(x) = f(x) \quad \text{for } 1 \leq n \leq m.$$

Theorem 117:
$$\left(\frac{1}{f(x)} \right)' = -\frac{f'(x)}{f^2(x)},$$

if the right-hand side is meaningful.

Proof: Suppose $f'(\xi)$ exists, and let

$$f(\xi) \neq 0.$$

Then there is a $p > 0$ such that, for $0 < |h| < p$,

$$f(\xi + h) \neq 0,$$

so that

$$\frac{\dfrac{1}{f(\xi + h)} - \dfrac{1}{f(\xi)}}{h} = - \frac{\dfrac{f(\xi + h) - f(\xi)}{h}}{f(\xi + h)f(\xi)} \to -\frac{f'(\xi)}{f^2(\xi)}.$$

Theorem 118:
$$\left(\frac{f(x)}{g(x)} \right)' = \frac{g(x)f'(x) - f(x)g'(x)}{g^2(x)},$$

if the right-hand side is meaningful.

Proof:
$$\frac{g(x)f'(x) - f(x)g'(x)}{g^2(x)} = f(x)\left(-\frac{g'(x)}{g^2(x)} \right) + f'(x)\frac{1}{g(x)}$$

$$= f(x)\left(\frac{1}{g(x)} \right)' + f'(x)\frac{1}{g(x)} = \left(f(x)\frac{1}{g(x)} \right)' = \left(\frac{f(x)}{g(x)} \right)'.$$

Theorem 119: *If* n *is an integer and* $x \neq 0$, *then* $(x^n)' = nx^{n-1}$.

Proof: The case $n > 0$ is contained in Theorem 103; the case $n = 0$ is obvious. If $n < 0$, then, by Theorem 117,

$$(x^n)' = \left(\frac{1}{x^{-n}}\right)' = -\frac{(x^{-n})'}{(x^{-n})^2} = -\frac{-nx^{-n-1}}{x^{-2n}} = nx^{n-1}.$$

Theorem 120: If $n > 0$ is integral and if $x > 0$, then $\left(\sqrt[n]{x}\right)' = \dfrac{\sqrt[n]{x}}{nx}$.

Proof: By Theorem 109, we have

$$\left(\sqrt[n]{x}\right)' = \left(x^{\frac{1}{n}}\right)' = \frac{1}{n}x^{\frac{1}{n}-1} = \frac{1}{n}x^{\frac{1}{n}}x^{-1} = \frac{\sqrt[n]{x}}{nx}.$$

Theorem 121: If $n > 0$ is an odd integer and if $x < 0$, then the equation

$$y^n = x$$

has exactly one solution, namely

$$y = -\sqrt[n]{-x}.$$

Proof: y must be negative. Our equation states that

$$(-y)^n = -x,$$

and this is equivalent to

$$-y = \sqrt[n]{-x},$$

i.e.

$$y = -\sqrt[n]{-x}.$$

Definition 26: The y of Theorem 121 is called $\sqrt[n]{x}$.

Theorem 122: $$\sqrt[1]{x} = x \text{ for } x < 0.$$

Proof: $$x^1 = x.$$

Theorem 123: If $n > 0$ is an odd integer and if $x < 0$, then

$$\left(\sqrt[n]{x}\right)' = \frac{\sqrt[n]{x}}{nx}.$$

Proof: By Theorems 101 (with

$$f(x) = -\sqrt[n]{x}, \quad g(x) = -x)$$

and 120, we have

$$\left(\sqrt[n]{x}\right)' = \left(-\sqrt[n]{-x}\right)' = \left(-\frac{\sqrt[n]{-x}}{n(-x)}\right)(-1) = \frac{-\sqrt[n]{-x}}{nx} = \frac{\sqrt[n]{x}}{nx}.$$

CHAPTER 7

INCREASE, DECREASE, MAXIMUM, MINIMUM

Introduction

If $h \neq 0$ and if $f(x)$ is defined in the interval $\xi \leqq x \leqq \xi + h$ or in the interval $\xi + h \leqq x \leqq \xi$, then the difference quotient $\dfrac{f(\xi + h) - f(\xi)}{h}$ measures, in a way, the steepness of the function in the interval. Consideration of the derivative (if it exists) will yield more delicate distinctions; the derivative at ξ measures, in a way, the steepness of the function at ξ.

Definition 27: *$f(x)$ is increasing at ξ if there exists an $\varepsilon > 0$ such that*

$$f(x) < f(\xi) \quad for \quad \xi - \varepsilon < x < \xi$$

and

$$f(x) > f(\xi) \quad for \quad \xi < x < \xi + \varepsilon.$$

Definition 28: *$f(x)$ is decreasing at ξ if there exists an $\varepsilon > 0$ such that*

$$f(x) > f(\xi) \quad for \quad \xi - \varepsilon < x < \xi,$$

and

$$f(x) < f(\xi) \quad for \quad \xi < x < \xi + \varepsilon.$$

Definition 29: *$f(x)$ has a maximum at ξ if there exists an $\varepsilon > 0$ such that*

$$f(x) < f(\xi) \quad for \quad 0 < |x - \xi| < \varepsilon.$$

Definition 30: *$f(x)$ has a minimum at ξ if there exists an $\varepsilon > 0$ such that*

$$f(x) > f(\xi) \quad for \quad 0 < |x - \xi| < \varepsilon.$$

Theorem 124: *For every $f(x)$ and each fixed ξ, at most one of the following four possibilities can be realized: $f(x)$ is increasing at ξ, $f(x)$ is decreasing at ξ, $f(x)$ has a maximum at ξ, $f(x)$ has a minimum at ξ.*

Proof: Obvious.

It may also happen that $f(x)$ is defined for $|x - \xi| < p$ with some $p > 0$, and yet that none of the four possibilities is realized. **Example:**

$$\xi = 0,$$

$$f(x) = \begin{cases} x^2 & \text{for rational } x, \\ -x^2 & \text{for irrational } x. \end{cases}$$

Here we have

$$f(0) = 0,$$

and for every $\varepsilon > 0$, there does exist an x for which

$$\begin{aligned} f(x) &< 0, & -\varepsilon < x < 0; \\ f(x) &> 0, & -\varepsilon < x < 0; \\ f(x) &< 0, & 0 < x < \varepsilon; \\ f(x) &> 0, & 0 < x < \varepsilon. \end{aligned}$$

Theorem 125: *If*
$$f'(\xi) > 0,$$
then $f(x)$ *is increasing at* ξ.

Proof: If
$$\frac{f(\xi + h) - f(\xi)}{h} \to t > 0 ,$$

then by Theorem 72 (applied to the function

$$F(h) = \begin{cases} \dfrac{f(\xi + h) - f(\xi)}{h} & \text{for } 0 < |h| < p, \\ t & \text{for } h = 0, \end{cases}$$

for suitable $p > 0$), there exists an $\varepsilon > 0$ such that

$$\frac{f(\xi + h) - f(\xi)}{h} > 0 \text{ for } 0 < |h| < \varepsilon,$$

so that

$$f(\xi + h) < f(\xi) \text{ for } -\varepsilon < h < 0,$$
$$f(\xi + h) > f(\xi) \text{ for } 0 < h < \varepsilon.$$

Theorem 126: *If*
$$f'(\xi) < 0,$$
then $f(x)$ *is decreasing at* ξ.

Proof: If we set
$$g(x) = -f(x)$$
then we have
$$g'(\xi) = -f'(\xi) > 0.$$

By Theorem 125, $g(x)$ is increasing at ξ. Hence there exists an $\varepsilon > 0$ such that

$$-f(x) < -f(\xi) \text{ for } \xi - \varepsilon < x < \xi,$$
$$-f(x) > -f(\xi) \text{ for } \xi < x < \xi + \varepsilon.$$

Theorem 127: *If* $f(x)$ *has a maximum or a minimum at* ξ, *and if* $f'(\xi)$ *exists, then*

$$f'(\xi) = 0.$$

Proof: Theorems 124, 125, and 126.

However, it should not be thought that if $f(x)$ has a maximum or a minimum at ξ, then we must have

$$f'(\xi) = 0.$$

$f'(\xi)$ need not even exist, as the example

$$f(x) = |x|, \xi = 0$$

shows. We know (example 3) at the beginning of Chap. 5) that $f'(0)$ does not exist. In spite of this, $f(x)$ clearly has a minimum at 0, since

$$f(0) = 0,$$
$$f(x) > 0 \quad \text{for} \quad x \neq 0.$$

When can we determine on the basis of our present knowledge, by considering $f'(\xi)$, that we have a maximum or that we have a minimum or even that we have one or the other? Never. For,

1) If $f'(\xi)$ does not exist, then we know nothing;

2) if $f'(\xi) > 0$ or if $f'(\xi) < 0$, then we know that neither a maximum nor a minimum is present;

3) if $f'(\xi) = 0$, then we know nothing.

For good measure, I shall give five examples which illustrate 3). In the first example, the function has a maximum, in the second, it has a minimum, in the third, it is increasing, in the fourth, it is decreasing, and in the fifth none of these situations occurs. In each of the examples, we have

$$\xi = 0, \; f(0) = f'(0) = 0.$$

I) $f(x) = -x^2$, and so is < 0 for $x \neq 0$.

II) $f(x) = x^2$, and so is > 0 for $x \neq 0$.

III) $f(x) = x^3$, and so is < 0 for $x < 0$, > 0 for $x > 0$.

IV) $f(x) = -x^3$, and so is > 0 for $x < 0$, < 0 for $x > 0$.

V) $f(x)$ is the example given after Theorem 124. Indeed,

$$f'(0) = \lim_{h=0} \frac{\pm h^2}{h} = 0.$$

In spite of this indecisive (but not undecidable) situation, we shall now work out an example to the point where we have determined all maxima and minima. Of course, we shall rely not only upon the theorems we have proved, but also on the original definitions. (Later, we shall have more theorems at our disposal.)

Example:
$$f(x) = \frac{1 - x}{1 + x^2}.$$

Now we have for all x that

$$f'(x) = \frac{-(1 + x^2) - (1 - x)2x}{(1 + x^2)^2} = \frac{-1 - 2x + x^2}{(1 + x^2)^2}.$$

$f'(x)$ is equal to zero only when

$$(x - 1)^2 - 2 = x^2 - 2x - 1 = 0,$$

and hence for the two numbers

$$x = 1 \pm \sqrt{2}$$

and no others.

Thus, $f(x)$ can have a maximum or a minimum only at $1 + \sqrt{2}$ and $1 - \sqrt{2}$.

I assert that it has a minimum at $1 + \sqrt{2}$ and a maximum at $1 - \sqrt{2}$.

In fact, if we set

$$\xi = 1 \pm \sqrt{2},$$

then for all $h \neq 0$,

$$f(\xi + h) - f(\xi) = \frac{1 - (\xi + h)}{1 + (\xi + h)^2} - \frac{1 - \xi}{1 + \xi^2}$$

is positive, negative, or zero according to whether

$$(1 - \xi - h)(1 + \xi^2) - (1 - \xi)(1 + \xi^2 + 2h\xi + h^2)$$
$$= -h(1 + \xi^2) - (1 - \xi)(2h\xi + h^2)$$
$$= h(-1 - \xi^2 - 2\xi + 2\xi^2) - h^2(1 - \xi) = h^2(\xi - 1)$$

is positive, negative, or zero. Hence we have for all $h \neq 0$ that

$$f(\xi + h) > f(\xi) \quad \text{if} \quad \xi = 1 + \sqrt{2},$$
$$f(\xi + h) < f(\xi) \quad \text{if} \quad \xi = 1 - \sqrt{2}.$$

This example may be misleading in that $f(x)$ has a value greater than all others at $1 - \sqrt{2}$, and a value less than all others at $1 + \sqrt{2}$, while only a neighborhood $0 < |x - \xi| < \varepsilon$ is taken into consideration for investigation of maxima and minima. However, the correct situation is apparent from Definitions 29 and 30.

An example of a minimum which is not smaller than all other values of the function is the following:

$$f(x) = x^2 - x^6, \quad \xi = 0.$$

0 is a minimum, since if $0 < |x| < 1$, then

$$f(0) = 0 < x^2(1 - x^4) = f(x);$$

nevertheless,

$$f(2) = 2^2 - 2^6 < 0 = f(0).$$

CHAPTER 8

GENERAL PROPERTIES OF A FUNCTION
CONTINUOUS IN A CLOSED INTERVAL

The contents of this chapter could have been discussed in connection with Chap. 3. However, I wanted to introduce the differential calculus first.

Definition 31: *A set of numbers $\mathfrak{M}$ is said to be bounded if there exists a c such that, for every x of $\mathfrak{M}$,*

$$|x| < c.$$

Definition 32: *A set of numbers $\mathfrak{M}$ is said to be bounded from above if there exists a c such that, for every x of $\mathfrak{M}$,*

$$x < c.$$

Definition 33: *A set of numbers $\mathfrak{M}$ is said to be bounded from below if there exists a c such that, for every x of $\mathfrak{M}$,*

$$x > c.$$

Theorem 128: *A set of numbers is bounded if and only if it is bounded from above and bounded from below:*

Proof: 1) If

$$|x| < c$$

then

$$-c < x < c.$$

2) If

$$c_1 < x < c_2$$

then

$$-x < -c_1,$$
$$|x| = \text{Max}(x, -x) < \text{Max}(c_2, -c_1).$$

Definition 34: *If $\mathfrak{M}$ is an infinite set of numbers, then ξ is called a limit point* (point of accumulation) *of $\mathfrak{M}$ if for every $\delta > 0$ there are infinitely many numbers of $\mathfrak{M}$ for which*

$$\xi - \delta < x < \xi + \delta.$$

Warning: "limit point" and "limit" are two different concepts.

Examples: 1) The set $\mathfrak{M}$ of integers does not have any limit points. For if $a < b$, there are never infinitely many integers x such that $a < x < b$.

2) If $\mathfrak{M}$ is the set of numbers $\dfrac{1}{n}$, where n is an integer ≥ 1, then it is clear that no $\xi \neq 0$ is a limit point. For, if we set

$$\delta = \frac{|\xi|}{2},$$

then there are not infinitely many integers $n \geq 1$ such that

$$\xi - \delta < \frac{1}{n} < \xi + \delta,$$

since either $\xi - \delta > 0$ or $\xi + \delta < 0$, and

$$\lim_{n=\infty} \frac{1}{n} = 0.$$

However, $\xi = 0$ is a limit point. For if δ is an arbitrarily chosen positive number, then for integral $n > \dfrac{1}{\delta}$ we have

$$0 - \delta < \frac{1}{n} < 0 + \delta.$$

This example shows that a limit point of $\mathfrak{M}$ need not belong to $\mathfrak{M}$. (Indeed, that it belong to $\mathfrak{M}$ was not required in Definition 34.)

Moreover, in Definition 34 it would have sufficed to require only that there exist, for every $\delta > 0$, at least **one** x of $\mathfrak{M}$ such that

$$(1) \qquad\qquad 0 < |x - \xi| < \delta.$$

For, employing 7) of the introduction, we may deduce from this that for every integer $n \geq 1$ there are at least n such x (hence that there are infinitely many). For, if $x = x_\nu$, $1 \leq \nu \leq n$, ν integral, are distinct numbers which satisfy (1), then we set

$$\delta_1 = \operatorname*{Min}_{1 \leq \nu \leq n} |x_\nu - \xi|,$$

and choose x_{n+1} in $\mathfrak{M}$ with

$$0 < |x_{n+1} - \xi| < \delta_1 \qquad (< \delta).$$

Then we have for $1 \leq \nu \leq n$ that

$$|x_{n+1} - \xi| < |x_\nu - \xi|,$$

so that

$$x_{n+1} \neq x_\nu.$$

Theorem 129:   *Every bounded infinite set of numbers has a limit point.*

Proof: There exists a c such that, for all x of the given set $\mathfrak{M}$,

$$-c < x < c.$$

We place a in

class I   if $x < a$ does not hold for infinitely many x of $\mathfrak{M}$,

class II   if $x < a$ holds for infinitely many x of $\mathfrak{M}$.

Every number a belongs to exactly one of these classes. Class I contains $-c$, and class II contains c. If a lies in class II, and if $\beta > a$, then we have for infinitely many x of $\mathfrak{M}$ that

$$x < a < \beta,$$

so that β lies in class II.

Hence there exists a ξ such that every $a < \xi$ belongs to class I and every $a > \xi$ belongs to class II.

This ξ is a limit point. For if $\delta > 0$ is given, then $\xi - \delta$ lies in class I, and $\xi + \delta$ lies in class II. Hence there are in $\mathfrak{M}$ infinitely many $x < \xi + \delta$, but not infinitely many $x < \xi - \delta$. If there were not infinitely many x in $\mathfrak{M}$ for which

$$\xi - \delta < x < \xi + \delta,$$

then, by Theorem 7, $\mathfrak{M}$ would not contain infinitely many $x < \xi + \delta$.

Theorem 130: *Suppose that $a < b$, and that, for all integers $n \geqq 1$,*

$$a \leqq \xi_n \leqq b.$$

(The ξ_n need not be distinct.) *Then there exists a ξ such that for every $\delta > 0$,*

$$\xi - \delta < \xi_n < \xi + \delta$$

for infinitely many n.

Preliminary Remark: Eo ipso, we then have

$$a \leqq \xi \leqq b.$$

Proof: 1) If there are infinitely many distinct ξ_n, then any limit point ξ of the bounded infinite set of points which consists of the distinct ξ_n satisfies the requirement, and by Theorem 129, there exists at least one such limit point.

2) In the other case, there exists a ξ, by Theorem 8, such that

$$\xi_n = \xi$$

for infinitely many n. This ξ is the desired number.

Theorem 131: *Let a set of numbers x be bounded from above. Then there exists exactly one number l such that*

$$every \ x \leqq l,$$

and, for every $\delta > 0$,

$$at \ least \ one \ x > l - \delta.$$

Proof: 1) There is at most one such l. For if both l_1 and $l_2 > l_1$ have the required properties, then we should have

$$\text{every } x \leqq l_1,$$

so that, if we set

$$\delta = l_2 - l_1 (> 0),$$

we have

$$\text{no } x > l_1 = l_2 - \delta.$$

2) We now show that there exists an l which has the required properties. We place a in

class I   if at least one $x \geqq a$,
class II if all $x < a$.

There exists an a which belongs to class I, namely any x; by hypothesis, there is an a which belongs to class II. If a is in class II, and if $\beta > a$, then

$$\text{every } x < a < \beta,$$

so that β is in class II.

Hence there exists an l such that every $a < l$ belongs to class I and every $a > l$ belongs to class II.

This number l satisfies our requirements. For,

a) If we had

$$\text{at least one } x > l,$$

then such an x would lie in class II. Thus, we should have

$$x < x.$$

Hence,

$$\text{every } x \leqq l.$$

b) If $\delta > 0$ is given, then $l - \dfrac{\delta}{2}$ lies in class I. Hence there exists

$$\text{at least one } x \geqq l - \frac{\delta}{2} > l - \delta.$$

Examples: 1) Let the x's be the numbers $\leqq c$. Then $l = c$.

2) In general, if the set contains a greatest number, then it is l.

3) Let the x's be the numbers $< c$. Once again $l = c$, but now l does not belong to the set.

4) Let the x's be the numbers $1 - \dfrac{1}{n}$, and n an integer $\geqq 1$. Then $l = 1$, and l does not belong to the set.

Definition 35:   *For every set of numbers which is bounded from above, the l of Theorem 131 is called the least upper bound (l.u.b.) of the set.*

Theorem 132: *Let a set of numbers x be bounded from below. Then there exists exactly one number λ such that*

$$\text{every } x \geqq \lambda,$$

and, for every $\delta > 0$,

$$\text{at least one } x < \lambda + \delta.$$

Proof: We apply Theorem 131 to the set of the $-x$'s and set

$$\lambda = -l.$$

Then we have

$$\text{every } (-x) \leqq l = -\lambda,$$

$$\text{at least one } (-x) > l - \delta = -\lambda - \delta.$$

Definition 36: *For every set of numbers which is bounded from below, the λ of Theorem 132 is called the greatest lower bound (g.l.b.) of the set.*

Example: Consider the set of all numbers x of the form

$$x = \sqrt{n^2 + 1} - n, \quad n \geqq 1 \text{ an integer}.$$

The set is bounded from below, since for each such x we have

$$x > 0.$$

If δ is given, then for $n > \dfrac{1}{2\delta}$ we have

$$n^2 + 1 < n^2 + 2\delta n < (n + \delta)^2,$$
$$\sqrt{n^2 + 1} < n + \delta,$$
$$x < \delta.$$

Thus, $\lambda = 0$.

Definition 37: *$f(x)$ is said to be continuous on the right at ξ if for every $\delta > 0$ there is an $\varepsilon > 0$ such that*

$$|f(\xi + h) - f(\xi)| < \delta \quad \text{for} \quad 0 < h < \varepsilon.$$

Definition 38: *$f(x)$ is said to be continuous on the left at ξ if for every $\delta > 0$ there is an $\varepsilon > 0$ such that*

$$|f(\xi + h) - f(\xi)| < \delta \quad \text{for} \quad -\varepsilon < h < 0.$$

Theorem 133: *$f(x)$ is continuous at ξ if and only if it is continuous on the left and on the right at ξ.*

Proof: Obvious.

Definition 39: *If $a < b$, then the set of x such that $a \leqq x \leqq b$ is called a closed interval and is denoted by $[a, b]$.*

Definition 40: *$f(x)$ is said to be continuous on $[a, b]$ if $f(x)$ is continuous at a on the right, continuous at b on the left, and continuous at every ξ such that $a < \xi < b$.*

Example: $\sqrt{x}$ is continuous on $[0, b]$ for $b > 0$. For, we already know that it is continuous at all $\xi > 0$. And $\sqrt{x}$ is continuous at 0 on the right, since for every $\delta > 0$ we have

$$\left|\sqrt{x}\right| < \delta \text{ for } 0 < x < \delta^2.$$

Theorem 134: $f(x)$ *is continuous on* $[a, b]$ *if and only if for every* ξ *in* $[a, b]$ *and for every* $\delta > 0$ *there exists an* $\varepsilon > 0$ *such that*

$$\left| f(\xi + h) - f(\xi) \right| < \delta \text{ for } \left| h \right| < \varepsilon, \ a \leqq \xi + h \leqq b.$$

Proof: Obvious.

Theorems 135 - 138: *If* $f(x)$ *and* $g(x)$ *are continuous at* ξ *on the right, then so are*

135) $\qquad\qquad f(x) + g(x),$

136) $\qquad\qquad f(x) - g(x),$

137) $\qquad\qquad f(x)g(x),$

138) $\qquad\qquad$ *if* $g(\xi) \neq 0, \ \dfrac{f(x)}{g(x)}$.

Theorems 139 - 142: *The same, but with left for right in both hypothesis and conclusion.*

Simultaneous proof of Theorems 135 - 142: In Theorems 135 - 138 or in Theorems 139 - 142, we define (by changing the old definitions if necessary, since nothing prevents $f(x)$ and $g(x)$ from being defined, for example, for all $x < \xi$ or all $x > \xi$ respectively)

$$\left.\begin{array}{l} f(x) = f(\xi) \\ g(x) = g(\xi) \end{array}\right\} \text{ for } x < \xi \text{ or for } x > \xi \text{ respectively.}$$

(This does not affect the hypothesis or the conclusion.) Then $f(x)$ and $g(x)$ are continuous at ξ, and the conclusions follow from Theorems 65, 68, 69, 75.

Theorem 143: *If* $f(x)$ *is continuous at* ξ *on the right, and if*

$$f(\xi) \neq 0,$$

then there exists an $\varepsilon > 0$ *such that*

$$f(x)f(\xi) > 0 \text{ for } \xi < x \leqq \xi + \varepsilon.$$

Theorem 144: *If* $f(x)$ *is continuous at* ξ *on the left, and if*

$$f(\xi) \neq 0,$$

then there exists an $\varepsilon > 0$ *such that*

$$f(x)f(\xi) > 0 \text{ for } \xi - \varepsilon \leqq x < \xi.$$

Simultaneous proof of Theorems 143 - 144: Both theorems follow from Theorems 72 and 73, if we define

$$f(x) = f(\xi) \text{ for } x < \xi \text{ or for } x > \xi, \text{ respectively.}$$

Common hypothesis of Theorems 145 - 152, 154, and 155: *Let $f(x)$ be continuous on $[a, b]$.*

Theorem 145: *The totality of values of $f(x)$ on $[a, b]$ forms a bounded set.*

Proof: Otherwise there would exist, for every c, an x on $[a, b]$ such that

$$| f(x) | \geqq c.$$

Accordingly, for every integral $n \geqq 1$, we choose a ξ_n on $[a, b]$ such that

$$| f(\xi_n) | \geqq n.$$

By Theorem 130, there exists a ξ on $[a, b]$ such that for every $\delta > 0$ we have, infinitely often,

$$\xi - \delta < \xi_n < \xi + \delta.$$

By Theorem 134 (with $\delta = 1$, and with δ in place of the ε appearing there), there is a $\delta > 0$ such that, for $\xi - \delta < x < \xi + \delta$, $a \leqq x \leqq b$, we have

$$| f(x) - f(\xi) | < 1,$$

so that

$$| f(x) | < 1 + | f(\xi) |.$$

Therefore we should have

$$n \leqq | f(\xi_n) | < 1 + | f(\xi) |,$$

for infinitely many n, which is false.

Theorem 146: *$f(x)$ takes on a largest value on $[a, b]$.*

In other words, there exists a γ such that

$$a \leqq \gamma \leqq b,$$

$$f(x) \leqq f(\gamma) \quad \text{for} \quad a \leqq x \leqq b.$$

Proof: Let l be the least upper bound of the various values of $f(x)$ on $[a, b]$; this exists, by virtue of Theorems 145 and 131. (Cf. Definition 35). More concisely, l is the l.u.b. of $f(x)$ on $[a, b]$. Then, for all x on $[a, b]$, we have

$$f(x) \leqq l.$$

If there did not exist a γ on $[a, b]$ such that

$$f(\gamma) = l,$$

then we should always have

$$f(x) < l,$$

$$l - f(x) > 0$$

on $[a, b]$, so that

$$\frac{1}{l - f(x)}$$

would be continuous on $[a, b]$, by Theorems 136, 138, 140, 142. Hence, by Theorem 145, it would be bounded from above, so that

$$\frac{1}{l - f(x)} < G,$$

$$f(x) < l - \frac{1}{G}.$$

Hence there would be no x such that

$$f(x) > l - \frac{1}{G},$$

which contradicts the definition of the l.u.b.

Theorem 147: $f(x)$ *takes on a least value on* $[a, b]$.

In other words, there exists an η such that

$$a \leqq \eta \leqq b,$$

$$f(x) \geqq f(\eta) \quad \text{for} \quad a \leqq x \leqq b.$$

Proof: By Theorems 137 and 141, $- f(x)$ is continuous on $[a, b]$. Hence, by Theorem 146, there exists an η on $[a, b]$ such that

$$-f(x) \leqq -f(\eta) \quad \text{for} \quad a \leqq x \leqq b.$$

Theorem 148: *If*

$$f(a) < 0 < f(b),$$

then there exists exactly one ξ such that

$$a < \xi < b,$$

$$f(\xi) = 0,$$

$$f(x) < 0 \quad \text{for} \quad a \leqq x < \xi.$$

Preliminary Remark: Even the part of the theorem which asserts the existence of a ξ such that

$$a < \xi < b, \; f(\xi) = 0,$$

though it is very plausible, is quite deep, and it is very important.

Proof: 1) That there is at most one such ξ, is obvious. For if ξ_1 and $\xi_2 > \xi_1$ are two such, then we should have both

$$f(\xi_1) = 0, \; f(\xi_1) < 0.$$

2) To prove that there is one such ξ, we proceed as follows. There exists an η such that

(1) $$a \leqq \eta \leqq b,$$

(2) $$f(x) < 0 \quad \text{for} \quad a \leqq x \leqq \eta,$$

namely $\eta = a$. Let ξ be the l.u.b. of the η's for which (1) and (2) hold. Then we have

$$a \leqq \xi \leqq b.$$

We have
(3)
$$f(x) < 0 \quad \text{for} \quad a \leqq x < \xi.$$

For, in case $\xi = a$, nothing is asserted here. And in case $\xi > a$, we choose, for every x_0 with $a \leqq x_0 < \xi$, an η with $x_0 < \eta \leqq \xi$ for which (2) holds, so that

$$f(x_0) < 0.$$

I assert that

$$f(\xi) = 0$$

(and hence $a < \xi < b$, so that everything will be proved).

If we had

$$f(\xi) < 0,$$

then we should have

$$a \leqq \xi < b,$$

so that, by Theorem 143, there would exist an ε such that

$$0 < \varepsilon < b - \xi,$$

(4)
$$f(x) < 0 \quad \text{for} \quad \xi \leqq x \leqq \xi + \varepsilon.$$

Then (3) and (4) would imply that

$$f(x) < 0 \quad \text{for} \quad a \leqq x \leqq \xi + \varepsilon,$$

and there would exist an $\eta > \xi$ with (1) and (2), namely $\eta = \xi + \varepsilon$.

If we had

$$f(\xi) > 0,$$

then we should have

$$a < \xi \leqq b,$$

so that, by Theorem 144, there would exist an η such that

$$a < \eta < \xi,$$

$$f(\eta) > 0,$$

contradicting (3).

Theorem 149: *If*

$$f(a) > 0 > f(b),$$

then there exists exactly one ξ such that

$$a < \xi < b,$$

$$f(\xi) = 0,$$

$$f(x) > 0 \quad \text{for} \quad a \leqq x < \xi.$$

Proof: Theorem 148 with $-f(x)$ in place of $f(x)$.

Theorem 150: *If*
$$f(a) < c < f(b),$$
then there exists exactly one ξ such that
$$a < \xi < b,$$
$$f(\xi) = c,$$
$$f(x) < c \quad \text{for } a \leqq x < \xi.$$

Theorem 151: *If*
$$f(a) > c > f(b),$$
then there exists exactly one ξ such that
$$a < \xi < b,$$
$$f(\xi) = c,$$
$$f(x) > c \quad \text{for } a \leqq x < \xi.$$

Simultaneous proof of Theorems 150 and 151: Theorem 148 and 149 respectively, with $f(x) - c$ in place of $f(x)$.

Theorem 152: *If l is the greatest value and λ the least value of $f(x)$ on $[a, b]$, and if*
$$\lambda \leqq c \leqq l,$$
then there exists a ξ such that
$$a \leqq \xi \leqq b, \quad f(\xi) = c.$$

Proof: This is trivial for $c = l$ and for $c = \lambda$. Therefore let
$$\lambda < c < l.$$
Choose u and v on $[a, b]$ such that
$$f(u) = \lambda, \quad f(v) = l,$$
and apply Theorem 150 or Theorem 151 to the interval $[u, v]$ or $[v, u]$ (according to whether $u < v$ or $v < u$).

Theorem 153: *If*
$$f(x) = \sum_{\nu=0}^{n} a_\nu x^\nu,$$
$$a_n \neq 0,$$
$$n \text{ an odd integer,}$$
then there exists a ξ such that
$$f(\xi) = 0.$$

Proof: W.l.g. let $a_n = 1 \left(\text{otherwise consider } \dfrac{f(x)}{a_n} \right)$.

By Theorem 148 it suffices to find an $a < 0$ with
$$f(a) < 0$$

and a $b > 0$ with

$$f(b) > 0.$$

Setting

$$\sum_{\nu=0}^{n-1} |a_\nu| = A,$$

we have for $|x| \geqq 1$ that

$$|f(x) - x^n| = \left|\sum_{\nu=0}^{n-1} a_\nu x^\nu\right| \leqq \sum_{\nu=0}^{n-1} |a_\nu| \, |x|^{n-1} = A \, |x|^{n-1},$$

so that, for $|x| = 1 + A$, it follows that

$$|f(x) - x^n| < |x| \, |x|^{n-1} = |x|^n.$$

Hence we have for $x = -1 - A$ that

$$f(x) < x^n + |x|^n = 0$$

and for $x = 1 + A$ that

$$f(x) > x^n - |x|^n = 0.$$

Theorem 154 (theorem on uniform continuity): *For every $\delta > 0$ there exists an $\varepsilon > 0$ such that*

$$|f(\alpha) - f(\beta)| < \delta \ \text{for} \ a \leqq \alpha \leqq b, \ a \leqq \beta \leqq b, \ |\alpha - \beta| < \varepsilon.$$

Preliminary Remark: Theorem 154 is not a special case of Theorem 134, since in that theorem ε depends on ξ.

Proof: If there were no such ε for some $\delta > 0$, then for every integer $n \geqq 1$ we could choose two numbers α_n, β_n on $[a, b]$ such that

$$|f(\alpha_n) - f(\beta_n)| \geqq \delta, \qquad |\alpha_n - \beta_n| < \frac{1}{n}.$$

Determine a ξ by Theorem 130 with $\xi_n = \alpha_n$. Since $f(x)$ is continuous on $[a, b]$, there would exist, by Theorem 134, an $\varepsilon > 0$ such that

$$(1) \qquad |f(x) - f(\xi)| < \frac{\delta}{2} \ \text{for} \ a \leqq x \leqq b, \ |x - \xi| < 2\varepsilon.$$

Choose n such that

$$n > \frac{1}{\varepsilon}$$

and

$$|\alpha_n - \xi| < \varepsilon.$$

Then we have

$$|\beta_n - \xi| = |(\alpha_n - \xi) - (\alpha_n - \beta_n)| \leqq |\alpha_n - \xi| + |\alpha_n - \beta_n|$$
$$< \varepsilon + \frac{1}{n} < 2\varepsilon,$$

so that, by (1),

$$\delta \leq |f(\alpha_n) - f(\beta_n)| = |(f(\alpha_n) - f(\xi)) - (f(\beta_n) -- f(\xi))|$$
$$\leq |f(\alpha_n) - f(\xi)| + |f(\beta_n) - f(\xi)| < \frac{\delta}{2} + \frac{\delta}{2} = \delta.$$

Example: $[a, b]$ arbitrary, $f(x)$ any entire rational function $\sum\limits_{\nu=0}^{n} a_\nu x^\nu$.
Here, however, the assertion of Theorem 154 may be verified directly, as follows. Set

$$M = \text{Max} (|a|, |b|).$$

W.l.g. let $n > 0$. Then if α and β are on $[a, b]$, we have

$$|f(\alpha) - f(\beta)| = \left| \sum_{\nu=1}^{n} a_\nu (\alpha^\nu - \beta^\nu) \right| = |\alpha - \beta| \left| \sum_{\nu=1}^{n} a_\nu \sum_{\mu=0}^{\nu-1} \alpha^{\nu-\mu-1} \beta^\mu \right|$$
$$\leq |\alpha - \beta| \sum_{\nu=1}^{n} |a_\nu| \sum_{\mu=0}^{\nu-1} M^{\nu-\mu-1} M^\mu = |\alpha - \beta| c,$$

where c is independent of α and β, so that

$$|f(\alpha) - f(\beta)| < \delta \text{ for } |\alpha - \beta| < \frac{\delta}{c+1}, \ \alpha \text{ and } \beta \text{ on } [a, b].$$

Theorem 155 (Weierstrass): *For every $\delta > 0$ there exists an entire rational function $P(x)$ such that*

$$|f(x) - P(x)| < \delta \text{ on } [a, b].$$

Preliminary Remark: Theorem 155 evidently implies Theorem 154 (knowing Theorem 154 for $P(x)$, which may be proved directly on the basis of the calculations of the last example). For, for $\delta > 0$ choose a $P(x)$ with

$$|f(x) - P(x)| < \frac{\delta}{3} \text{ on } [a, b],$$

and for this $P(x)$ (which depends on δ), choose an $\varepsilon > 0$ such that

$$|P(\alpha) - P(\beta)| < \frac{\delta}{3} \text{ for } |\alpha - \beta| < \varepsilon, \ \alpha \text{ and } \beta \text{ on } [a, b].$$

Then we have for these α, β that

$$|f(\alpha) - f(\beta)| = |(f(\alpha) - P(\alpha)) - (f(\beta) - P(\beta)) + (P(\alpha) - P(\beta))|$$
$$< \frac{\delta}{3} + \frac{\delta}{3} + \frac{\delta}{3} = \delta.$$

The proof of Theorem 154 is not, however, unnecessary, since Theorem 154 is needed in the proof of Theorem 155.

Proof: For integral $n > 0$, we set

$$\varphi_n(x) = \sum_{i=0}^{n} \left(1 - \left(\frac{i}{n} - x\right)^2\right)^n,$$

$$K_n = \varphi_n(0) \qquad (\geq 1),$$

$$\tau_n(x) = \frac{\varphi_n(x)}{2K_n},$$

and we begin by proving the existence of two positive absolute constants p_1, p_2 such that

(1) $$K_n > p_1\sqrt{n},$$

(2) $$1 - \frac{p_2}{\sqrt{n}} \leq \tau_n(x) \leq 1 \quad \text{for } \tfrac{1}{3} \leq x \leq \tfrac{2}{3}.$$

For this, we use the fact $\left(\text{known from Theorem 38 with } x = 1 - \frac{1}{n}\right)$ that, for $n \geq 2$,

$$\log\left(1 - \frac{1}{n}\right) \geq 1 - \frac{n}{n-1} = -\frac{1}{n-1} \geq -\frac{2}{n},$$

so that

$$\left(1 - \frac{1}{n}\right)^n = e^{n \log\left(1 - \frac{1}{n}\right)} \geq e^{-2},$$

and that $(n+1)\vartheta^n$ is bounded for fixed ϑ with $0 < \vartheta < 1$ and for $n \geq 1$. Indeed, we have

$$(n+1)\vartheta^n \leq \sum_{\nu=0}^{n} \vartheta^\nu = \frac{1 - \vartheta^{n+1}}{1 - \vartheta} < \frac{1}{1 - \vartheta}.$$

For $n \geq 2$, we have that

$$K_n = \sum_{i=0}^{n}\left(1 - \frac{i^2}{n^2}\right)^n \geq \sum_{i=0}^{[\sqrt{n}]}\left(1 - \frac{i^2}{n^2}\right)^n \geq \sum_{i=0}^{[\sqrt{n}]}\left(1 - \frac{n}{n^2}\right)^n$$

$$= \left([\sqrt{n}] + 1\right)\left(1 - \frac{1}{n}\right)^n > e^{-2}\sqrt{n},$$

and for $n = 1$ that

$$K_n = 1 > e^{-2}\sqrt{n}.$$

Hence we have established (1).

For $\tfrac{1}{3} \leq x \leq \tfrac{2}{3}$, we set

$$l = [nx];$$

then we have

$$l \leqq nx < l + 1,$$

$$\frac{l}{n} \leqq x < \frac{l+1}{n},$$

$$0 \leqq l \leqq \tfrac{2}{3} n < n,$$

$$\varphi_n(x) = \sum_{i=0}^{l} \left(1 - \left(x - \frac{i}{n}\right)^2\right)^n + \sum_{i=l+1}^{n} \left(1 - \left(\frac{i}{n} - x\right)^2\right)^n$$

$$\leqq \sum_{i=0}^{l} \left(1 - \left(\frac{l}{n} - \frac{i}{n}\right)^2\right)^n + \sum_{i=l+1}^{n} \left(1 - \left(\frac{i}{n} - \frac{l+1}{n}\right)^2\right)^n$$

$$= \sum_{\nu=0}^{l} \left(1 - \left(\frac{\nu}{n}\right)^2\right)^n + \sum_{\nu=0}^{n-l-1} \left(1 - \left(\frac{\nu}{n}\right)^2\right)^n \leqq K_n + K_n = 2K_n,$$

$$\tau_n(x) \leqq 1.$$

If we further set

$$k = \left[\frac{n}{3}\right],$$

then we have

$$k + 1 > \frac{n}{3},$$

$$\left(\frac{k+1}{n}\right)^2 > \frac{1}{9},$$

$$l + 1 > nx \geqq \frac{n}{3} \geqq k,$$

$$n - l \geqq n - nx \geqq \frac{n}{3} \geqq k,$$

$$\varphi_n(x) \geqq \sum_{i=0}^{l} \left(1 - \left(\frac{l+1}{n} - \frac{i}{n}\right)^2\right)^n + \sum_{i=l+1}^{n} \left(1 - \left(\frac{i}{n} - \frac{l}{n}\right)^2\right)^n$$

$$= \sum_{\nu=1}^{l+1} \left(1 - \left(\frac{\nu}{n}\right)^2\right)^n + \sum_{\nu=1}^{n-l} \left(1 - \left(\frac{\nu}{n}\right)^2\right)^n \geqq 2 \sum_{\nu=1}^{k} \left(1 - \left(\frac{\nu}{n}\right)^2\right)^n,$$

$$= 2 \left(K_n - 1 - \sum_{\nu=k+1}^{n} \left(1 - \left(\frac{\nu}{n}\right)^2\right)^n\right) \geqq 2 \left(K_n - 1 - \sum_{\nu=k+1}^{n} \left(1 - \frac{1}{9}\right)^n\right)$$

$$\geqq 2 \left(K_n - 1 - n \left(\frac{8}{9}\right)^n\right) \geqq 2 \left(K_n - p_3\right),$$

where p_3 is an absolute constant, so that

$$\tau_n(x) \geqq 1 - \frac{p_3}{K_n} > 1 - \frac{p_3}{p_1 \sqrt{n}}.$$

Hence we have established (2).

First case: Let

$$\left.\begin{array}{l} f(x) \text{ be continuous} \\ |f(x)| \leqq 1 \end{array}\right\} \text{ on } [0, 1].$$

We set

$$P_n(x) = \frac{1}{2K_n} \sum_{i=0}^{n} f\left(\frac{i}{n}\right)\left(1 - \left(\frac{i}{n} - x\right)^2\right)^n,$$

and assert that for every $\delta > 0$ there exists an n independent of x (thus depending only on δ and f) such that

(3) $\qquad |f(x) - P_n(x)| < \delta \text{ for } \frac{1}{3} \leqq x \leqq \frac{2}{3}.$

This will yield a completely general proof of the assertion of Theorem 155 in case $a = \frac{1}{3}$, $b = \frac{2}{3}$. For, if $F(x)$ is continuous on $[\frac{1}{3}, \frac{2}{3}]$, let M be the largest value of $|F(x)|$ on $[\frac{1}{3}, \frac{2}{3}]$, and define

$$f(x) = \begin{cases} \dfrac{F(x)}{M+1} & \text{for } [\frac{1}{3}, \frac{2}{3}], \\ f(\frac{1}{3}) & \text{for } 0 \leqq x < \frac{1}{3}, \\ f(\frac{2}{3}) & \text{for } \frac{2}{3} < x \leqq 1. \end{cases}$$

This $f(x)$ is continuous on $[a, b]$ and is, in absolute value, $\leqq 1$. If we choose n such that

$$|f(x) - P_n(x)| < \frac{\delta}{M+1} \text{ for } \frac{1}{3} \leqq x \leqq \frac{2}{3},$$

then we have

$$|F(x) - (M+1)P_n(x)| < \delta \text{ for } \frac{1}{3} \leqq x \leqq \frac{2}{3}.$$

And $(M+1)P_n(x)$ is clearly an entire rational function of x.

We shall now proceed to prove (3). By Theorem 154, choose an ε independent of x and ξ such that

$$0 < \varepsilon < \frac{1}{3},$$

$$|f(x) - f(\xi)| < \frac{\delta}{2} \text{ for } \frac{1}{3} \leqq x \leqq \frac{2}{3}, \ |x - \xi| < \varepsilon.$$

Then if an empty sum means 0, we have for $\frac{1}{3} \leqq x \leqq \frac{2}{3}$ that

$$|f(x)\tau_n(x) - P_n(x)| = \left| \frac{1}{2K_n} \sum_{i=0}^{n} \left(f(x) - f\left(\frac{i}{n}\right)\right)\left(1 - \left(\frac{i}{n} - x\right)^2\right)^n \right|$$

$$\leq \frac{1}{2K_n} \sum_{\substack{i=0 \\ \left|\frac{i}{n}-x\right|<\varepsilon}}^{n} \left| f(x) - f\left(\frac{i}{n}\right) \right| \left(1 - \left(\frac{i}{n} - x\right)^2\right)^n$$

$$+ \frac{1}{2K_n} \sum_{\substack{i=0 \\ \left|\frac{i}{n}-x\right|\geq\varepsilon}}^{n} \left| f(x) - f\left(\frac{i}{n}\right) \right| \left(1 - \left(\frac{i}{n} - x\right)^2\right)^n$$

$$\leq \frac{\delta}{4K_n} \sum_{\substack{i=0 \\ \left|\frac{i}{n}-x\right|<\varepsilon}}^{n} \left(1 - \left(\frac{i}{n} - x\right)^2\right)^n + \frac{1}{K_n} \sum_{\substack{i=0 \\ \left|\frac{i}{n}-x\right|\geq\varepsilon}}^{n} \left(1 - \left(\frac{i}{n} - x\right)^2\right)^n$$

$$\leq \frac{\delta}{4K_n} \varphi_n(x) + \frac{1}{K_n} \sum_{i=0}^{n} (1 - \varepsilon^2)^n = \frac{\delta}{2} \tau_n(x) + \frac{1}{K_n}(n + 1)(1 - \varepsilon^2)^n$$

$$< \frac{\delta}{2} + \frac{p(\delta, f)}{\sqrt{n}},$$

where $p(\delta, f)$ depends only on δ and f. Furthermore, we have

$$\left| f(x) - f(x)\tau_n(x) \right| = \left| f(x) \right| \left| 1 - \tau_n(x) \right| \leq \left| 1 - \tau_n(x) \right| \leq \frac{p_2}{\sqrt{n}},$$

so that

$$\left| f(x) - P_n(x) \right| < \frac{\delta}{2} + \frac{p(\delta, f) + p_2}{\sqrt{n}}.$$

Hence (3) is true for a suitable n independent of x.

Second case: Let $[a, b]$ be arbitrary. The function

$$g(x) = f(a + (3x - 1)(b - a))$$

is evidently continuous on $[\frac{1}{3}, \frac{2}{3}]$. Hence by the first case, there exists an entire rational function $Q(x)$ with

$$\left| g(x) - Q(x) \right| < \delta \text{ on } [\tfrac{1}{3}, \tfrac{2}{3}].$$

Hence we have on $[a, b]$ that

$$\left| f(x) - Q\left(\frac{1}{3}\frac{x-a}{b-a} + \frac{1}{3}\right) \right| = \left| g\left(\frac{1}{3}\frac{x-a}{b-a} + \frac{1}{3}\right) - Q\left(\frac{1}{3}\frac{x-a}{b-a} + \frac{1}{3}\right) \right|$$

$$< \delta.$$

$Q\left(\dfrac{1}{3}\dfrac{x-a}{b-a} + \dfrac{1}{3}\right)$ is evidently an entire rational function of x.

CHAPTER 9

ROLLE'S THEOREM AND THE
THEOREM OF THE MEAN

We now return to the differential calculus.

Theorem 156 (Rolle's theorem) : *Let $f(x)$ be continuous on $[a, b]$. Let*

$$f(a) = f(b) = 0.$$

Let $f'(x)$ exist for $a < x < b$. Then there is a ξ such that

$$a < \xi < b, \ f'(\xi) = 0.$$

Preliminary Remark: If a number ξ is such that $a < \xi < b$, then we shall say that it lies between a and b or that it lies between b and a.

Proof: 1) Let

$$f(x) = 0 \ \text{for} \ a \leqq x \leqq b.$$

Then

$$f'\left(\frac{a + b}{2}\right) = 0.$$

2) Let $f(x)$ be positive somewhere on $[a, b]$. Then by Theorem 146, there is a ξ such that

$$a < \xi < b, \ f(x) \leqq f(\xi) \ \text{for} \ a \leqq x \leqq b.$$

If $f'(\xi) > 0$, then $f(x)$ would be increasing at ξ; if $f'(\xi) < 0$ then $f(x)$ would be decreasing at ξ. In both cases, there would exist an x on $[a, b]$ such that

$$f(x) > f(\xi).$$

Thus we have

$$f'(\xi) = 0.$$

3) Let

$$f(x) \leqq 0 \ \text{for} \ a \leqq x \leqq b,$$

but < 0 at some place in that interval. Then for $-f(x)$ we have case 2). Thus there exists a ξ such that

$$a < \xi < b, \; -f'(\xi) = 0.$$

Theorem 157: *If*

$$f(x) = \sum_{\nu=0}^{n} a_{\nu}x^{\nu},$$

$$a_n \neq 0,$$

then

$$f(x) = 0$$

has at most n solutions.

Proofs: The assertion is obvious for $n = 0$, since, if $a_0 \neq 0$, then

$$a_0 = 0$$

has no solution.

Let $n > 0$, and assume that our statement is true for $n - 1$.

1) If

$$f(x) = 0$$

has no solution, then we are done.

Otherwise, let ξ be a solution. Then

$$f(x) = f(x) - f(\xi) = \sum_{\nu=0}^{n} a_{\nu}x^{\nu} - \sum_{\nu=0}^{n} a_{\nu}\xi^{\nu} = \sum_{\nu=1}^{n} a_{\nu}(x^{\nu} - \xi^{\nu})$$

$$= (x - \xi) \sum_{\nu=1}^{n} a_{\nu} \sum_{\mu=0}^{\nu-1} x^{\mu}\xi^{\nu-1-\mu} = (x - \xi) \sum_{\mu=0}^{n-1} x^{\mu} \sum_{\nu=\mu+1}^{n} a_{\nu}\xi^{\nu-1-\mu}$$

$$= (x - \xi)g(x),$$

where

$$g(x) = \sum_{\mu=0}^{n-1} b_{\mu}x^{\mu}, \quad b_{n-1} = a_n, \quad b_{n-1} \neq 0.$$

If

$$f(\eta) = 0, \quad \eta \neq \xi,$$

then

$$(\eta - \xi)g(\eta) = 0,$$
$$g(\eta) = 0.$$

If

$$f(x) = 0$$

had at least $n + 1$ solutions (i.e. an infinite number or a finite number $\geqq n + 1$), then

$$g(x) = 0$$

would have at least n solutions, which is a contradiction.

2) Suppose that

$$f(x) = 0$$

had a system of $n + 1$ solutions. Then by Theorem 156, between any two consecutive solutions there would be at least one solution of

$$f'(x) = 0.$$

But, since

$$f'(x) = \sum_{\nu=0}^{n-1} (\nu + 1)a_{\nu+1}x^\nu, \ na_n \neq 0,$$

we see that

$$f'(x) = 0$$

can have at most $n - 1$ solutions.

Theorem 158: *If*

$$f(x) = \sum_{\nu=0}^{n} a_\nu x^\nu,$$

$$n > 1,$$

$$a_n \neq 0,$$

and if

(1) $$f(x) = 0$$

has exactly n solutions, then

(2) $$f'(x) = 0$$

has exactly $n - 1$ solutions.

Proof: By Theorem 156, between any two consecutive solutions of (1) there is at least one solution of (2). Thus (2) has at least $n - 1$ solutions. But since

$$f'(x) = \sum_{\nu=0}^{n-1} (\nu + 1)a_{\nu+1}x^\nu, \ na_n \neq 0,$$

(2) has, by Theorem 157, at most $n - 1$ solutions. Thus it has exacctly $n - 1$ solutions.

Theorem 159 (The theorem of the mean, or mean value theorem): *Let $f(x)$ be continuous on $[a, b]$. Let $f'(x)$ exist for $a < x < b$. Then there is a ξ such that*

$$a < \xi < b, \quad \frac{f(b) - f(a)}{b - a} = f'(\xi).$$

Proof: $$\varphi(x) = f(x) - f(a) - \frac{x - a}{b - a}\left(f(b) - f(a)\right)$$

is continuous on $[a, b]$. If $a < x < b$, we have

$$\varphi'(x) = f'(x) - \frac{f(b) - f(a)}{b - a}.$$

Furthermore,

$$\varphi(a) = 0 = \varphi(b).$$

Thus, by Theorem 156, there exists a ξ such that

$$a < \xi < b, \quad 0 = \varphi'(\xi) = f'(\xi) - \frac{f(b) - f(a)}{b - a}.$$

Theorem 160: *Let $f(x)$ be continuous on $[a, b]$. Let*

$$f'(x) \geqq 0 \text{ for } a < x < b.$$

Then

$$f(b) \geqq f(a).$$

Proof: In Theorem 159, we have

$$f'(\xi) \geqq 0.$$

Thus

$$\frac{f(b) - f(a)}{b - a} \geqq 0,$$

$$f(b) \geqq f(a).$$

Example: If $\quad f(x) = e^x - x, \quad a = 0, \quad b > 0,$
then

$$f'(x) = e^x - 1 \geqq 0 \text{ for } x \geqq 0,$$
$$e^b - b \geqq 1 \text{ for } b > 0$$

(which is already known from Theorem 37 with $x = e^b$).

Theorem 161: *Let $f(x)$ and $g(x)$ be continuous on $[a, b]$. Let*

$$f'(x) \geqq g'(x) \text{ for } a < x < b.$$

Then

$$f(b) - f(a) \geqq g(b) - g(a).$$

Proof: By Theorem 160, using $f(x) - g(x)$ in place of $f(x)$, we have

$$f(b) - g(b) \geqq f(a) - g(a).$$

Theorem 162: *Let $f(x)$ and $g(x)$ be continuous on $[a, b]$. Let*

$$f'(x) = g'(x) \text{ for } a < x < b.$$

Then

$$f(x) = g(x) + \big(f(a) - g(a)\big) \text{ for } a \leqq x \leqq b$$

(so that $f(x) - g(x)$ is constant in that interval).

Proof: Let $a \leqq \xi \leqq b$. If $\xi = a$, then

$$f(\xi) = g(\xi) + \big(f(a) - g(a)\big).$$

If $a < \xi \leqq b$, then by applying Theorem 161 to $[a, \xi]$, we obtain

$$f(\xi) - f(a) \geqq g(\xi) - g(a).$$

But, since our hypotheses are symmetric in $f(x)$ and $g(x)$, we have

$$g(\xi) - g(a) \geqq f(\xi) - f(a)$$

and therefore

$$f(\xi) - f(a) = g(\xi) - g(a),$$
$$f(\xi) = g(\xi) + (f(a) - g(a)).$$

Theorem 163: *Let $f(x)$ be continuous on $[a, b]$. Let*

$$f'(x) = 0 \ for \ a < x < b.$$

Then

$$f(x) = f(a) \ for \ a \leqq x \leqq b$$

(i.e. $f(x)$ is constant therein).

Proof: Theorem 162, with

$$g(x) = 0.$$

Theorem 164: *Let $a < b$, and let $f'(x)$ exist for $a \leqq x \leqq b$. Let*

$$f'(a) < c < f'(b)$$

or

$$f'(a) > c > f'(b).$$

Then there is a ξ such that

$$a < \xi < b, \quad f'(\xi) = c.$$

Proof: W.l.g. let $c = 0$. (Otherwise we would consider $f(x) - cx$). W.l.g. let

$$f'(a) > 0 > f'(b).$$

(Otherwise we would consider $-f(x)$.)

By Theorem 146, there is a ξ such that

$$a \leqq \xi \leqq b, \ f(x) \leqq f(\xi) \ \text{for} \ a \leqq x \leqq b.$$

Since $f(x)$ increases at a and decreases at b, we have

$$a < \xi < b.$$

If

$$f'(\xi) > 0,$$

then $f(x)$ would be increasing at ξ and would be $> f(\xi)$ somewhere on $[a, b]$; if

$$f'(\xi) < 0,$$

then $f(x)$ would be decreasing at ξ and would be $> f(\xi)$ somewhere on $[a, b]$.

Thus, we have

$$f'(\xi) = 0.$$

Is Theorem 164 contained in Theorems 150 and 151 as a special case? No; for we have not assumed that $f'(x)$ is continuous on $[a, b]$. But can this perhaps be proved? No, as the following theorem shows.

Theorem 165: *There is an everywhere differentiable function $f(x)$ such that $f'(x)$ is not everywhere continuous on the right.*

Proof: For all z, set

$$\varphi(z) = ((z - [z])(1 - z + [z]))^2.$$

Then, we have for all z that

(1) $$0 \leq \varphi(z) \leq (1 \cdot 1)^2 = 1.$$

If $-1 < z < 0$, then

$$\varphi(z) = ((z + 1)z)^2;$$

if $0 \leq z < 1$, then

$$\varphi(z) = (z(1 - z))^2.$$

Thus,

$$\varphi'(0) = \lim_{z=0} \frac{\varphi(z)}{z} = \lim_{z=0} (z(1 \pm z)^2) = 0,$$

$$\varphi'(z) = \begin{cases} 2(z + 1)z(2z + 1) & \text{for } -1 < z < 0, \\ 2z(1 - z)(1 - 2z) & \text{for } 0 < z < 1, \end{cases}$$

$$\varphi'(\tfrac{1}{4}) \neq 0.$$

$\varphi'(z)$ exists for $|z| < 1$. If n is an integer, then

$$\varphi(z + n) = \varphi(z).$$

Thus, $\varphi'(z)$ exists everywhere (since for every ζ there exists an integer n such that $|\zeta + n| < 1$). If z is an integer, then

$$\varphi'(z + \tfrac{1}{4}) = \varphi'(\tfrac{1}{4}).$$

Now we set

$$f(x) = \begin{cases} 0 & \text{for } x = 0, \\ x^2\varphi\left(\dfrac{1}{x}\right) & \text{for } x \neq 0. \end{cases}$$

Then, by (1),

$$f'(0) = \lim_{x=0} x\,\varphi\left(\frac{1}{x}\right) = 0$$

and if $x \neq 0$,

$$f'(x) = 2x\,\varphi\left(\frac{1}{x}\right) - \varphi'\left(\frac{1}{x}\right).$$

Suppose that $f'(x)$ were continuous on the right at 0. Then, since

$$\lim_{x=0} 2x\, \varphi\left(\frac{1}{x}\right) = 0,$$

the function

$$F(x) = \begin{cases} 0 & \text{for } x = 0, \\ \varphi'\left(\dfrac{1}{x}\right) & \text{for } x > 0 \end{cases}$$

would be continuous on the right at 0. But for integral $z > 0$,

$$\varphi'\left(\frac{1}{\dfrac{1}{z + \frac{1}{4}}}\right) = \varphi'\left(z + \tfrac{1}{4}\right) = \varphi'(\tfrac{1}{4}) \neq 0.$$

CHAPTER 10

DERIVATIVES OF HIGHER ORDER; TAYLOR'S THEOREM

Definition 41: *Let $f(x)$ be given. Then we set*

$$f^{(0)}(x) = f(x)$$

for those x at which $f(x)$ is defined;

$$f^{(1)}(x) = f'(x)$$

for those x at which $f(x)$ is differentiable;

$$f^{(2)}(x) = \left(f^{(1)}(x)\right)'$$

for those x at which $f^{(1)}(x)$ is differentiable; in general, if $n \geqq 0$ is an integer (and if $f^{(n)}(x)$ is defined), then

$$f^{(n+1)}(x) = \left(f^{(n)}(x)\right)' \; .$$

for those x at which $f^{(n)}(x)$ is differentiable.

If $f^{(n)}(\xi)$ exists, then we say that the function $f(x)$ is n times differentiable at ξ.

$f^{(n)}(x)$ *is called the n-th derivative of $f(x)$. We also write* $\dfrac{d^n f(x)}{dx^n}$ *or* $\dfrac{d^n}{dx^n} f(x)$ *and, when no confusion is possible, also* $(f(x))^{(n)}$. *We also write* $f''(x)$ *or* $(f(x))''$ *for* $f^{(2)}(x)$, *and* $f'''(x)$ *or* $(f(x))'''$ *for* $f^{(3)}(x)$, *and so on.*
If

$$y = f(x),$$

then we also write (when no confusion is possible) $y^{(0)}, y^{(1)}, y^{(2)}, \ldots$ *or* $y^{(0)}, y', y'', \ldots$.

Examples: 1) If $y = x^3$ then we have that, everywhere

$$y' = 3x^2, \; y'' = 6x, \; y''' = 6, \; y'''' = 0,$$

so that

$$y^{(n)} = 0 \text{ for integral } n > 3.$$

2) For $y = \dfrac{1}{x}$, $x \neq 0$ we have

$$y^{(n)} = \frac{(-1)^n n!}{x^{n+1}}.$$

For $n = 0$ this is given. $n + 1$ follows from n since

$$y^{(n+1)} = (y^{(n)})' = \left(\frac{(-1)^n n!}{x^{n+1}}\right)' = (-1)^n n! (x^{-n-1})' = (-1)^n n! (-n-1) x^{-n-2}$$

$$= \frac{(-1)^{n+1}(n+1)!}{x^{n+2}}.$$

Theorem 166: $\big(f(x) + g(x)\big)^{(n)} = f^{(n)}(x) + g^{(n)}(x)$,

if the right-hand side is meaningful.

Proof: $n = 0$: Obvious. To proceed from n to $n + 1$:

$$f^{(n+1)} + g^{(n+1)} = (f^{(n)})' + (g^{(n)})' = (f^{(n)} + g^{(n)})' = \big((f+g)^{(n)}\big)' = (f+g)^{(n+1)}.$$

Theorem 167: $\left(\displaystyle\sum_{\nu=1}^{m} f_\nu(x)\right)^{(n)} = \displaystyle\sum_{\nu=1}^{m} f_\nu^{(n)}(x)$,

if the right-hand side is meaningful.

Proof: $m = 1$: Obvious. To proceed from m to $m + 1$ (for fixed n):

$$\sum_{\nu=1}^{m+1} f_\nu^{(n)} = \sum_{\nu=1}^{m} f_\nu^{(n)} + f_{m+1}^{(n)} = \left(\sum_{\nu=1}^{m} f_\nu\right)^{(n)} + f_{m+1}^{(n)} = \left(\sum_{\nu=1}^{m} f_\nu + f_{m+1}\right)^{(n)} = \left(\sum_{\nu=1}^{m+1} f_\nu\right)^{(n)}$$

Theorem 168: $\big(cf(x)\big)^{(n)} = c f^{(n)}(x)$,

if the right-hand side is meaningful.

Proof: $n = 0$: Obvious. To proceed from n to $n + 1$:

$$c f^{(n+1)} = c(f^{(n)})' = (c f^{(n)})' = \big((cf)^{(n)}\big)' = (cf)^{(n+1)}.$$

Theorem 169: $\big(f(x) - g(x)\big)^{(n)} = f^{(n)}(x) - g^{(n)}(x)$,

if the right-hand side is meaningful.

Proof: $\qquad\qquad f - g = f + (-1)g$,

Theorems 166, and 168.

Definition 42: *For integral $n \geqq 0$ and for every α, we define*

$$\binom{\alpha}{n} = \begin{cases} 1 & , \text{ if } \quad n = 0, \\[2mm] \dfrac{\displaystyle\prod_{m=0}^{n-1}(\alpha - m)}{n!} & , \text{ if } \quad n > 0. \end{cases}$$

To be read: α above n.

Example: For integral $n \geqq 0$, we have

$$\binom{n}{n} = 1.$$

Theorem 170: *Let α be an integer $\geqq 0$. Then for all x, if n is an integer $\geqq 0$,*

$$(x^\alpha)^{(n)} = \binom{\alpha}{n} n!\, x^{\alpha-n} \ \textit{for} \ n \leqq \alpha,$$

so that

$$(x^\alpha)^{(\alpha)} = \alpha!,$$

and

$$(x^\alpha)^{(n)} = 0 \ \textit{for} \ n > \alpha.$$

Proof: For $n = 0$, our assertion follows from

$$(x^\alpha)^{(0)} = x^\alpha = \binom{\alpha}{0} 0!\, x^{\alpha-0}.$$

If the assertion is true for n, and if $0 \leqq n < \alpha$, then it follows for $n+1$ since

$$(x^\alpha)^{(n+1)} = \left((x^\alpha)^{(n)}\right)' = \left(\binom{\alpha}{n} n!\, x^{\alpha-n}\right)' = \binom{\alpha}{n} n!\, (\alpha-n)x^{\alpha-n-1}$$

$$= \binom{\alpha}{n+1} (n+1)!\, x^{\alpha-(n+1)}.$$

Theorem 171: *For $x > 0$ and every α, we have for integral $n \geqq 0$ that*

$$(x^\alpha)^{(n)} = \binom{\alpha}{n} n!\, x^{\alpha-n}.$$

If α is an integer, then this holds even for $x < 0$.

Proof: $n = 0$ is obvious. $n+1$ follows from n by the calculations occurring in the preceding proof.

Theorem 172: *For every α and integral $\nu \geqq 1$, we have*

$$\binom{\alpha}{\nu} + \binom{\alpha}{\nu-1} = \binom{\alpha+1}{\nu}.$$

Proof: Both sides equal $\alpha + 1$ for $\nu = 1$. If $\nu > 1$, the left-hand side is

$$\frac{\prod\limits_{m=0}^{\nu-1} (\alpha - m)}{\nu!} + \frac{\prod\limits_{m=0}^{\nu-2} (\alpha - m)}{(\nu-1)!} = \frac{\prod\limits_{m=0}^{\nu-2} (\alpha - m)}{\nu!} \left((\alpha - \nu + 1) + \nu\right)$$

$$= \frac{(\alpha + 1) \prod\limits_{m=0}^{\nu-2} (\alpha - m)}{\nu!} = \frac{\prod\limits_{k=0}^{\nu-1} (\alpha + 1 - k)}{\nu!} = \binom{\alpha+1}{\nu}.$$

Theorem 173: *If $f^{(n)}(x)$ and $g^{(n)}(x)$ exist, then*

$$(f(x)g(x))^{(n)} = \sum_{\nu=0}^{n} \binom{n}{\nu} f^{(n-\nu)}(x) \; g^{(\nu)}(x).$$

Proof: $n = 0$: Obvious, because

$$(fg)^{(0)} = fg = \binom{0}{0} f^{(0)} g^{(0)}.$$

To proceed from n to $n + 1$: By Theorems 111, 107, and 172, we have

$$(fg)^{(n+1)} = ((fg)^{(n)})' = \left(\sum_{\nu=0}^{n} \binom{n}{\nu} f^{(n-\nu)} g^{(\nu)} \right)' = \sum_{\nu=0}^{n} \binom{n}{\nu} (f^{(n-\nu)} g^{(\nu)})'$$

$$= \sum_{\nu=0}^{n} \binom{n}{\nu} (f^{(n-\nu+1)} g^{(\nu)} + f^{(n-\nu)} g^{(\nu+1)})$$

$$= \sum_{\nu=0}^{n} \binom{n}{\nu} f^{(n-\nu+1)} g^{(\nu)} + \sum_{\nu=0}^{n} \binom{n}{\nu} f^{(n-\nu)} g^{(\nu+1)}$$

$$= \sum_{\nu=0}^{n} \binom{n}{\nu} f^{(n-\nu+1)} g^{(\nu)} + \sum_{\nu=1}^{n+1} \binom{n}{\nu-1} f^{(n-\nu+1)} g^{(\nu)}$$

$$= f^{(n+1)} g^{(0)} + \sum_{\nu=1}^{n} \left(\binom{n}{\nu} + \binom{n}{\nu-1} \right) f^{(n+1-\nu)} g^{(\nu)} + f^{(0)} g^{(n+1)}$$

(the last Σ means 0 if $n = 0$)

$$= \sum_{\nu=0}^{n+1} \binom{n+1}{\nu} f^{(n+1-\nu)} g^{(\nu)}.$$

Example:
$$(fg)''' = f'''g + 3f''g' + 3f'g'' + fg''',$$

if both f''' and g''' exist.

Theorem 174:
$$(f(cx))^{(n)} = c^n f^{(n)}(cx),$$

if the right-hand side is meaningful.

Proof: $n = 0$ obvious. To proceed from n to $n + 1$: By Theorem 101, we have

$$(f^{(n)}(cx))' = c f^{(n+1)}(cx),$$

so that

$$c^{n+1} f^{(n+1)}(cx) = c^n (f^{(n)}(cx))' = (c^n f^{(n)}(cx))' = ((f(cx))^{(n)})' = (f(cx))^{(n+1)}.$$

Theorem 175:
$$(f(x+c))^{(n)} = f^{(n)}(x+c),$$

if the right-hand side is meaningful.

Proof: $n = 0$: Obvious. To proceed from n to $n + 1$: By Theorem 101, we have

$$f^{(n+1)}(x+c) = (f^{(n)}(x+c))' = ((f(x+c))^{(n)})' = (f(x+c))^{(n+1)}.$$

Theorem 176: *Let $h > 0$. Let $f^{(n-1)}(x)$ be continuous for $0 \leqq x \leqq h$, and let $f^{(n)}(x)$ exist for $0 < x < h$. Set*

$$\Phi = f(h) - \sum_{\nu=0}^{n-1} \frac{f^{(\nu)}(0)}{\nu!} h^\nu.$$

(This number is independent of x.) *Then there is an x such that*

$$0 < x < h, \quad \Phi = \frac{h^n}{n!} f^{(n)}(x).$$

Proof: If we set

(1) $$g(x) = f(x) - \sum_{\nu=0}^{n-1} \frac{f^{(\nu)}(0)}{\nu!} x^\nu - \Phi \frac{x^n}{h^n},$$

then by Theorems 167 and 170, we have for integral m such that $0 \leqq m < n$ and for all x such that $0 \leqq x \leqq h$, that

$$g^{(m)}(x) = f^{(m)}(x) - \sum_{\nu=m}^{n-1} \frac{f^{(\nu)}(0)}{\nu!} \binom{\nu}{m} m! \, x^{\nu-m} - \frac{\Phi}{h^n} \binom{n}{m} m! \, x^{n-m}$$

(2) $$= f^{(m)}(x) - \sum_{\nu=m}^{n-1} \frac{f^{(\nu)}(0)}{(\nu-m)!} x^{\nu-m} - \Phi \frac{n!}{(n-m)!} \frac{x^{n-m}}{h^n}.$$

If, in particular, $m = n - 1$ then (2) becomes

$$g^{(n-1)}(x) = f^{(n-1)}(x) - f^{(n-1)}(0) - \Phi \frac{n!}{h^n} x,$$

so that, if $0 < x < h$,

(3) $$g^{(n)}(x) = f^{(n)}(x) - \Phi \frac{n!}{h^n}.$$

From (1) we obtain

$$g(h) = 0,$$

and from (2),

$$g^{(m)}(0) = f^{(m)}(0) - f^{(m)}(0) = 0 \text{ for } 0 \leqq m < n.$$

I assert that

$$g^{(m)}(x) = 0$$

has a solution between 0 and h for all m with $1 \leqq m \leqq n$. For $m = 1$, this follows from Theorem 156, since

$$g(0) = 0 = g(h).$$

If $1 \leqq m < n$, and the assertion is true for m, then it is true for $m + 1$ by Theorem 156, since

$$g^{(m)}(0) = 0, \quad g^{(m)}(\eta) = 0 \text{ for an } \eta \text{ with } 0 < \eta < h.$$

Thus there is an x such that

$$0 < x < h, \quad g^{(n)}(x) = 0.$$

For this x, we have by (3),

$$f^{(n)}(x) - \Phi \, \frac{n!}{h^n} = 0,$$

$$\Phi = \frac{h^n}{n!} \, f^{(n)}(x).$$

Theorem 177 (Taylor): *Let $h > 0$. Let $f^{(n-1)}(x)$ be continuous for $\xi \leqq x \leqq \xi + h$ and let $f^{(n)}(x)$ exist for $\xi < x < \xi + h$. Then there is an x such that*

$$\xi < x < \xi + h,$$

$$f(\xi + h) = \sum_{\nu=0}^{n-1} \frac{f^{(\nu)}(\xi)}{\nu!} \, h^\nu + \frac{h^n}{n!} \, f^{(n)}(x).$$

Proof: Using Theorem 176 with

$$F(x) = f(\xi + x)$$

(in place of $f(x)$), we have, with the help of Theorem 175, that for a suitable y

$$0 < y < h,$$

$$f(\xi + h) = F(h) = \sum_{\nu=0}^{n-1} \frac{F^{(\nu)}(0)}{\nu!} \, h^\nu + \frac{h^n}{n!} \, F^{(n)}(y)$$

$$= \sum_{\nu=0}^{n-1} \frac{f^{(\nu)}(\xi)}{\nu!} \, h^\nu + \frac{h^n}{n!} \, f^{(n)}(\xi + y).$$

Theorem 178: *Let $h < 0$. Let $f^{(n-1)}(x)$ be continuous for $\xi + h \leqq x \leqq \xi$ and let $f^{(n)}(x)$ exist for $\xi + h < x < \xi$. Then there is an x such that*

$$\xi + h < x < \xi,$$

$$f(\xi + h) = \sum_{\nu=0}^{n-1} \frac{f^{(\nu)}(\xi)}{\nu!} \, h^\nu + \frac{h^n}{n!} \, f^{(n)}(x).$$

Proof: We apply Theorem 177 to

$$F(x) = f(-x)$$

(in place of $f(x)$), using $-\xi$ in place of ξ and $-h$ in place of h. Then, by Theorem 174 (with $c = -1$), we obtain a y such that

$$-\xi < y < -\xi - h,$$

$$f(\xi + h) = F(-\xi - h) = \sum_{\nu=0}^{n-1} \frac{F^{(\nu)}(-\xi)}{\nu!}(-h)^\nu + \frac{(-h)^n}{n!} F^{(n)}(y)$$

$$= \sum_{\nu=0}^{n-1} \frac{f^{(\nu)}(\xi)}{\nu!} h^\nu + \frac{h^n}{n!} f^{(n)}(-y).$$

Theorem 179: *If*

$$f(x) = \sum_{\nu=0}^{n} a_\nu x^\nu,$$

then

$$f(\xi + h) = \sum_{\nu=0}^{n} \frac{f^{(\nu)}(\xi)}{\nu!} h^\nu.$$

Proof: This is obvious for $h = 0$. By Theorem 170,

$$(x^\nu)^{(n+1)} = 0 \text{ for } 0 \leq \nu \leq n,$$

so that

$$f^{(n+1)}(x) = 0.$$

Thus, our assertion is obvious if $h > 0$ (or $h < 0$) by Theorem 177 (or 178), with $n + 1$ instead of n.

Theorem 180 (the binomial theorem): *We have for integral $n \geq 0$ that*

$$(a + b)^n = \sum_{\nu=0}^{n} \binom{n}{\nu} a^{n-\nu} b^\nu.$$

Proofs: 1) By Theorem 179, with

$$f(x) = x^n, \quad \xi = a, \quad h = b,$$

we obtain, using Theorem 170, that

$$(a + b)^n = \sum_{\nu=0}^{n} \frac{1}{\nu!} \binom{n}{\nu} \nu! \, a^{n-\nu} b^\nu.$$

2) (Direct proof.) $n = 0$ is obvious. By Theorem 172, $n + 1$ follows from n since

$$(a + b)^{n+1} = (a + b)^n (a + b) = \sum_{\nu=0}^{n} \binom{n}{\nu} a^{n-\nu} b^\nu (a + b)$$

$$= \sum_{\nu=0}^{n} \binom{n}{\nu} a^{n+1-\nu} b^\nu + \sum_{\nu=0}^{n} \binom{n}{\nu} a^{n-\nu} b^{\nu+1}$$

$$= \sum_{\nu=0}^{n} \binom{n}{\nu} a^{n+1-\nu} b^\nu + \sum_{\nu=1}^{n+1} \binom{n}{\nu-1} a^{n+1-\nu} b^\nu$$

$$= a^{n+1} + \sum_{\nu=1}^{n} \left(\binom{n}{\nu} + \binom{n}{\nu-1} \right) a^{n+1-\nu} b^\nu + b^{n+1}$$

(the last Σ means 0 if $n = 0$)

$$= \sum_{\nu=0}^{n+1} \binom{n+1}{\nu} a^{n+1-\nu} b^{\nu}.$$

3) By Theorem 173, with

$$f(x) = e^{ax}, \quad g(x) = e^{bx}$$

and Theorem 174, we obtain

$$(a+b)^n e^{(a+b)x} = (e^{(a+b)x})^{(n)} = (e^{ax}e^{bx})^{(n)} = \sum_{\nu=0}^{n} \binom{n}{\nu} (e^{ax})^{(n-\nu)} (e^{bx})^{(\nu)}$$

$$= \sum_{\nu=0}^{n} \binom{n}{\nu} a^{n-\nu} e^{ax} \, b^{\nu} e^{bx} = \sum_{\nu=0}^{n} \binom{n}{\nu} a^{n-\nu} b^{\nu} \cdot e^{(a+b)x}.$$

Theorem 181: *For integral $m \geqq 0$, and $x > 0$, there is a y such that*

$$1 < y < 1 + x, \quad \sqrt{1+x} = \sum_{\nu=0}^{m} \binom{\frac{1}{2}}{\nu} x^{\nu} + \binom{\frac{1}{2}}{m+1} \frac{x^{m+1}}{y^{m+\frac{1}{2}}}.$$

Proof: If

$$f(x) = x^{\frac{1}{2}} \ (x > 0),$$

then, by Theorem 171,

$$f^{(\nu)}(x) = \binom{\frac{1}{2}}{\nu} \nu! \, x^{\frac{1}{2}-\nu}.$$

for integral $\nu \geqq 0$. Theorem 177 with $\xi = 1$, $h = x$, and $n = m+1$, therefore insures the existence of a y such that

$$1 < y < 1 + x,$$

$$\sqrt{1+x} = \sum_{\nu=0}^{m} \frac{1}{\nu!} \binom{\frac{1}{2}}{\nu} \nu! \, x^{\nu} + \frac{x^{m+1}}{(m+1)!} \binom{\frac{1}{2}}{m+1} (m+1)! \, y^{\frac{1}{2}-m-1}.$$

Theorem 182: *If $0 < x < 1$ then*

$$\lim_{m=\infty} \sum_{\nu=0}^{m} \binom{\frac{1}{2}}{\nu} x^{\nu} = \sqrt{1+x}.$$

Proof: For integral $m \geqq 0$, we have

$$\left| \binom{\frac{1}{2}}{m+1} \right| = \frac{\left| \prod_{k=0}^{m} (\frac{1}{2}-k) \right|}{(m+1)!} \leqq \frac{\prod_{k=0}^{m} (k+\frac{1}{2})}{(m+1)!} < \frac{\prod_{k=0}^{m} (k+1)}{(m+1)!} = 1,$$

so that, in the formula of Theorem 181,

$$\left| \binom{\frac{1}{2}}{m+1} \frac{x^{m+1}}{y^{m+\frac{1}{2}}} \right| < x^{m+1} \to 0.$$

Theorem 183: *For integral $m \geqq 1$, and $x > 0$, there is a y such that*

$$1 < y < 1 + x, \ \log(1+x) = \sum_{\nu=1}^{m} \frac{(-1)^{\nu-1}}{\nu} x^\nu + \frac{(-1)^m x^{m+1}}{(m+1)y^{m+1}}.$$

Proof: If

$$f(x) = \log x \qquad (x > 0)$$

then

$$f'(x) = \frac{1}{x},$$

so that (by Example 2) to Definition 41) we have for integral $\nu \geqq 1$ that

$$f^{(\nu)}(x) = \left(\frac{1}{x}\right)^{(\nu-1)} = \frac{(-1)^{\nu-1}(\nu-1)!}{x^\nu},$$

$$\frac{f^{(\nu)}(1)}{\nu!} = \frac{(-1)^{\nu-1}}{\nu}.$$

Theorem 177 with $\xi = 1$, $h = x$, and $n = m + 1$, therefore insures the existence of a y with the desired properties.

Theorem 184: *If $0 < x \leqq 1$, then*

$$\lim_{m=\infty} \sum_{\nu=1}^{m} \frac{(-1)^{\nu-1}}{\nu} x^\nu = \log(1+x).$$

Proof: In the formula of Theorem 183, we have

$$\left| \frac{(-1)^m x^{m+1}}{(m+1) y^{m+1}} \right| < \frac{1}{m+1} \to 0.$$

Theorem 183 is true for every $x > 1$, but the formula of Theorem 184 is true for no $x > 1$. Indeed, suppose

$$\lim_{m=\infty} \sum_{\nu=1}^{m} \frac{(-1)^{\nu-1}}{\nu} x^\nu = \varphi(x)$$

existed. Then it would immediately follow that, if $m > 1$, we would have

$$\frac{(-1)^{m-1}}{m} x^m = \sum_{\nu=1}^{m} \frac{(-1)^{\nu-1}}{\nu} x^\nu - \sum_{\nu=1}^{m-1} \frac{(-1)^{\nu-1}}{\nu} x^\nu \to \varphi(x) - \varphi(x) = 0$$

as $m \to \infty$, or

$$\frac{x^m}{m} \to 0.$$

But by Theorem 180, if $m \geqq 2$ then

$$\frac{x^m}{m} = \frac{(1 + (x - 1))^m}{m} > \frac{\binom{m}{2}(x - 1)^2}{m} = (m - 1)\frac{(x-1)^2}{2} \geqq \frac{(x-1)^2}{2} \quad (>0).$$

Now, the following theorem expresses a very remarkable fact.

Theorem 185: *There exists a function $f(x)$ which is everywhere arbitrarily often differentiable, and for which*

$$\lim_{m=\infty} \sum_{\nu=0}^{m} \frac{f^{(\nu)}(0)}{\nu!} h^\nu$$

exists for every h, but has the value $f(h)$ only at $h = 0$.

Proof: Let

$$f(x) = \begin{cases} 0 & \text{for } x = 0, \\ e^{-\frac{1}{x^2}} & \text{for } x \neq 0. \end{cases}$$

I first show that, for every integral $\nu \geqq 0$,

(1)
$$f^{(\nu)}(x) = \begin{cases} 0 & \text{for } x = 0, \\ P_\nu\left(\frac{1}{x}\right)e^{-\frac{1}{x^2}} & \text{for } x \neq 0, \end{cases}$$

where $P_\nu(z)$ is a polynomial in z.

By the example to Theorem 160, we have

$$e^b > b \quad \text{for} \quad b > 0.$$

Thus for every $x \neq 0$ and for every integral $n \geqq 0$,

$$e^{\frac{1}{x^2}} = \left(e^{\frac{1}{(n+1)x^2}}\right)^{n+1} > \left(\frac{1}{(n+1)x^2}\right)^{n+1},$$

$$\frac{1}{|x|^n} e^{-\frac{1}{x^2}} < (n+1)^{n+1} |x|^{n+2},$$

so that, for integral $n \geqq 0$,

$$\lim_{x=0} \frac{1}{x^n} e^{-\frac{1}{x^2}} = 0.$$

Thus for every polynomial $P(z)$,

(2) $$\lim_{x=0} P\left(\frac{1}{x}\right) e^{-\frac{1}{x^2}} = 0.$$

(1) is obvious for $v = 0$ (with $P_0(z) = 1$). $v + 1$ follows from v, since

$$f^{(v+1)}(0) = \lim_{x=0} \frac{f^{(v)}(x)}{x} = \lim_{x=0} \frac{1}{x} P_v\left(\frac{1}{x}\right) e^{-\frac{1}{x^2}} = 0,$$

by (2) ($zP_v(z)$ is also a polynomial) and since, if $x \neq 0$,

$$f^{(v+1)}(x) = \left(P_v\left(\frac{1}{x}\right) e^{-\frac{1}{x^2}}\right)' = P_v'\left(\frac{1}{x}\right)\left(-\frac{1}{x^2}\right) e^{-\frac{1}{x^2}} + P_v\left(\frac{1}{x}\right)\frac{2}{x^3} e^{-\frac{1}{x^2}}$$

$$= P_{v+1}\left(\frac{1}{x}\right) e^{-\frac{1}{x^2}}.$$

Thus (1) is proved. Therefore,

$$\sum_{v=0}^{m} \frac{f^{(v)}(0)}{v!} h^v = 0,$$

for all h and all integral $m \geq 0$, so that

$$\lim_{m=\infty} \sum_{v=0}^{m} \frac{f^{(v)}(0)}{v!} h^v = 0$$

for all h. But 0 is, for $h \neq 0$, different from

$$f(h) = e^{-\frac{1}{h^2}}.$$

Theorem 186: *Let n be an integer ≥ 2. Let*

$$f^{(v)}(\xi) = 0 \text{ for } 1 \leq v \leq n - 1,$$

$$f^{(n)}(\xi) \neq 0.$$

1) *If n is even and $f^{(n)}(\xi) > 0$, then $f(x)$ has a minimum at ξ.*
2) *If n is even and $f^{(n)}(\xi) < 0$, then $f(x)$ has a maximum at ξ.*
3) *If n is odd and $f^{(n)}(\xi) > 0$, then $f(x)$ increases at ξ.*
4) *If n is odd and $f^{(n)}(\xi) < 0$, then $f(x)$ decreases at ξ.*

Proof: There exists an $\varepsilon > 0$ such that $f^{(n-1)}(x)$ exists for $|x - \xi| < \varepsilon$. By Theorems 177 and 178 (with $n - 1$ for n), there is, for $0 < |h| < \varepsilon$, a y between ξ and $\xi + h$ such that

(1) $$f(\xi + h) - f(\xi) = \frac{h^{n-1}}{(n-1)!} f^{(n-1)}(y).$$

$f^{(n-1)}(x)$ increases or decreases at ξ according to whether $f^{(n)}(\xi) > 0$ or < 0.

Thus there is an ε_1 with $0 < \varepsilon_1 < \varepsilon$ such that for $0 < |h| < \varepsilon_1$ and all y between ξ and $\xi + h$, we have

(2) $$h f^{(n-1)}(y) f^{(n)}(\xi) > 0.$$

Hence, using (1) and the y appearing in (1), we obtain for $0 < |h| < \varepsilon_1$ that

$$h^n f^{(n)}(\xi)\big(f(\xi + h) - f(\xi)\big) = \frac{(h^{n-1})^2}{(n-1)!}\, h f^{(n-1)}(y) f^{(n)}(\xi) > 0.$$

1) Thus if n is even and if $f^{(n)}(\xi) > 0$, we obtain

$$f(\xi + h) - f(\xi) > 0.$$

2) If n is even and if $f^{(n)}(\xi) < 0$, then

$$f(\xi + h) - f(\xi) < 0.$$

3) If n is odd and if $f^{(n)}(\xi) > 0$, then

$$h\big(f(\xi + h) - f(\xi)\big) > 0.$$

4) If n is odd and if $f^{(n)}(\xi) < 0$, then

$$h\big(f(\xi + h) - f(\xi)\big) < 0.$$

Examples $\Big(\mathrm{I}) - \mathrm{IV}\Big)$ are the same as those toward the end of Chapter $7\Big)$:

I) $f(x) = -x^2$, $f'(0) = 0$, $f''(0) = -2 < 0$: Maximum at 0.

II) $f(x) = \quad x^2$, $f'(0) = 0$, $f''(0) = 2 > 0$: Minimum at 0.

III) $f(x) = \quad x^3$, $f'(0) = 0$, $f''(0) = 0$, $f'''(0) = 6 > 0$: Increases at 0.

IV) $f(x) = -x^3$, $f'(0) = 0$, $f''(0) = 0$, $f'''(0) = -6 < 0$: Decreases at 0.

V) Let

$$f(x) = \frac{(x + 1)^3}{x^2} \quad \text{for } x \neq 0.$$

We wish to find all maxima and minima. Since $f(x)$ is, evidently, arbitrarily often differentiable at $x \neq 0$ (as indeed, x^{-2} and $(x + 1)^3$ are), we need only worry about the zeros of $f'(x)$ (i.e. the x such that $f'(x) = 0$). Now, if $x \neq 0$ then

$$f'(x) = \big(x^{-2}(x+1)^3\big)' = -2x^{-3}(x+1)^3 + 3x^{-2}(x+1)^2$$

$$= x^{-3}(x+1)^2(-2x-2+3x) = x^{-3}(x+1)^2(x-2).$$

Thus we need only discuss $x = -1$ and $x = 2$. We shall now apply our criterion without, however, evaluating terms we do not need.

Investigation of $x = -1$:

$$f''(x) = \left((x+1)^2 \frac{x-2}{x^3}\right)' = (x+1)^2 \left(\frac{x-2}{x^3}\right)' + 2(x+1)\frac{x-2}{x^3},$$

$$f''(-1) = 0,$$

$$f'''(x) = \left((x+1)^2 \frac{x-2}{x^3}\right)'' = (x+1)^2 \left(\frac{x-2}{x^3}\right)'' + 4(x+1)\left(\frac{x-2}{x^3}\right)' + 2\frac{x-2}{x^3},$$

$$f'''(-1) = 0 + 0 + 2\frac{-3}{-1} > 0.$$

Increasing, no maximum or minimum.
  Investigation of $x = 2$:

$$f''(2) = \lim_{x=2} \frac{f'(x)}{x-2} = \lim_{x=2} \frac{(x+1)^2}{x^3} > 0.$$

Minimum.

CHAPTER 11

" $\dfrac{0}{0}$ " AND SIMILAR MATTERS

Introduction

$\dfrac{0}{0}$ has had no meaning until now, nor will it be given one. Rather, its significance is as follows:

We know that

$$\lim_{x=0} \frac{x}{x} = 1 \, ,$$

$$\lim_{x=0} \frac{x^2}{x} = 0,$$

$$\lim_{x=0} \frac{x}{x^2} \text{ does not exist,}$$

$$\lim_{x=0} \frac{\dfrac{x^2}{x}}{\dfrac{x^2}{x}} = 1.$$

All four of the expressions following the limit sign have the form

$$\varphi(x) = \frac{f(x)}{g(x)} \, ,$$

where

$$\lim_{x=0} f(x) = 0, \quad \lim_{x=0} g(x) = 0 \, .$$

If

$$\varphi(x) = \frac{f(x)}{g(x)} \, ,$$

where

$$\lim_{x=\xi} f(x) = \eta, \quad \lim_{x=\xi} g(x) = \zeta \, ,$$

then for

$$\zeta \neq 0$$

we have by Theorem 92 that

$$\lim_{x=\xi} \varphi(x) = \frac{\eta}{\zeta}.$$

Thus only the case $\zeta = 0$ (as in the above four examples) is of interest. If

$$\zeta = 0, \quad \eta \neq 0,$$

then $\lim\limits_{x=\xi} \varphi(x)$ evidently does not exist. For otherwise we should have

$$\eta = \lim_{x=\xi} f(x) = \lim_{x=\xi} \big(g(x)\, \varphi(x) \big) = \lim_{x=\xi} g(x) \lim_{x=\xi} \varphi(x)$$

$$= 0 \cdot \lim_{x=\xi} \varphi(x) = 0.$$

It is with the case

$$\eta = 0, \quad \zeta = 0$$

that the first investigations of this chapter will deal.

Theorem 187: *Let*

$$\lim_{x=\xi} f(x) = 0,$$

$$\lim_{x=\xi} g(x) = 0,$$

$$f'(\xi) \; exist \;,$$

$$g'(\xi) \neq 0.$$

Then

$$\lim_{x=\xi} \frac{f(x)}{g(x)} = \frac{f'(\xi)}{g'(\xi)}.$$

Proof: $f(x)$ and $g(x)$ are differentiable at ξ, and hence are continuous. Thus

$$f(\xi) = g(\xi) = 0,$$

$$f'(\xi) = \lim_{x=\xi} \frac{f(x)}{x-\xi},$$

$$g'(\xi) = \lim_{x=\xi} \frac{g(x)}{x-\xi},$$

so that, by Theorem 92,

$$\frac{f'(\xi)}{g'(\xi)} = \lim_{x=\xi} \frac{\dfrac{f(x)}{x-\xi}}{\dfrac{g(x)}{x-\xi}} = \lim_{x=\xi} \frac{f(x)}{g(x)}.$$

Examples: 1) $\xi = 0$, $f(x) = \log(1+x^2)$, $g(x) = e^{2x} - 1$. Here, we have

$$f(0) = 0 = g(0),$$

$$f'(x) = \frac{2x}{1+x^2}, \quad g'(x) = 2e^{2x},$$

$$f'(0) = 0, \qquad g'(0) = 2.$$

Thus

$$\lim_{x=0} \frac{\log(1+x^2)}{e^{2x}-1} = \frac{0}{2} = 0.$$

2)
$$\xi = 0, \quad f(x) = x, \quad g(x) = 1 - e^{-x}.$$

Here, we have

$$f(0) = 0 = g(0),$$

$$f'(x) = 1, \quad g'(x) = e^{-x},$$

$$f'(0) = 1, \quad g'(0) = 1,$$

so that

$$\lim_{x=0} \frac{x}{1 - e^{-x}} = \frac{1}{1} = 1.$$

Theorem 188: *Let* $h \neq 0$. *Let* $f(x)$ *and* $g(x)$ *be continuous on* $[\xi, \xi + h]$ *(or* $[\xi + h, \xi]$*). Let* $f(x)$ *and* $g(x)$ *be differentiable between* ξ *and* $\xi + h$, *and let*

$$g'(x) \neq 0.$$

Let

$$f(\xi) = g(\xi) = 0.$$

Then there is a y *between* ξ *and* $\xi + h$ *such that*

$$\frac{f(\xi + h)}{g(\xi + h)} = \frac{f'(y)}{g'(y)}.$$

Proof: We have

$$g(\xi + h) \neq 0,$$

since otherwise, by Theorem 156, we should have

$$g'(x) = 0$$

somewhere between ξ and $\xi + h$.

The function

$$\Phi(x) = f(x) - g(x) \frac{f(\xi + h)}{g(\xi + h)}$$

is continuous on $[\xi, \xi + h]$ (or $[\xi + h, \xi]$).

$$\Phi'(x) = f'(x) - g'(x) \frac{f(\xi + h)}{g(\xi + h)}$$

between ξ and $\xi + h$. Furthermore,

$$\Phi(\xi) = 0 = \Phi(\xi + h).$$

Thus by Theorem 156, there exists a y between ξ and $\xi + h$ such that

$$0 = \Phi'(y) = f'(y) - g'(y) \frac{f(\xi + h)}{g(\xi + h)}.$$

Theorem 189: *Let*

$$\lim_{x=\xi} f(x) = 0,$$

$$\lim_{x=\xi} g(x) = 0,$$

$$(1) \qquad \lim_{x=\xi} \frac{f'(x)}{g'(x)} = l.$$

Then

$$\lim_{x=\xi} \frac{f(x)}{g(x)} = l.$$

Proof: W.l.g. let

$$f(\xi) = g(\xi) = 0,$$

which may be accomplished by introducing or changing the definition of $f(x)$ or $g(x)$ at ξ without influencing the hypothesis or conclusion.

For a suitable $p > 0$, the hypotheses of Theorem 188 are fulfilled for $0 < |h| < p$. In particular, it is to be noted that the functions $f(x)$ and $g(x)$ are, by (1), differentiable in a neighborhood of ξ exclusive of ξ, and that

$$g'(x) \neq 0$$

therein.

Hence, for $0 < |x - \xi| < p$, there is a y between ξ and x such that

$$\frac{f(x)}{g(x)} = \frac{f'(y)}{g'(y)}.$$

y depends on x. But on the other hand, by (1) we have

$$\lim_{x=\xi} \frac{f'(y)}{g'(y)} = l.$$

Thus

$$\lim_{x=\xi} \frac{f(x)}{g(x)} = l.$$

Example: $\quad \xi = 0, \quad f(x) = x^2, \quad g(x) = -1 + x + e^{-x}.$

Here we have

$$f(x) \to 0, \qquad g(x) \to 0,$$
$$f'(x) = 2x, \qquad g'(x) = 1 - e^{-x}.$$

By example 2) to Theorem 187, we have

$$\frac{f'(x)}{g'(x)} \to 2,$$

so that, by Theorem 189,

$$\frac{f(x)}{g(x)} \to 2.$$

Theorem 190: *Let $f(x)$ be continuous at ξ. Let*

$$\lim_{x=\xi} f'(x) = l.$$

Then

$$f'(\xi) = l.$$

Preliminary Remark: A very wonderful theorem: Wherever the derivative has a limit, the derivative exists and assumes this limit as a value, and is thus continuous.

Proof: By Theorem 189, with $f(x) - f(\xi)$ in place of $f(x)$ and with

$$g(x) = x - \xi,$$

we have

$$\lim_{x=\xi} \frac{f(x) - f(\xi)}{x - \xi} = l.$$

Theorem 191: *Let n be an integer ≥ 1. For all integral ν with $0 \leq \nu < n$,*

let

$$\lim_{x=\xi} f^{(\nu)}(x) = 0,$$

$$\lim_{x=\xi} g^{(\nu)}(x) = 0.$$

Let

$$\lim_{x=\xi} \frac{f^{(n)}(x)}{g^{(n)}(x)} = l.$$

Then

$$\lim_{x=\xi} \frac{f(x)}{g(x)} = l.$$

Proof: This is the statement of Theorem 189 for $n = 1$. Let $n > 1$, and let the theorem be true for $n - 1$. If we apply Theorem 189 with $f^{(n-1)}(x)$ for $f(x)$ and $g^{(n-1)}(x)$ for $g(x)$, we have that if

$$\lim_{x=\xi} \frac{f^{(n)}(x)}{g^{(n)}(x)} = l,$$

then

$$\lim_{x=\xi} \frac{f^{(n-1)}(x)}{g^{(n-1)}(x)} = l.$$

Thus (since the theorem is true for $n - 1$)

$$\lim_{x=\xi} \frac{f(x)}{g(x)} = l.$$

Example (for $n = 2$): The example to Theorem 189. Since

$$f'(x) \to 0, \quad g'(x) \to 0,$$

$$\frac{f''(x)}{g''(x)} = \frac{2}{e^{-x}} \to 2,$$

we have

$$\frac{f(x)}{g(x)} \to 2.$$

Theorem 192: *Let n be an integer $\geqq 1$. Let*

$$\lim_{x=\xi} f^{(\nu)}(x) = 0,$$

$$\lim_{x=\xi} g^{(\nu)}(x) = 0$$

for all integral ν with $0 \leqq \nu < n$. Let

$$f^{(n)}(\xi) \quad exist,$$

$$g^{(n)}(\xi) \neq 0.$$

Then

$$\lim_{x=\xi} \frac{f(x)}{g(x)} = \frac{f^{(n)}(\xi)}{g^{(n)}(\xi)}.$$

Preliminary Remark: Theorem 192 is evidently not contained in Theorem 191, nor conversely.

Proof: For $n = 1$, this is the statement of Theorem 187. Therefore let $n > 1$. Applying Theorem 187, with $f^{(n-1)}(x)$ for $f(x)$ and with $g^{(n-1)}(x)$ for $g(x)$, we obtain

$$\lim_{x=\xi} \frac{f^{(n-1)}(x)}{g^{(n-1)}(x)} = \frac{f^{(n)}(\xi)}{g^{(n)}(\xi)}.$$

Therefore by Theorem 191, with $n - 1$ for n, we have

$$\lim_{x=\xi} \frac{f(x)}{g(x)} = \frac{f^{(n)}(\xi)}{g^{(n)}(\xi)}.$$

Definition 43: *If for every ω there exists an $\varepsilon > 0$ such that*

$$f(x) > \omega \quad for \ \ 0 < |x - \xi| < \varepsilon,$$

then we say that

$$\lim_{x=\xi} f(x) = \infty,$$

or for short that

$$f(x) \to \infty$$

("as $x \to \xi$").

Example: $\xi = 0,$

$$f(x) = \frac{1}{|x|} \quad for \ \ x \neq 0.$$

Theorem 193: $\lim_{x=\xi} |f(x)| = \infty$

is equivalent to

$$\lim_{x=\xi} \frac{1}{f(x)} = 0.$$

Proof: Both state that for every $\delta > 0$ there exists an ε such that

$$\left| \frac{1}{f(x)} \right| < \delta \text{ for } 0 < |x - \xi| < \varepsilon.$$

Definition 44: *If*

$$\lim_{x = \xi} \left(- f(x) \right) = \infty,$$

then we say that

$$\lim_{x = \xi} f(x) = - \infty,$$

or for short that

$$f(x) \to - \infty$$

("*as* $x \to \xi$").

— ∞ is to be read: minus infinity.

Example:
$$\xi = 0,$$
$$f(x) = \log | x | \text{ for } x \neq 0.$$
$$\lim_{x = \xi} f(x) = - \infty$$

holds, because

$$- \log | x | > \omega \text{ for } 0 < | x | < e^{-\omega}.$$

Theorem 194: *If*

$$\lim_{x = \xi} | g(x) | = \infty,$$

$$\lim_{x = \xi} \frac{f'(x)}{g'(x)} = 0,$$

then

$$\lim_{x = \xi} \frac{f(x)}{g(x)} = 0.$$

Proof: There exists a $p > 0$ such that

$$g'(x) \neq 0 \text{ for } 0 < | x - \xi | < p.$$

Therefore, by Theorem 164, $g'(x)$ is always positive or always negative for $- p < x - \xi < 0$. The same is true for $0 < x - \xi < p$. W.l.g. let $g'(x)$ be positive in both cases; for otherwise, we could replace $g(x)$ by $- g(x)$ for $- p < x - \xi < 0$, or for $0 < x - \xi < p$, or for both, without affecting. the hypotheses or conclusion.

Let $\delta > 0$. For a suitable positive $\varepsilon < p$, we have, for all y such that $0 < | y - \xi | \leqq \varepsilon$,

$$| f'(y) | \leqq \frac{\delta}{2} | g'(y) | = \frac{\delta}{2} g'(y),$$

so that

$$-\frac{\delta}{2}\,g'(y) \leqq f'(y) \leqq \frac{\delta}{2}\,g'(y).$$

Therefore, by Theorem 161, if $\xi - \varepsilon < x < \xi$ then

$$-\frac{\delta}{2}\,\big(g(x) - g(\xi - \varepsilon)\big) \leqq f(x) - f(\xi - \varepsilon) \leqq \frac{\delta}{2}\,\big(g(x) - g(\xi - \varepsilon)\big),$$

and if $\xi < x < \xi + \varepsilon$ then

$$-\frac{\delta}{2}\,\big(g(\xi + \varepsilon) - g(x)\big) \leqq f(\xi + \varepsilon) - f(x) \leqq \frac{\delta}{2}\,\big(g(\xi + \varepsilon) - g(x)\big).$$

Therefore, if $\xi - \varepsilon < x < \xi$, then

$$\big|\,f(x) - f(\xi - \varepsilon)\,\big| \leqq \frac{\delta}{2}\,\big|\,g(x) - g(\xi - \varepsilon)\,\big|,$$

$$\big|\,f(x)\,\big| \leqq \frac{\delta}{2}\,\big|\,g(x)\,\big| + \frac{\delta}{2}\,\big|\,g(\xi - \varepsilon)\,\big| + \big|\,f(\xi - \varepsilon)\,\big|,$$

and if $\xi < x < \xi + \varepsilon$, then

$$\big|\,f(\xi + \varepsilon) - f(x)\,\big| \leqq \frac{\delta}{2}\,\big|\,g(\xi + \varepsilon) - g(x)\,\big|,$$

$$\big|\,f(x)\,\big| \leqq \frac{\delta}{2}\,\big|\,g(x)\,\big| + \frac{\delta}{2}\,\big|\,g(\xi + \varepsilon)\,\big| + \big|\,f(\xi + \varepsilon)\,\big|.$$

Hence if $0 < \big|\,x - \xi\,\big| < \varepsilon$, then

$$\big|\,f(x)\,\big| \leqq \frac{\delta}{2}\,\big|\,g(x)\,\big| + c,$$

where c is independent of x.

Thus for a suitable $\eta > 0$, we have for $0 < \big|\,x - \xi\,\big| < \eta$ that

$$\left|\frac{f(x)}{g(x)}\right| \leqq \frac{\delta}{2} + \frac{c}{\big|\,g(x)\,\big|} < \delta.$$

Example (I purposely choose an easy one, where the theorem is not even necessary, to illustrate Theorem 194. I will do this sort of thing frequently) :

$$\xi = 0,$$

$$f(x) = x + \sqrt[3]{x}, \quad g(x) = \frac{1}{x} + 1 \text{ for } x \neq 0.$$

If $x \neq 0$, we have

$$f'(x) = 1 + \frac{\sqrt[3]{x}}{3x}, \quad g'(x) = -\frac{1}{x^2},$$

$$\frac{f'(x)}{g'(x)} = -x^2 - \tfrac{1}{3}x\sqrt[3]{x} \to 0.$$

Thus

$$\frac{f(x)}{g(x)} \to 0.$$

Theorem 195: *If*

$$\lim_{x=\xi} |g(x)| = \infty,$$

$$\lim_{x=\xi} \frac{f'(x)}{g'(x)} = l,$$

then

$$\lim_{x=\xi} \frac{f(x)}{g(x)} = l.$$

Proof: If

$$\Phi(x) = f(x) - lg(x)$$

then we have

$$\lim_{x=\xi} \frac{\Phi'(x)}{g'(x)} = \lim_{x=\xi} \left(\frac{f'(x)}{g'(x)} - l\right) = 0.$$

Therefore, by Theorem 194 (with $\Phi(x)$ for $f(x)$), we have

$$\lim_{x=\xi} \frac{\Phi(x)}{g(x)} = 0,$$

$$\lim_{x=\xi} \left(\frac{f(x)}{g(x)} - l\right) = 0,$$

$$\lim_{x=\xi} \frac{f(x)}{g(x)} = l.$$

Example: $\xi = 0,$

$f(x) = \log |x|$ for $x \neq 0$, $g(x) = \log(e^{|x|} - 1)$ for $x \neq 0$.

Here, we have

$$\lim_{x=0} |g(x)| = \infty,$$

$$f'(x) = \frac{1}{x}, \quad g'(x) = \frac{|x|}{x} \frac{e^{|x|}}{e^{|x|} - 1} \quad \text{for } x \neq 0,$$

$$\frac{f'(x)}{g'(x)} = \frac{e^{|x|} - 1}{|x|} \frac{1}{e^{|x|}} \to 1 \cdot 1 = 1,$$

so that
$$\frac{f(x)}{g(x)} \to 1.$$

Definition 45:
$$\lim_{x=\infty} f(x) = l,$$

or for short
$$f(x) \to l$$

("as $x \to \infty$"), *if*
$$\lim_{z=0} f\left(\frac{1}{|z|}\right) = l.$$

In other words, if for every $\delta > 0$ there exists an $\omega > 0$ such that

$$|f(x) - l| < \delta \text{ for } x > \omega.$$

Example:
$$\lim_{x=\infty} \left(1 + \frac{1}{x}\right) = \lim_{z=0} (1 + |z|) = 1.$$

Unfortunately, the symbol $\lim\limits_{n=\infty}$ has been used before (Definition 9), and any number may be called n or x. Thus, we must sometimes pay attention to whether the variable involved is increasing through all large values or through all large integral values. Hence, if we take x and n in their usual sense, we have that

$$\lim_{n=\infty} (n - [n]) = 0,$$
$$\lim_{x=\infty} (x - [x]) \text{ is meaningless.}$$

Definition 46:
$$\lim_{x=\infty} f(x) = \infty$$

if
$$\lim_{z=0} f\left(\frac{1}{|z|}\right) = \infty.$$

Example:
$$f(x) = \sqrt{x}.$$

Definition 47:
$$\lim_{x=-\infty} f(x) = l,$$

or for short
$$f(x) \to l$$

("as $x = -\infty$"), *if*
$$\lim_{x=\infty} f(-x) = l.$$

Definition 48:
$$\lim_{x=-\infty} f(x) = \infty$$

if
$$\lim_{x=\infty} f(-x) = \infty.$$

Definition 49:
$$\lim_{x=\infty} f(x) = -\infty$$

if

$$\lim_{x=\infty} (-f(x)) = \infty.$$

Definition 50:
$$\lim_{x=-\infty} f(x) = -\infty$$

if

$$\lim_{x=\infty} (-f(-x)) = \infty.$$

Definitions 43, 44, 46, 48, 49, and 50, are applied only in this chapter. Thus, if we later speak of the existence of $\lim f(x)$, we always mean the existence of a number l such that

$$\lim f(x) = l.$$

Theorem 196: *If*

$$\lim_{x=\infty} \frac{f'(x)}{g'(x)} = l$$

and if we set

$$F(z) = f\left(\frac{1}{|z|}\right), \quad G(z) = g\left(\frac{1}{|z|}\right),$$

then

$$\lim_{z=0} \frac{F'(z)}{G'(z)} = l.$$

Proof: For a suitable $p > 0$, both $f(x)$ and $g(x)$ are differentiable for $x > p$, and

$$g'(x) \neq 0.$$

The above definition of $F(z)$ and $G(z)$ therefore holds for $0 < |z| < \dfrac{1}{p}$.
If $z \neq 0$, then

$$\left(\frac{1}{|z|}\right)' = -\frac{|z|'}{z^2} = -\frac{1}{z|z|}.$$

Therefore if $0 < |z| < \dfrac{1}{p}$, we have

$$F'(z) = -f'\left(\frac{1}{|z|}\right) \frac{1}{z|z|}, \quad G'(z) = -g'\left(\frac{1}{|z|}\right) \frac{1}{z|z|},$$

$$g'\left(\frac{1}{|z|}\right) \neq 0,$$

$$\frac{F'(z)}{G'(z)} = \frac{f'\left(\dfrac{1}{|z|}\right)}{g'\left(\dfrac{1}{|z|}\right)}.$$

By

$$\lim_{x=\infty} \frac{f'(x)}{g'(x)} = l$$

and Definition 45,

$$\lim_{z=0} \frac{f'\left(\dfrac{1}{|z|}\right)}{g'\left(\dfrac{1}{|z|}\right)} = l,$$

and therefore

$$\lim_{z=0} \frac{F'(z)}{G'(z)} = l.$$

Theorem 197: *If*

$$\lim_{x=\infty} f(x) = 0,$$

$$\lim_{x=\infty} g(x) = 0,$$

$$\lim_{x=\infty} \frac{f'(x)}{g'(x)} = l,$$

then

$$\lim_{x=\infty} \frac{f(x)}{g(x)} = l.$$

Proof: Using Theorem 196 and the notation therein, we have

$$\lim_{z=0} \frac{F'(z)}{G'(z)} = l.$$

By Definition 45,

$$\lim_{z=0} F(z) = 0,$$

$$\lim_{z=0} G(z) = 0.$$

Thus, by Theorem 189,

$$\lim_{z=0} \frac{F(z)}{G(z)} = l,$$

and so, by Definition 45,

$$\lim_{x=\infty} \frac{f(x)}{g(x)} = l.$$

Example: $$f(x) = \log\left(1 - \frac{1}{x}\right), \ g(x) = \frac{1}{x},$$

$$\frac{f'(x)}{g'(x)} = \frac{\dfrac{1}{1 - \dfrac{1}{x}} \cdot \dfrac{1}{x^2}}{-\dfrac{1}{x^2}} = -\frac{1}{1 - \dfrac{1}{x}} \to -1,$$

and therefore

$$\frac{f(x)}{g(x)} \to -1.$$

Theorem 198: *If*

$$\lim_{x=\infty} |g(x)| = \infty,$$

$$\lim_{x=\infty} \frac{f'(x)}{g'(x)} = l,$$

then

$$\lim_{x=\infty} \frac{f(x)}{g(x)} = l.$$

Proof: Using Theorem 196, and the notation therein, we have

$$\lim_{z=0} \frac{F'(z)}{G'(z)} = l.$$

By Definition 46,

$$\lim_{z=0} |G(z)| = \infty.$$

Therefore, by Theorem 195,

$$\lim_{z=0} \frac{F(z)}{G(z)} = l,$$

and so, by Definition 45,

$$\lim_{x=\infty} \frac{f(x)}{g(x)} = l.$$

Example: $$f(x) = \log x, \ g(x) = x,$$

$$\frac{f'(x)}{g'(x)} = \frac{\dfrac{1}{x}}{1} \to 0,$$

and therefore

$$\frac{f(x)}{g(x)} \to 0.$$

Theorems 187, 189, 191, 192, and 197, concern themselves, so to speak, with $\dfrac{0}{0}$; and Theorems 194, 195, and 198, with $\dfrac{\infty}{\infty}$. The possibilities $0 \cdot \infty$, 0^0, 1^∞, ∞^0, $\infty - \infty$ (by this we mean the corresponding limits as $x \to \xi$ or as $x \to \infty$) may all be reduced to $\dfrac{0}{0}$, in the following way.

1) "$0 \cdot \infty$." Let

$$f(x) \to 0, \ |g(x)| \to \infty.$$

Then, in certain cases, our theorems yield the existence of

$$\lim \big(f(x)g(x)\big).$$

For, "ultimately" (i.e. in a suitable neighborhood of ξ excluding ξ itself, or for all sufficiently large x) we have

$$g(x) \neq 0,$$

$$f(x)g(x) = \frac{f(x)}{\dfrac{1}{g(x)}},$$

$$\frac{1}{g(x)} \to 0.$$

Example: $\qquad f(x) = x^2, \quad g(x) = \dfrac{1}{x}$

and $x \to 0$. Then

$$f(x)g(x) = \frac{x^2}{x} \to 0.$$

2) "0^0." (It is irrelevent that we have defined

$$0^0 = 1$$

under all circumstances.) Let

$$f(x) \to 0$$

and let, ultimately,

$$f(x) > 0.$$

Furthermore, let

$$g(x) \to 0.$$

We will consider (if it exists) the

$$\lim f(x)^{g(x)}.$$

In any case, we have, ultimately,

(1) $\qquad\qquad f(x)^{g(x)} = e^{g(x)\log f(x)}.$

Since

$$|\log f(x)| \to \infty,$$

$g(x)\log f(x)$ belongs to type 1). If

$$g(x)\log f(x) \to l,$$

then, by the continuity of e^z,

$$f(x)^{g(x)} \to e^l.$$

Examples: I) $f(x) = |x|, \; g(x) = |x|, \; x \to 0.$

$$f(x)^{g(x)} = e^{|x|\log|x|} \to e^0 = 1.$$

II) $f(x) = e^{-x}, \; g(x) = \dfrac{1}{x}, \; x \to \infty.$

$$f(x)^{g(x)} = e^{\frac{1}{x}(-x)} = e^{-1} \to e^{-1}.$$

III) $f(x) = e^{-x}, \; g(x) = \dfrac{x - [x]}{x}, \; x \to \infty.$

$$f(x)^{g(x)} = e^{[x] - x}$$

has no limit.

3) "1^∞." Let

$$f(x) \to 1, \quad |g(x)| \to \infty.$$

We concern ourselves with

$$\lim f(x)^{g(x)}.$$

We ultimately have

$$f(x) > 0,$$

so that (1) holds. Since

$$\log f(x) \to 0,$$

$\log f(x) \cdot g(x)$ belongs to type 1).

Example: $f(x) = 1 + \dfrac{c}{x}, \; g(x) = x, \; x \to \infty.$

Since

$$\lim_{z=0} \frac{1}{z} \log(1 + cz) = c,$$

we have that

$$\lim_{z=0} \frac{1}{|z|} \log(1 + c|z|) = c,$$

$$\lim_{x=\infty} x \log\left(1 + \frac{c}{x}\right) = c,$$

$$\lim_{x=\infty} g(x) \log f(x) = c.$$

Thus

$$\lim_{x=\infty} \left(1 + \frac{c}{x}\right)^x = e^c.$$

In particular, if x increases through integral values, we obtain

$$\lim_{n=\infty} \left(1 + \frac{c}{n}\right)^n = e^c,$$

i. e. we have for all x that

$$\lim_{n=\infty} \left(1 + \frac{x}{n}\right)^n = e^x,$$

a formula which should be noted. As a special case, we obtain

$$\lim_{n=\infty} \left(1 + \frac{1}{n}\right)^n = e.$$

4) "∞^0." Let

$$f(x) \to \infty, \quad g(x) \to 0.$$

We concern ourselves with

$$\lim f(x)^{g(x)}.$$

We ultimately have

$$f(x) > 0,$$

so that (1) holds. **Since**

$$|\log f(x)| \to \infty,$$

$g(x) \log f(x)$ belongs to type 1).

Example: $\qquad f(x) = e^x, \ g(x) = \frac{1}{x}, \ x \to \infty.$

$$f(x)^{g(x)} = e^{\frac{1}{x}x} = e \to e.$$

5) "$\infty - \infty$." Let

$$f(x) \to \infty, \quad g(x) \to \infty.$$

We concern ourselves with the

$$\lim \left(f(x) - g(x)\right).$$

We ultimately have that

$$g(x) > 0,$$

$$f(x) - g(x) = \left(\frac{f(x)}{g(x)} - 1\right) g(x).$$

If

$$\lim_{x=\infty} \frac{f(x)}{g(x)} = l,$$

then we evidently have that

$$f(x) - g(x) \begin{cases} \to \infty & \text{for } l > 1, \\ \to -\infty & \text{for } l < 1. \end{cases}$$

If $l = 1$, then this reduces to the case $0 \cdot \infty$ of 1).

Example: $f(x) = \sqrt{x^2 - 1},\ g(x) = x,\ x \to \infty.$

$f(x)$ and $g(x)$ are defined for $x \geq 1,$ and

$$f(x) - g(x) = \left(\sqrt{1 - \frac{1}{x^2}} - 1 \right) x.$$

Here, we have the case $0 \cdot \infty$. If $x \geq 1$, then

$$f(x) - g(x) = \frac{\sqrt{1 - \dfrac{1}{x^2}} - 1}{\dfrac{1}{x}}.$$

By Theorem 197 $\left(\text{ with } F(x) = \sqrt{1 - \dfrac{1}{x^2}} - 1 \text{ in place of } f(x) \text{ and}\right.$

$G(x) = \dfrac{1}{x}$ in place of $g(x) \Big)$, this approaches 0, since

$$\frac{F'(x)}{G'(x)} = \frac{\dfrac{1}{\sqrt{1 - \dfrac{1}{x^2}}} \cdot \dfrac{1}{2} \cdot \dfrac{2}{x^3}}{-\dfrac{1}{x^2}} = -\frac{1}{x\sqrt{1 - \dfrac{1}{x^2}}} = -\frac{1}{\sqrt{x^2 - 1}} \to 0.$$

CHAPTER 12

INFINITE SERIES

In this·chapter, n, N, m, M, p, q, r, t, v, v, u, always denote integers.
If a_n is given for $n \geqq N$, then we shall set

$$s_m = \sum_{n=N}^{m} a_n \text{ for } 'm \geqq N$$

for the remainder of this chapter.

Definition 51: $\qquad \sum_{n=N}^{\infty} a_n = s$

(to be read: the sum from $n = N$ to ∞), *if a_n is given for $n \geqq N$ and if*

$$\lim_{m=\infty} s_m = s.$$

We also say that *the infinite series*

$$\sum_{n=N}^{\infty} a_n$$

converges and has the value (sum) *s, or that it converges to s, or that it converges and $= s$.*

Example: If $|\vartheta| < 1$, then

$$\sum_{n=0}^{\infty} \vartheta^n = \frac{1}{1-\vartheta},$$

by example 5 to Definition 9.

Definition 52: *If a_n is given for $n \geqq N$, and if*

$$\lim_{m=\infty} s_m$$

does not exist, then the infinite series

$$\sum_{n=N}^{\infty} a_n$$

is called divergent (meaningless).

Example:
$$a_n = 1 \text{ for } n \geq 1.$$
Here, we have
$$s_m = m \text{ for } m \geq 1.$$

Theorem 199:
$$\sum_{n=N}^{\infty} a_n = \sum_{n=N+M}^{\infty} a_{n-M},$$

if one of the sides is meaningful.

Preliminary Remark: In considering the question of whether a given numerical series, like

$$1 + \tfrac{1}{2} + \tfrac{1}{4} + \tfrac{1}{8} + \ldots$$

(the reader will know what is meant), converges, and if so to what value, it does not matter, by Theorem 199, whether we label its terms $a_1, a_2, a_3, \ldots$ or $a_0, a_1, a_3, \ldots$ or $a_{-4}, a_{-3}, a_{-2}, \ldots$ or, in general, $a_p, a_{p+1}, a_{p+2}, \ldots$ for any p.

Proof: If one side is meaningful, then a_n is given for $n \geq N$. If s_m has the usual meaning, and if

$$S_m = \sum_{n=N+M}^{m} a_{n-M} \text{ for } m \geq N + M,$$

then

$$S_m = s_{m-M} \text{ for } m \geq N + M.$$

Evidently,

$$s_{m-M} \to s$$

if and only if

$$s_m \to s.$$

For, both statement say that for every $\delta > 0$ we ultimately (i.e. for all q from some value on) have

$$|s_q - s| < \delta.$$

Example:
$$\sum_{n=0}^{\infty} a_n = \sum_{n=1}^{\infty} a_{n-1},$$

if one of the sides is meaningful.

Theorem 200: *For $n \geq N$, let*
$$h_n \text{ be an integer,}$$
$$h_n < h_{n+1}.$$
Furthermore, let
$$h_N \geq N.$$

Let a_n be given for $n \geq N$. Set
$$b_{h_n} = a_n,$$
$$b_n = 0 \text{ for those } n \geq N \text{ which are not equal to any } h_p.$$

Then

$$\sum_{n=N}^{\infty} a_n = \sum_{n=N}^{\infty} b_n,$$

if one of the sides is meaningful.

Preliminary Remark: In other words, we may remove a finite or an infinite number of zeros from a convergent series (if we do not change the order of its terms). And we may introduce a finite number of zeros between any two successive terms of a convergent series, or in front of the first term. Every such altered series converges, and, moreover, to the same value.

Proof: Set

$$S_m = \sum_{n=N}^{m} b_n \text{ for } m \geq N.$$

For every $m \geq h_N$ there exists exactly one $p \geq N$ such that

$$h_p \leq m < h_{p+1}.$$

Therefore, if $m \geq h_N$ we have

$$S_m = s_p,$$

where $p = p(m)$ was defined above.

Evidently,

$$\lim_{m=\infty} S_m = s$$

if and only if

$$\lim_{p=\infty} s_p = s$$

For, both statements say that for every $\delta > 0$ we have ultimately (i.e. for all p from some value on), that

$$\left| s_p - s \right| < \delta.$$

Example: $N = 1$, $h_n = 2n - 1$ for $n \geq 1$, so that one zero is introduced after every term of the series.

Theorem 201: *Let* $M \geq N$ *and let* a_n *be given for* $n \geq N$. *Set*

$$b_n = 0 \text{ for } N \leq n < M,$$

$$b_n = a_{n-M+N} \text{ for } n \geq M.$$

Then

$$\sum_{n=N}^{\infty} a_n = \sum_{n=N}^{\infty} b_n,$$

if one of the sides is meaningful.

Preliminary Remark: Hence, we may introduce a finite number of zeros in front of a convergent series or we may omit such a finite number of zeros from the series. This, without affecting convergence or changing the value of the sum.

Proof: Theorem 200 with

$$h_n = n + M - N.$$

Theorem 202: *If* $M > N$, *then*

$$\sum_{n=N}^{\infty} a_n = \sum_{n=N}^{M-1} a_n + \sum_{n=M}^{\infty} a_n,$$

if one of the sides is meaningful.

Preliminary Remark: Thus, every convergent series equals its "beginning" + its "remainder," and conversely.

Proof: If $m \geq M$ then

$$\sum_{n=N}^{m} a_n = \sum_{n=N}^{M-1} a_n + \sum_{n=M}^{m} a_n.$$

Both assertions are proved if we let $m \to \infty$.

Example: $\quad \sum\limits_{n=2}^{\infty} \vartheta^n = \dfrac{1}{1-\vartheta} - (1 + \vartheta)$ for $|\vartheta| < 1$.

Theorem 203: *If*

$$\sum_{n=N}^{\infty} a_n$$

converges, then for every $\delta > 0$ *there exists a* $p \geq N$ *such that*

$$|s_q - s_r| < \delta \text{ for } q \geq p, \ r \geq p.$$

Proof: Let

$$\sum_{n=N}^{\infty} a_n = s.$$

For a given $\delta > 0$, choose a $p > 0$ such that

$$|s_m - s| < \frac{\delta}{2} \text{ for } m \geq p.$$

Then we have for $q \geq p$, $r \geq p$, that

$$|s_q - s_r| = |(s_q - s) - (s_r - s)| \leq |s_q - s| + |s_r - s| < \frac{\delta}{2} + \frac{\delta}{2} = \delta.$$

Theorem 204: *If*

$$\sum_{n=N}^{\infty} a_n$$

converges, then

$$a_n \to 0.$$

Proof: Let $\delta > 0$ be given. By Theorem 203 there exists a p such that, for $r \geq p$,

$$|a_{r+1}| = |s_{r+1} - s_r| < \delta.$$

Hence we have for $n \geq p + 1$ that

$$|a_n| < \delta.$$

Example:
$$\sum_{n=0}^{\infty} (-1)^n$$

diverges, since $(-1)^n$ does not approach 0.

Theorem 205: *The so-called harmonic series*

$$\sum_{n=1}^{\infty} \frac{1}{n}$$

diverges.

Preliminary Remark: Therefore the converse of Theorem 204 is not true, even when a_n is defined for $n \geq N$.

Proof: If $m \geq 0$, we have

$$s_{2^{m+1}} - s_{2^m} = \sum_{n=2^m+1}^{2^{m+1}} \frac{1}{n} \geq \sum_{n=2^m+1}^{2^{m+1}} \frac{1}{2^{m+1}} = \frac{2^{m+1} - 2^m}{2^{m+1}} = \tfrac{1}{2}.$$

But, by Theorem 203 with $\delta = \tfrac{1}{2}$ convergence of the series would imply the existence of an $m \geq 0$ such that

$$\left|s_{2^{m+1}} - s_{2^m}\right| < \tfrac{1}{2}$$

(since for every p there exists an $m \geq 0$ such that $2^m \geq p$).

Theorem 206: *Let a_n be given for $n \geq N$. For every $\delta > 0$, let there exist a $p \geq N$ such that*

$$|s_q - s_p| < \delta \text{ for } q > p.$$

Then

$$\sum_{n=N}^{\infty} a_n$$

converges.

Preliminary Remark: By Theorem 203, our condition is also necessary for convergence.

Proof: There exists a $p \geq N$ such that

$$|s_q - s_p| < 1 \text{ for } q > p.$$

Hence if $q > p$, we have

$$|s_q| = |(s_q - s_p) + s_p| \leq |s_q - s_p| + |s_p| < 1 + |s_p|.$$

Therefore if $q \geq N$, we have

$$|s_q| < 1 + \max_{N \leq r \leq p} |s_r|.$$

Thus s_q is bounded for $q \geq N$.

Therefore, by Theorem 130 (with $\xi_n = s_{n+N-1}$), there exists an s such that for every $\delta > 0$ we have, infinitely often (i.e. for infinitely many $t \geqq N$),

$$(1) \qquad |s_t - s| < \frac{\delta}{2}.$$

By hypothesis (with $\dfrac{\delta}{4}$ for δ), there exists an r such that

$$|s_q - s_r| < \frac{\delta}{4} \quad \text{for } q > r.$$

Hence if $n > r$, $t > r$, we have

$$(2) \quad |s_n - s_t| = |(s_n - s_r) - (s_t - s_r)| \leqq |s_n - s_r| + |s_t - s_r| < \frac{\delta}{4} + \frac{\delta}{4} = \frac{\delta}{2}.$$

Since (1) is true infinitely often, there exists a $t > r$ such that (1) holds. Thus by (2), if t is such a number, we have for all $n > r$ that

$$|s_n - s| = |(s_n - s_t) + (s_t - s)| \leqq |s_n - s_t| + |s_t - s| < \frac{\delta}{2} + \frac{\delta}{2} = \delta.$$

Theorem 207: *If $p > 0$ and if*

$$\sum_{n=N}^{\infty} a_{nq} = A_q \quad \text{for } 1 \leqq q \leqq p,$$

then

$$\sum_{n=N}^{\infty} \sum_{q=1}^{p} a_{nq} = \sum_{q=1}^{p} A_q.$$

Preliminary Remark: In particular ($p = 2$), if

$$\sum_{n=N}^{\infty} a_n = A,$$

$$\sum_{n=N}^{\infty} b_n = B,$$

then

$$\sum_{n=N}^{\infty} (a_n + b_n) = A + B = \sum_{n=N}^{\infty} a_n + \sum_{n=N}^{\infty} b_n.$$

Proof: As $m \to \infty$, we have

$$S_{mq} = \sum_{n=N}^{m} a_{nq} \to A_q \quad \text{for } 1 \leqq q \leqq p,$$

so that, by Theorem 15,

$$\sum_{n=N}^{m} \sum_{q=1}^{p} a_{nq} = \sum_{q=1}^{p} \sum_{n=N}^{m} a_{nq} = \sum_{q=1}^{p} S_{mq} \to \sum_{q=1}^{p} A_q.$$

Example:
$$\sum_{n=0}^{\infty} \frac{1}{2^n} = \frac{1}{1-\frac{1}{2}} = 2,$$

$$\sum_{n=0}^{\infty} \frac{1}{3^n} = \frac{1}{1-\frac{1}{3}} = \frac{3}{2},$$

so that
$$\sum_{n=0}^{\infty} \left(\frac{1}{2^n} + \frac{1}{3^n} \right) = 2 + \frac{3}{2} = \frac{7}{2}.$$

Theorem 208: *If*
$$\sum_{n=N}^{\infty} a_n = s$$

then
$$\sum_{n=N}^{\infty} ca_n = cs.$$

Proof: By Theorem 16, we have for $m \geqq N$ that
$$\sum_{n=N}^{m} ca_n = c \sum_{n=N}^{m} a_n \to cs.$$

Example: If $|\vartheta| < 1$, $p > 0$, then
$$\sum_{n=p}^{\infty} \vartheta^n = \vartheta^p \sum_{n=p}^{\infty} \vartheta^{n-p} = \vartheta^p \sum_{n=0}^{\infty} \vartheta^n = \frac{\vartheta^p}{1-\vartheta}.$$

Theorem 209: *If*
$$\sum_{n=N}^{\infty} a_n = A,$$

$$\sum_{n=N}^{\infty} b_n = B$$

then
$$\sum_{n=N}^{\infty} (a_n - b_n) = A - B.$$

Proof: By Theorem 208 with $c = -1$, we have
$$\sum_{n=N}^{\infty} (-b_n) = -B,$$

so that, by Theorem 207 with $p = 2$,
$$\sum_{n=N}^{\infty} (a_n - b_n) = A - B.$$

Theorem 210: *If*
$$a_n \geqq 0 \ \textit{for} \ n \geqq N,$$

$$s_n \leqq g \ \textit{for} \ n \geqq N,$$

then

$$\sum_{n=N}^{\infty} a_n$$

converges, and

$$0 \leqq a_N \leqq \sum_{n=N}^{\infty} a_n \leqq g.$$

Preliminary Remark: The hypothesis $a_n \geqq 0$ may not be omitted, even if the other hypothesis is strengthened to read $|s_n| \leqq g$. For,

$$\sum_{n=0}^{\infty} (-1)^n$$

diverges, even though

$$s_n = 1 \text{ or } 0 \text{ for } n \geqq 0,$$

so that

$$|s_n| \leqq 1.$$

Proof: Theorem 27.

Example: (cf. that to Theorem 27): $\sum_{n=1}^{\infty} \dfrac{1}{n^2}$ converges.

Theorem 211: *If*

$$a_n \geqq 0 \text{ for } n \geqq N$$

and

$$\sum_{n=N}^{\infty} a_n = A,$$

then

$$s_m \leqq A \text{ for } m \geqq N$$

(so that

$$A \geqq 0).$$

Proof: For fixed $m \geqq N$ and for $p \geqq 0$, we have

$$s_m \leqq s_{m+p},$$

so that, by Theorem 22,

$$s_m \leqq \lim_{p=\infty} s_{m+p} = A.$$

Theorem 212: *If*

$$\sum_{n=N}^{\infty} a_n$$

converges, and if

$$0 \leqq b_n \leqq a_n \text{ for } n \geqq N,$$

then

$$\sum_{n=N}^{\infty} b_n$$

converges, and

$$0 \leq \sum_{n=N}^{\infty} b_n \leq \sum_{n=N}^{\infty} a_n.$$

Proof: Set

$$\sum_{n=N}^{\infty} a_n = A.$$

By Theorem 211, we have for $m \geq N$ that

$$\sum_{n=N}^{m} b_n \leq \sum_{n=N}^{m} a_n \leq A,$$

so that, by Theorem 210 (with b_n for a_n, $g = A$)

$$\sum_{n=N}^{\infty} b_n$$

converges, and

$$0 \leq \sum_{n=N}^{\infty} b_n \leq A.$$

Example: (cf. that of Theorem 27) : $a_n = \dfrac{1}{(n-1)n}$, $b_n = \dfrac{1}{n^2}$ for $n \geq 2$.

$$\sum_{n=2}^{\infty} \frac{1}{(n-1)n}$$

converges, since

$$\sum_{n=2}^{m} \frac{1}{(n-1)n} = \sum_{n=2}^{m} \left(\frac{1}{n-1} - \frac{1}{n} \right) = 1 - \frac{1}{m} \to 1;$$

and, therefore, so does

$$\sum_{n=2}^{\infty} \frac{1}{n^2}.$$

Theorem 213: *If*

$$\sum_{n=N}^{\infty} |a_n|$$

converges, then

$$\sum_{n=N}^{\infty} a_n$$

converges, and

$$\left| \sum_{n=N}^{\infty} a_n \right| \leq \sum_{n=N}^{\infty} |a_n|.$$

Proof: $\qquad 0 \leq |a_n| + a_n \leq |a_n| + |a_n|.$

By Theorem 207 (with $p = 2$),

$$\sum_{n=N}^{\infty} (|a_n| + |a_n|)$$

converges. Thus, by Theorem 212, so does

$$\sum_{n=N}^{\infty} (|a_n| + a_n),$$

and we have

$$0 \leq \sum_{n=N}^{\infty} (|a_n| + a_n) \leq \sum_{n=N}^{\infty} (|a_n| + |a_n|),$$

so that, by Theorem 209, we have

$$-\sum_{n=N}^{\infty} |a_n| \leq \sum_{n=N}^{\infty} (|a_n| + a_n) - \sum_{n=N}^{\infty} |a_n| = \sum_{n=N}^{\infty} a_n$$

$$\leq \sum_{n=N}^{\infty} (|a_n| + |a_n|) - \sum_{n=N}^{\infty} |a_n| = \sum_{n=N}^{\infty} |a_n|.$$

Example: $\sum_{n=0}^{\infty} \varepsilon_n \dfrac{1}{2^n}$ converges if each $|\varepsilon_n| = 1$.

Definition 53:
$$\sum_{n=N}^{\infty} a_n$$

converges absolutely if

$$\sum_{n=N}^{\infty} |a_n|$$

converges.

Examples: 1) Every convergent series whose terms are ≥ 0 converges absolutely.

2) By Theorem 208 (with $c = -1$), every convergent series whose terms are ≤ 0 converges absolutely.

Theorem 214: *Let*

$$(-1)^n a_n \text{ be always } \geq 0 \text{ or always } \leq 0 \text{ for } n \geq N,$$

$$|a_n| \geq |a_{n+1}| \text{ for } n \geq N,$$

$$a_n \to 0.$$

Then

$$\sum_{n=N}^{\infty} a_n$$

converges.

Proof: W.l.g. let $N = 0$ (for otherwise we may consider $b_n = a_{n+N}, n \geq 0$ instead of a_n, $n \geq N$).

W.l.g. let

$$(-1)^n a_n \geq 0 \text{ for } n \geq 0.$$

For, in the other case, we may replace a_n by $-a_n$, which does not affect either the hypotheses or (by Theorem 208 with $c = -1$) the conclusion.

If $n \geq 0$ then

$$a_{2n} \geq 0 \geq a_{2n+1},$$

$$a_{2n} + a_{2n+1} = |a_{2n}| - |a_{2n+1}| \geq 0,$$

and, if $m \geq 0$,

$$\sum_{n=0}^{m} (a_{2n} + a_{2n+1}) = \sum_{n=0}^{m} (|a_{2n}| - |a_{2n+1}|)$$

$$= |a_0| - \sum_{n=0}^{m} (|a_{2n+1}| - |a_{2n+2}|) - |a_{2m+2}| \leq |a_0|.$$

Therefore, by Theorem 27,

$$\lim_{m=\infty} \sum_{n=0}^{m} (a_{2n} + a_{2n+1}) = \lim_{m=\infty} s_{2m+1}$$

exists. We set

(1)
$$\lim_{m=\infty} s_{2m+1} = s.$$

Since

$$\lim_{m=\infty} a_{2m+1} = 0,$$

we have

(2)
$$\lim_{m=\infty} s_{2m} = \lim_{m=\infty} (s_{2m+1} - a_{2m+1}) = s.$$

(1) and (2) together imply

$$\lim_{m=\infty} s_m = s.$$

Theorem 215: *Not every convergent series converges absolutely.*
Proof: If

$$a_n = \frac{(-1)^n}{n},$$

then

$$\sum_{n=1}^{\infty} a_n$$

converges by Theorem 214, since we have for $n \geq 1$ that

$$(-1)^n a_n = \frac{1}{n} \geq 0,$$

$$|a_n| = \frac{1}{n} \geq \frac{1}{n+1} = |a_{n+1}|,$$

$$|a_n| = \frac{1}{n} \to 0.$$

But, by Theorem 205,

$$\sum_{n=1}^{\infty} |a_n|$$

diverges.

Definition 54:
$$\sum_{n=N}^{\infty} a_n$$
converges conditionally, if this series converges but does not converge absolutely.

Definition 55: *A sequence λ_n $(n \geqq 1)$ is called a rearrangement of the integers $\geqq N$, if every λ_n is an integer $\geqq N$ and if every integer $\geqq N$ has the value λ_n for exactly one $n \geqq 1$.*

Example: $N = 1$, $\lambda_n = n + 1$ for odd $n \geqq 1$, $\lambda_n = n - 1$ for even $n \geqq 1$.

Theorem 216: *Let*
$$\sum_{n=N}^{\infty} a_n = s$$
and let this series converge absolutely. Let λ_n be some rearrangement of the $n \geqq N$. Then
$$\sum_{n=1}^{\infty} a_{\lambda_n}$$
converges, and we have
$$\sum_{n=1}^{\infty} a_{\lambda_n} = s.$$

Proof: If $M > N$, we have by Theorem 202 that
$$\sum_{n=M}^{\infty} |a_n| = \sum_{n=N}^{\infty} |a_n| - \sum_{n=N}^{M-1} |a_n|.$$

The right-hand side approaches 0 as $M \to \infty$, and therefore so does the left-hand side. Let $\delta > 0$ be given. Choose an $M > N$ such that
$$\sum_{n=M}^{\infty} |a_n| < \delta.$$

Now choose an r such that all of the n for which $N \leqq n < M$ occur among the λ_n with $n \leqq r$. For $m \geqq r$, let h_ν, $\nu \geqq 1$ be the sequence of the $n \geqq N$ arranged in ascending order, excluding those numbers λ_n with $n \leqq m$. Then $h_1 \geqq M$, and for all large t we have
$$\sum_{n=1}^{m} a_{\lambda_n} + \sum_{n=1}^{t} a_{h_n} = \sum_{n=N}^{N+t+m-1} a_n.$$
Letting $t \to \infty$, we obtain
$$\sum_{n=1}^{\infty} a_{h_n} = s - \sum_{n=1}^{m} a_{\lambda_n},$$
$$\left| \sum_{n=1}^{m} a_{\lambda_n} - s \right| = \left| \sum_{n=1}^{\infty} a_{h_n} \right| \leqq \sum_{n=1}^{\infty} |a_{h_n}| \leqq \sum_{n=M}^{\infty} |a_n| < \delta.$$

Thus we have

$$\lim_{m=\infty} \sum_{n=1}^{m} a_{\lambda_n} = s.$$

Theorem 217: *Let*

(1)
$$\sum_{n=1}^{\infty} a_n$$

converge conditionally. Then

1) *Given any* S, *we may find a rearrangement* λ_n *of the integers* $\geqq 1$ *such that*

$$\sum_{n=1}^{\infty} a_{\lambda_n} = S.$$

2) *We may find a rearrangement* λ_n *of the integers* $\geqq 1$ *such that*

$$\sum_{n=1}^{\infty} a_{\lambda_n}$$

diverges.

Proof: If we arrange the $a_n \geqq 0$ according to increasing subscripts, then we obtain a sequence b_n, $n \geqq 1$. Moreover,

(2)
$$\sum_{n=1}^{\infty} b_n$$

diverges. For otherwise, there would be no $a_n \geqq 0$, or only a finite number, or infinitely many such that (2) converges. Then, by Theorems 200 and 209, the series which is obtained from (1) by replacing each $a_n \geqq 0$ by 0 would converge. This series has no positive terms, and so would converge absolutely. Thus, (1) would converge absolutely.

If we arrange the $a_n < 0$ according to increasing subscripts, then we obtain a sequence c_n, $n \geqq 1$. Moreover,

(3)
$$\sum_{n=1}^{\infty} c_n$$

diverges. For otherwise, there would be no $a_n < 0$, or only a finite number, or infinitely many such that (3) converges. Then, by Theorems 200 and 207 (with $p = 2$), the series which is obtained from (1) by replacing each $a_n < 0$ by 0 would converge. This series has no negative terms, and so would converge absolutely. Thus (1) would converge absolutely.

Since

$$a_n \to 0,$$

we have

$$b_n \to 0, \quad c_n \to 0.$$

Set

$$B_m = \sum_{n=1}^{m} b_n \text{ for } m \geq 1,$$

$$C_M = \begin{cases} 0 & \text{for } M = 0, \\ \sum_{n=1}^{M} c_n & \text{for } M \geq 1. \end{cases}$$

By what has just been said, and by Theorem 210, we have for every $\omega > 0$ that, ultimately,

$$B_m > \omega$$

and, ultimately,

$$C_M < -\omega.$$

1) For every $m \geq 1$, there is therefore an M such that
$$B_m + C_M < S.$$
Let $M = M(m)$ be the least such number and let $M(0)$ mean 0. Then we evidently have that
$$M(m-1) \leq M(m) \quad \text{for} \quad m \geq 1$$
and that $M(m)$ is unbounded. By what has been said, we have for $M(m) \geq 1$ that
$$B_m + C_{M(m)-1} \geq S,$$
and so
$$B_m + C_{M(m)} \geq S + c_{M(m)}.$$

We obtain a new arrangement of the a's as follows: The arrangement of the b_n among themselves is retained. Similarly for the c_n. For $m \geq 1$, we place between b_m and b_{m+1} those c_n for which
$$M(m-1) + 1 \leq n \leq M(m),$$
so that none occurs if $M(m-1) = M(m)$.

Every sum
$$\sum_{n=1}^{p} a_{\lambda_n}$$
which already contains b_2 and c_1, and which contains b_m but not b_{m+1} ($m = m(p) \geq 2$), is therefore
$$\leq B_m + C_{M(m-1)} = B_{m-1} + C_{M(m-1)} + b_m < S + b_m$$
and is
$$\geq B_m + C_{M(m)} \geq S + c_{M(m)}.$$

Thus we have for large p that
$$\left| \sum_{n=1}^{p} a_{\lambda_n} - S \right| \leq \text{Max} \left(b_{m(p)}, \ -c_{M(m(p))} \right) \to 0,$$

so that

$$\sum_{n=1}^{\infty} a_{\lambda_n} = S.$$

2) For every $m \geq 1$, choose the smallest $M = M(m)$ for which

$$B_m + C_M < -m;$$

let $M(0) = 0$. For the new arrangement of the a, use the method of 1) but with the new definition of $M(m)$. Then for every $m \geq 1$, there exists a sum

$$\sum_{n=1}^{p} a_{\lambda_n} < -m.$$

Thus,

$$\sum_{n=1}^{p} a_{\lambda_n}$$

is not bounded, so that

$$\sum_{n=1}^{\infty} a_{\lambda_n}$$

diverges by Theorem 26.

Theorem 218: *Let*

$$\sum_{n=N}^{\infty} a_n = s$$

and let the series converge absolutely. Let the integers $n \geq N$ be partitioned into a finite $(1 \leq q \leq v)$ or an infinite $(q \geq 1)$ sequence of sets $\mathfrak{R}_q$ such that each $\mathfrak{R}_q$ is either a finite $(n_{qt}, \ 1 \leq t \leq t_q$, where t_q is an integer$)$ or an infinite sequence $(n_{qt}, t \geq 1)$.

1) *Then*

$$\sum_{t=1}^{\infty} a_{n_{qt}} = A_q$$

converges absolutely for those q for which $\mathfrak{R}_q$ is infinite.

2) *In addition, set*

$$\sum_{t=1}^{t_q} a_{n_{qt}} = A_q$$

for those q for which $\mathfrak{R}_q$ is finite.

Then, if there are an infinite number of $\mathfrak{R}_q$,

$$\sum_{q=1}^{\infty} A_q$$

converges absolutely, and we have

$$\sum_{q=1}^{\infty} A_q = s.$$

If there are a finite number of $\mathfrak{N}_q$, then

$$\sum_{q=1}^{v} A_q = s.$$

Preliminary Remark: Theorem 216 is the special case of Theorem 218 in which there are infinitely many $\mathfrak{N}_q$ each containing exactly one number.

Proof: 1) If $\mathfrak{N}_q$ is infinite, then we have for every $u \geq 1$ that

$$\sum_{t=1}^{u} | a_{n_{qt}} | \leq \sum_{n=N}^{\infty} | a_n |.$$

Thus, Theorem 210 yields the convergence of

$$\sum_{t=1}^{\infty} | a_{n_{qt}} |.$$

2) If there are only a finite number of $\mathfrak{N}_q$, then we have, by Theorems 216, 200, and 207, that

$$\sum_{q=1}^{v} A_q = s.$$

Now, let there be infinitely many $\mathfrak{N}_q$. Let $\delta > 0$ be given. Choose an $M > N$ such that

$$\sum_{n=M}^{\infty} | a_n | < \delta,$$

and an r such that the $\mathfrak{N}_q$ with $q \leq r$ contain all of the n with $N \leq n < M$. Then if $m \geq r$, we have

$$s - \sum_{q=1}^{m} A_q = \sum_{n=1}^{\infty} a_{h_n},$$

where h_n are those $n \geq N$, arranged in natural order, which do not occur in any $\mathfrak{N}_q$ with $q \leq m$. Thus $h_1 \geq M$, and

$$\left| \sum_{q=1}^{m} A_q - s \right| \leq \sum_{n=1}^{\infty} | a_{h_n} | \leq \sum_{n=M}^{\infty} | a_n | < \delta.$$

The convergence of

$$\sum_{q=1}^{\infty} | A_q |,$$

in the case of infinitely many $\mathfrak{N}_q$, follows from

$$\sum_{q=1}^{m} | A_q | \leq \sum_{n=N}^{\infty} | a_n |.$$

Example: $N = 1$. For every $q \geq 1$, $\mathfrak{N}_q$ contains all the numbers $q + \dfrac{(u-1)u}{2}$ with $u \geq q$. This satisfies the conditions of Theorem 218. For,

1) $\dfrac{(u-1)u}{2}$ is always an integer, since $\dfrac{u}{2}$ is an integer for even u and $\dfrac{u-1}{2}$ is an integer for odd u.

2) Every $n \geqq 1$ belongs to exactly one interval

$$\frac{(u-1)u}{2} < n \leqq \frac{u(u+1)}{2}, \quad u \geqq 1$$

and, since

$$\frac{u(u+1)}{2} - \frac{(u-1)u}{2} = u,$$

therefore has the form

$$n = q + \frac{(u-1)u}{2}, \quad 1 \leqq q \leqq u.$$

3) This representation is unique. For it implies that

$$\frac{(u-1)u}{2} < n \leqq u + \frac{(u-1)u}{2} = \frac{u(u+1)}{2}.$$

Theorem 219: *If*

$$\sum_{q=N}^{\infty} \left| a_{pq} \right|$$

converges for all $p \geqq N$, and if

$$\sum_{p=N}^{\infty} \sum_{q=N}^{\infty} \left| a_{pq} \right|$$

converges, then

$$\sum_{p=N}^{\infty} \sum_{q=N}^{\infty} a_{pq} = \sum_{q=N}^{\infty} \sum_{p=N}^{\infty} a_{pq}.$$

Proof: W.l.g. let $N = 0$. If we arrange the a_{pq}, $p \geqq 0$, $q \geqq 0$, according to increasing $p + q$, and according to increasing p for those with equal $p + q$, then we obtain a sequence which we denote by a_n, $n \geqq 0$. If we then set

$$\sum_{p=0}^{\infty} \sum_{q=0}^{\infty} \left| a_{pq} \right| = A,$$

we have, for each $m \geqq 1$,

$$\sum_{n=0}^{m} \left| a_n \right| \leqq \sum_{p=0}^{m} \sum_{q=0}^{m} \left| a_{pq} \right| \leqq \sum_{p=0}^{m} \sum_{q=0}^{\infty} \left| a_{pq} \right| \leqq A.$$

$$\sum_{n=0}^{\infty} a_n = s$$

therefore converges absolutely. Thus, by Theorem 218,

$$s = \sum_{p=0}^{\infty} \sum_{q=0}^{\infty} a_{pq},$$

on the one hand, and on the other hand

$$s = \sum_{q=0}^{\infty} \sum_{p=0}^{\infty} a_{pq}.$$

Theorem 220: *Let*

$$\sum_{n=0}^{\infty} a_n = A$$

converge absolutely, let

$$\sum_{n=0}^{\infty} b_n = B$$

converge, and let

$$c_n = \sum_{\nu=0}^{n} a_\nu b_{n-\nu} \quad for \ n \geq 0.$$

Then

$$\sum_{n=0}^{\infty} c_n$$

converges, and we have

$$\sum_{n=0}^{\infty} c_n = AB.$$

Preliminary Remark: In particular, this holds if both of the given series are absolutely convergent.

Proof: Setting

$$\sum_{n=0}^{m} a_n = A_m, \quad \sum_{n=0}^{m} b_n = B_m$$

for $m \geq 0$, we have for $m \geq 0$ that

$$\sum_{n=0}^{m} c_n = \sum_{n=0}^{m} \sum_{\nu=0}^{n} a_\nu b_{n-\nu} = \sum_{\nu=0}^{m} a_\nu \sum_{n=\nu}^{m} b_{n-\nu} = \sum_{\nu=0}^{m} a_\nu B_{m-\nu} \, ,$$

$$\sum_{n=0}^{m} c_n - A_m B_m = \sum_{\nu=0}^{m} a_\nu B_{m-\nu} - \sum_{\nu=0}^{m} a_\nu B_m = \sum_{\nu=0}^{m} a_\nu (B_{m-\nu} - B_m).$$

Set

$$\sum_{\nu=0}^{\infty} |a_\nu| = g \, ;$$

by Theorem 26, we have for $\nu \geq 0$ and for a suitable h independent of ν, that

$$|B_v| < h.$$

Let $\delta > 0$ be given. By Theorem 203, choose a $t > 0$ so that

$$|B_u - B_m| < \frac{\delta}{2(g+1)} \quad \text{for } u \geq t, \ m \geq t$$

and

$$\sum_{\nu=\left[\frac{m}{2}\right]}^{m} |a_\nu| < \frac{\delta}{4h} \text{ for } m \geq 2t.$$

Then we have that

$$|B_{m-\nu} - B_m| < 2h \text{ for } 0 \leq \nu \leq m,$$

$$|B_{m-\nu} - B_m| < \frac{\delta}{2(g+1)} \text{ for } m \geq 2t, \ 0 \leq \nu \leq \frac{m}{2}.$$

Hence if $m \geq 2t$, we have

$$\left| \sum_{n=0}^{m} c_n - A_m B_m \right| \leq \sum_{\nu=0}^{m} |a_\nu| |B_{m-\nu} - B_m|$$

$$= \sum_{\nu=0}^{\left[\frac{m}{2}\right]-1} |a_\nu| |B_{m-\nu} - B_m| + \sum_{\nu=\left[\frac{m}{2}\right]}^{m} |a_\nu| |B_{m-\nu} - B_m|$$

$$\leq \sum_{\nu=0}^{\left[\frac{m}{2}\right]-1} |a_\nu| \frac{\delta}{2(g+1)} + \sum_{\nu=\left[\frac{m}{2}\right]}^{m} |a_\nu| 2h$$

$$< \frac{\delta}{2(g+1)} g + 2h \frac{\delta}{4h} < \delta.$$

Therefore,

$$\sum_{n=0}^{m} c_n - A_m B_m \to 0,$$

and since

$$A_m B_m \to AB,$$

we finally obtain

$$\sum_{n=0}^{m} c_n \to AB,$$

$$\sum_{n=0}^{\infty} c_n = AB.$$

Example: $|\vartheta| < 1, \ a_n = b_n = \vartheta^n.$

Then, we have

$$A = \frac{1}{1-\vartheta}, \quad B = \frac{1}{1-\vartheta},$$

$$c_n = \sum_{\nu=0}^{n} \vartheta^\nu \vartheta^{n-\nu} = (n+1)\vartheta^n,$$

so that

$$\sum_{n=0}^{\infty} (n+1)\vartheta^n = \frac{1}{(1-\vartheta)^2}.$$

To be sure, even the special case given in the preliminary remark to Theorem 220 covers this example.

Theorem 221: *Let $0 < \vartheta < 1$. Let a_n be given for $n \geqq N$. Let there exist a $p \geqq N$ such that*

$$| a_{n+1} | \leqq \vartheta | a_n | \quad \text{for} \ n \geqq p.$$

Then

$$\sum_{n=N}^{\infty} a_n$$

converges, and in fact, absolutely.

Proofs: For $n \geqq p$, we have

(1) $$| a_n | \leqq \vartheta^{n-p} | a_p |,$$

since this is true for $n = p$, and $n + 1$ follows from n ($\geqq p$) because

$$| a_{n+1} | \leqq \vartheta | a_n | \leqq \vartheta \cdot \vartheta^{n-p} | a_p | = \vartheta^{n+1-p} | a_p | .$$

1) Therefore we have for $m \geqq p$ that

$$\sum_{n=p}^{m} | a_n | \leqq \sum_{n=p}^{m} \vartheta^{n-p} | a_p | = | a_p | \sum_{q=0}^{m-p} \vartheta^q = | a_p | \frac{1 - \vartheta^{m-p+1}}{1 - \vartheta} \leqq \frac{| a_p |}{1 - \vartheta},$$

so that the sum on the left is bounded. Hence

$$\sum_{n=N}^{m} | a_n |$$

is bounded for $m \geqq N$. This shows the convergence of

$$\sum_{n=N}^{\infty} | a_n | .$$

2) We may also proceed from (1) as follows:

$$\sum_{n=p}^{\infty} \vartheta^{n-p} = \sum_{q=0}^{\infty} \vartheta^q$$

converges, therefore so does

$$\sum_{n=p}^{\infty} | a_n |$$

and so does

$$\sum_{n=N}^{\infty} | a_n | .$$

Theorem 222: *Let $| \Theta | < 1$ and let a_n be given for $n \geqq N$. Let*

$$\frac{a_{n+1}}{a_n} \to \Theta.$$

Then

$$\sum_{n=N}^{\infty} a_n$$

converges absolutely.

Proof: If we set

$$\vartheta = \frac{1 + |\Theta|}{2},$$

then we have

$$0 \leqq |\Theta| < \vartheta < 1,$$

so that, ultimately,

$$\left| \frac{a_{n+1}}{a_n} \right| \leqq \vartheta,$$

$$|a_{n+1}| \leqq \vartheta |a_n|,$$

so that Theorem 221 is applicable.

Theorem 223 (the so-called decimal representation of real numbers):
Every a may be written uniquely in the following form:

(1)
$$\begin{cases} a = \sum_{n=0}^{\infty} \frac{x_n}{10^n}, \\[2mm] x_n \text{ integral}, \\[2mm] 0 \leqq x_n \leqq 9 \text{ for } n > 0. \\[2mm] \text{For no } m \geqq 0 \text{ is } x_n = 9 \text{ for all } n > m. \end{cases}$$

Proof: 1) If (1) holds, we have for every integral $m \geqq 0$ that

$$10^m a - 10^m \sum_{n=0}^{m} \frac{x_n}{10^n} = 10^m \sum_{n=m+1}^{\infty} \frac{x_n}{10^n} \begin{cases} \geqq 0, \\[2mm] < 10^m \sum_{n=m+1}^{\infty} \frac{9}{10^n} = 1, \end{cases}$$

so that the integer

$$10^m \sum_{n=0}^{m} \frac{x_n}{10^n} = [10^m a],$$

$$\sum_{n=0}^{m} \frac{x_n}{10^n} = \frac{[10^m a]}{10^m},$$

so that

(2)
$$\begin{cases} x_0 = [a], \\[2mm] \frac{x_n}{10^n} = \frac{[10^n a]}{10^n} - \frac{[10^{n-1} a]}{10^{n-1}} \text{ for } n > 0. \end{cases}$$

Therefore there is at most one representation of the required kind.

2) The x_n determined by (2) have the required properties. For,

a) We have for integral $m > 0$ that

$$\sum_{n=0}^{m} \frac{x_n}{10^n} = [a] + \sum_{n=1}^{m} \left(-\frac{[10^{n-1}a]}{10^{n-1}} + \frac{[10^n a]}{10^n} \right) = \frac{[10^m a]}{10^m}$$

$$\begin{cases} \leqq \dfrac{10^m a}{10^m} = a, \\[2ex] > \dfrac{10^m a - 1}{10^m} = a - \dfrac{1}{10^m}, \end{cases}$$

so that the left-hand side approaches a as $m \to \infty$.

b)
$$x_n = \begin{cases} [a] & \text{for } n = 0, \\ [10^n a] - 10[10^{n-1}a] & \text{for } n > 0 \end{cases}$$

is an integer.

c) If $n > 0$, we have

$$x_n \begin{cases} < 10^n a - 10(10^{n-1}a - 1) = 10, \\ > (10^n a - 1) - 10 \cdot 10^{n-1}a = -1, \end{cases}$$

so that

$$0 \leqq x_n \leqq 9.$$

d) If for some $m \geqq 0$ we had

$$x_n = 9 \text{ for } n > m,$$

then we would have

$$10^m \sum_{n=m+1}^{\infty} \frac{x_n}{10^n} = 10^m \sum_{n=m+1}^{\infty} \frac{9}{10^m} = 1,$$

$$b = 10^m a$$

an integer, and

$$9 = x_{m+1} = [10^{m+1}a] - 10[10^m a] = [10b] - 10[b] = 10b - 10b = 0.$$

CHAPTER 13

UNIFORM CONVERGENCE

Introduction

We have learned in Theorem 66 that a sum

$$f(x) = \sum_{n=1}^{m} f_n(x)$$

is continuous at ξ if each $f_n(x)$ is. Is this also true, at a ξ such that $a < \xi < b$, of an infinite series

$$f(x) = \sum_{n=1}^{\infty} f_n(x)$$

which converges for all x on $[a, b]$?

No. **Example:**

$$\xi = 0, \quad f_n(x) = x^2(1 - x^2)^{n-1} \text{ for } |x| < \sqrt{2}.$$

Indeed, we have for $n \geq 1$ that

$$f_n(0) = 0,$$

so that

$$\sum_{n=1}^{\infty} f_n(0)$$

converges, and

$$f(0) = 0;$$

but for $0 < |x| < \sqrt{2}$ we have

$$-1 < 1 - x^2 < 1,$$

so that

$$\sum_{n=1}^{\infty} f_n(x) = x^2 \sum_{n=1}^{\infty} (1 - x^2)^{n-1} = x^2 \sum_{\nu=0}^{\infty} (1 - x^2)^{\nu} = \frac{x^2}{1 - (1 - x^2)} = 1,$$

$$f(x) = 1.$$

$f(x)$ is discontinuous at 0; in fact it is continuous neither on the right nor on the left, although the $f_n(x)$ are continuous there.

By imposing a suitable restriction, we will be able to save Theorem 66 from failing for infinite series. And with this we come to the important concept of uniform convergence.

In this chapter, n, N, μ, m, u, v, μ_1, μ_2 always denote integers.

Definition 56: *Let $\mathfrak{M}$ be a set of numbers, let $f_n(x)$ be defined for $n \geqq N$ and for every x in $\mathfrak{M}$, and let $f(x)$ be defined for all x in $\mathfrak{M}$. For every $\delta > 0$, let there exist a $\mu \geqq N$ (independent of x) such that for every x in $\mathfrak{M}$ we have*

$$\left| \sum_{n=N}^{m} f_n(x) - f(x) \right| < \delta \ \text{for} \ m \geqq \mu.$$

We then say that

$$\sum_{n=N}^{\infty} f_n(x)$$

converges uniformly to $f(x)$ on (in) $\mathfrak{M}$.

(That the series converges and to the sum $f(x)$, follows from Definition 51.)

Example: Let $\mathfrak{M}$ consist of a single number. Then every series which converges in $\mathfrak{M}$ converges uniformly therein.

Theorem 224: *Not every series*

$$\sum_{n=N}^{\infty} f_n(x)$$

convergent in some $\mathfrak{M}$ converges uniformly therein.

Proof: Let $N = 1$, and let $\mathfrak{M}$ be the set of x such that $|x| < \sqrt{2}$ or, in general, the set of x such that $0 < |x| < p$ where $0 < p \leqq \sqrt{2}$. Let

$$f_n(x) = x^2(1 - x^2)^{n-1}$$

(our example of the introduction, where we have already proved convergence). Set

$$\sum_{n=1}^{\infty} f_n(x) = f(x).$$

From the introduction, we know that

$$f(x) = 1 \ \text{for} \ 0 < |x| < p.$$

If the series were uniformly convergent for $0 < |x| < p$, then there would exist a $\mu \geqq 1$ such that

$$\left| \sum_{n=1}^{\mu} f_n(x) - 1 \right| < \tfrac{1}{2} \ \text{for} \ 0 < |x| < p.$$

(In more than one respect, the conditions of uniform convergence are not fully exploited.) Since

$$\sum_{n=1}^{\mu} f_n(x) = x^2 \sum_{n=1}^{\mu} (1-x^2)^{n-1} = x^2 \sum_{v=0}^{\mu-1} (1-x^2)^v = x^2 \frac{1-(1-x^2)^\mu}{1-(1-x^2)} = 1-(1-x^2)^\mu,$$

we should have

$$\left| (1-x^2)^\mu \right| < \tfrac{1}{2} \text{ for } 0 < |x| < p.$$

But, since

$$\lim_{x=0} (1-x^2)^\mu = 1,$$

this is not true.

Theorem 225: *Let every* $f_n(x)$, $n \geqq N$, *be defined for* x *in* $\mathfrak{M}$. *Then*

$$(1) \qquad \sum_{n=N}^{\infty} f_n(x)$$

is uniformly convergent in $\mathfrak{M}$ *if and only if for every* $\delta > 0$ *there exists a* $\mu \geqq N$ *(independent of* x*) such that we have for every* x *in* $\mathfrak{M}$ *that*

$$\left| \sum_{n=u}^{v} f_n(x) \right| < \delta \text{ for } v \geqq u > \mu.$$

Proof: 1) If this last condition is satisfied, then (1) converges in $\mathfrak{M}$ by Theorem 206. Therefore if we set

$$(2) \qquad \sum_{n=N}^{\infty} f_n(x) = f(x),$$

then we have for $m \geqq \mu$ that

$$\left| \sum_{n=N}^{m} f_n(x) - f(x) \right| = \left| \sum_{n=m+1}^{\infty} f_n(x) \right| \leqq \delta < 2\delta,$$

so that (1) converges uniformly by Definition 56 (since 2δ is an arbitrary positive number).

2) If (1) is uniformly convergent in $\mathfrak{M}$ and if $f(x)$ is defined by (2), then we choose a μ as in Definition 56 with $\dfrac{\delta}{2}$ for δ. Then we have for $v \geqq u > \mu$ that

$$\left| \sum_{n=N}^{u-1} f_n(x) - f(x) \right| < \frac{\delta}{2}$$

and

$$\left| \sum_{n=N}^{v} f_n(x) - f(x) \right| < \frac{\delta}{2},$$

so that

$$\left| \sum_{n=u}^{v} f_n(x) \right| = \left| \left(\sum_{n=N}^{v} f_n(x) - f(x) \right) - \left(\sum_{n=N}^{u-1} f_n(x) - f(x) \right) \right| < \frac{\delta}{2} + \frac{\delta}{2} = \delta.$$

Theorem 226: *If $\mathfrak{M}$ and $\mathfrak{N}$ are sets of numbers having no numbers in common, and if*

$$\sum_{n=N}^{\infty} f_n(x)$$

converges uniformly in $\mathfrak{M}$ and in $\mathfrak{N}$, then the series converges uniformly in the union of $\mathfrak{M}$ and $\mathfrak{N}$.

Proof: Given a $\delta > 0$, choose a suitable μ_1 for $\mathfrak{M}$ and a suitable μ_2 for $\mathfrak{N}$ by Definition 56. The number $\mu = \text{Max } (\mu_1, \mu_2)$ is the required number for the union.

Theorem 227: *If*

$$\sum_{n=N}^{\infty} f_n(x) \qquad \left(= f(x)\right)$$

converges uniformly in $\mathfrak{M}$, and if $g(x)$ is defined and bounded in $\mathfrak{M}$, then

$$\sum_{n=N}^{\infty} f_n(x) g(x) \qquad \left(= f(x) g(x)\right)$$

converges uniformly in $\mathfrak{M}$.

Proof: For a suitable c independent of x, we have that

$$|g(x)| < c \text{ in } \mathfrak{M}.$$

For any $\delta > 0$, choose a μ independent of x such that

$$\left| \sum_{n=N}^{m} f_n(x) - f(x) \right| < \frac{\delta}{c} \text{ for } m \geq \mu, \ x \text{ in } \mathfrak{M}.$$

Then we have for $m \geq \mu$ and x in $\mathfrak{M}$ that

$$\left| \sum_{n=N}^{m} f_n(x) g(x) - f(x) g(x) \right| = \left| g(x) \left(\sum_{n=N}^{m} f_n(x) - f(x) \right) \right|$$

$$= |g(x)| \left| \sum_{n=N}^{m} f_n(x) - f(x) \right| < c \frac{\delta}{c} = \delta.$$

Theorem 228: *Let $f_n(x)$ be defined for $n \geq N$ and for x in $\mathfrak{M}$. Let there exist for $n \geq N$ a sequence p_n independent of x such that*

$$|f_n(x)| \leq p_n$$

for x in $\mathfrak{M}$ (in other words, let each $f_n(x)$ be bounded in $\mathfrak{M}$) and let

$$\sum_{n=N}^{\infty} p_n$$

converge. Then

$$\sum_{n=N}^{\infty} f_n(x)$$

converges uniformly in $\mathfrak{M}$.

Preliminary Remark: This sufficient condition for uniform convergence is not a necessary condition. **Counter-example:** $\mathfrak{M}$ arbitrary, $N = 1$,

$$f_n(x) = \frac{(-1)^n}{n} \text{ for } n \geq 1.$$

Proof: For every $\delta > 0$, choose a $\mu \geq N$ by Theorem 203 such that

$$\sum_{n=u}^{v} p_n < \delta \text{ for } v \geq u > \mu.$$

Then we have for these u, v that

$$\left| \sum_{n=u}^{v} f_n(x) \right| \leq \sum_{n=u}^{v} |f_n(x)| \leq \sum_{n=u}^{v} p_n < \delta,$$

so that Theorem 225 proves our assertion.

Theorem 229: *Let* $p > 0$, *and let*

$$\sum_{n=N}^{\infty} f_n(x)$$

converge uniformly for $\xi < x < \xi + p$. *Let every* $f_n(x)$ *be continuous at* ξ *on the right. Then the series converges at* $x = \xi$. *If furthermore we set*

$$\sum_{n=N}^{\infty} f_n(x) = f(x) \text{ for } \xi \leq x < \xi + p,$$

then $f(x)$ *is continuous on the right.*

Preliminary Remark: This theorem verifies once again that the particular series given in the proof of Theorem 224 is not uniformly convergent for $0 < |x| < p$. For, its sum, as was calculated in the introduction, is not continuous at 0 on the right.

Proof: 1) We have for $v \geq u \geq N$ that

$$\sum_{n=u}^{v} f_n(x)$$

is continuous on the right at ξ, as can be seen, say, from Theorem 66 by noting that the $f_n(x)$ are continuous at ξ if we define them to be $f_n(\xi)$ for $\xi - 1 < x < \xi$. Let $\delta > 0$ be given. By Theorem 225, we choose a $\mu \geq N$ independent of x such that

$$\left| \sum_{n=u}^{v} f_n(x) \right| < \frac{\delta}{2} \text{ for } v \geq u \geq \mu, \xi < x < \xi + p.$$

Then we have

$$\left| \sum_{n=u}^{v} f_n(\xi) \right| \leq \frac{\delta}{2} < \delta \text{ for } v \geq u \geq \mu,$$

so that

$$\sum_{n=N}^{\infty} f_n(x)$$

converges at $x = \xi$ (and so, by Theorem 226, is uniformly convergent for $\xi \leq x < \xi + p$).

2) Let $\delta > 0$ be given. Choose a $\mu_1 \geq N$ independent of x such that

$$\left| \sum_{n=N}^{\mu_1} f_n(x) - f(x) \right| < \frac{\delta}{3} \text{ for } \xi \leq x < \xi + p.$$

If we set

$$G(x) = \sum_{n=N}^{\mu_1} f_n(x),$$

then $G(x)$ is continuous at ξ on the right. Hence there exists a positive $\varepsilon < p$ such that

$$| G(\xi + h) - G(\xi) | < \frac{\delta}{3} \text{ for } 0 < h < \varepsilon.$$

Now we have for $0 < h < \varepsilon$ that

$$| f(\xi + h) - f(\xi) |$$
$$= | - (G(\xi + h) - f(\xi + h)) + (G(\xi) - f(\xi)) + (G(\xi + h) - G(\xi)) |$$
$$\leq | G(\xi + h) - f(\xi + h) | + | G(\xi) - f(\xi) | + | G(\xi + h) - G(\xi) |$$
$$< \frac{\delta}{3} + \frac{\delta}{3} + \frac{\delta}{3} = \delta.$$

Theorem 230: *Let $p > 0$, and let*

$$\sum_{n=N}^{\infty} f_n(x)$$

converge uniformly for $\xi - p < x < \xi$. Let every $f_n(x)$ be continuous at ξ on the left. Then the series converges at ξ and its sum is continuous at ξ on the left.

Proof: Theorem 229 with $f_n(-x)$ in place of $f_n(x)$ and $-\xi$ in place of ξ.

Theorem 231: *Let $p > 0$, and let*

$$\sum_{n=N}^{\infty} f_n(x)$$

converge uniformly for $0 < | x - \xi | < p$. Let every $f_n(x)$ be continuous at ξ. Then the series converges at ξ and its sum is continuous at ξ.

Proof: Theorems 229 and 230.

Theorem 232: *Let $\varepsilon > 0$ and let $f_n(x)$ be continuous at ξ for every $n \geq N$. Let*

$$\sum_{n=N}^{\infty} f_n(x) = f(x)$$

converge for $|x - \xi| < \varepsilon$ and be continuous at ξ. Then for any $p > 0$, the series may fail to converge uniformly for every $p > 0$ in one or both of the sets $\xi < x < \xi + p$ or $\xi - p < x < \xi$.

Preliminary Remark: Thus, the sufficient condition for continuity given in Theorem 231, for continuity on the right given in Theorem 229, and for continuity on the left given in Theorem 230, is not a necessary condition.

Proof: For every x let

$$f_n(x) = n^2 x^2 e^{-nx^2} - (n-1)^2 x^2 e^{-(n-1)x^2} \text{ for } n \geq 1,$$

so that $f_n(x)$ is continuous everywhere for every $n \geq 1$ and

$$s_m(x) = \sum_{n=1}^{m} f_n(x) = m^2 x^2 e^{-mx^2} \text{ for } m \geq 1.$$

Then we have

$$s_m(0) = 0$$

and we have for $x \neq 0$ that

$$0 < s_m(x) = \frac{m^2 x^2}{\left(e^{\frac{mx^2}{3}}\right)^3} < \frac{m^2 x^2}{\left(\frac{mx^2}{3}\right)^3} = \frac{27}{mx^4} \to 0$$

as $m \to \infty$. The series

$$\sum_{n=1}^{\infty} f_n(x)$$

thus converges everywhere to

$$f(x) = 0.$$

We consider $\xi = 0$. $f(x)$ is continuous at 0.

If the series were uniformly convergent for $0 < x < p$ or for $-p < x < 0$ for some $p > 0$, then there would exist a $\mu \geq 1$ such that for $0 < x < p$ or $-p < x < 0$ respectively and for $m \geq \mu$ we would have

$$|s_m(x) - f(x)| = s_m(x) = m^2 x^2 e^{-mx^2} < e^{-1}.$$

Then $x = \dfrac{1}{\sqrt{m}}$ or $x = -\dfrac{1}{\sqrt{m}}$ would, for suitable $m \geq \mu$, be smaller than p or larger than $-p$, respectively. We would thus have

$$e^{-1} \leq me^{-1} = m^2 \frac{1}{m} e^{-\frac{m}{m}} < e^{-1}.$$

Theorem 233: *Let $a < b$. Let*

$$(1) \qquad \sum_{n=N}^{\infty} f_n(x)$$

converge for an $x = \eta$ such that $a < \eta < b$. Let

$$\sum_{n=N}^{\infty} f_n'(x)$$

converge uniformly for $a < x < b$ (which implicitly contains the hypothesis that every $f_n(x)$ is differentiable there). *Then* (1) *converges for $a < x < b$, and in fact uniformly. If we set*

$$\sum_{n=N}^{\infty} f_n(x) = f(x),$$

$$\sum_{n=N}^{\infty} f_n'(x) = g(x),$$

then $f(x)$ is differentiable for $a < x < b$ and we have

$$f'(x) = g(x).$$

Proof: (one of the most difficult of the book): Set

$$\sum_{n=u}^{v} f_n(x) = \varphi(x)$$

for $v \geqq u \geqq N$ and $a < x < b$. Then we have for $a < x < b$ that

$$\sum_{n=u}^{v} f_n'(x) = \varphi'(x).$$

By Theorem 159, if $h \neq 0$, $a < \xi < b$, $a < \xi + h < b$, then we have for a suitable y between ξ and $\xi + h$ that

$$\frac{\varphi(\xi + h) - \varphi(\xi)}{h} = \varphi'(y),$$

so that

$$(2) \qquad \sum_{n=u}^{v} \frac{f_n(\xi + h) - f_n(\xi)}{h} = \sum_{n=u}^{v} f_n'(y).$$

(y depends on u, v, ξ, h, but not on n.)

By Theorem 225, there exists for every $\delta > 0$ a $\mu \geqq N$ independent of y such that we have for $v \geqq u > \mu$ and for $a < y < b$ that

$$\left| \sum_{n=u}^{v} f_n'(y) \right| < \delta.$$

Hence by (2), we have for $v \geqq u > \mu$, $h \neq 0$, $a < \xi < b$, $a < \xi + h < b$. that

$$\left| \sum_{n=u}^{v} \frac{f_n(\xi + h) - f_n(\xi)}{h} \right| < \delta.$$

Thus, by Theorem 225,

$$(3) \qquad \sum_{n=N}^{\infty} \frac{f_n(\xi + h) - f_n(\xi)}{h}$$

converges uniformly in h for fixed ξ and $h \neq 0$, $a < \xi < b$, and $a < \xi + h < b$.

The convergence of this series implies that

$$(4) \qquad \sum_{n=N}^{\infty} \left(f_n(\xi + h) - f_n(\xi) \right)$$

converges for $a < \xi < b$, $a < \xi + h < b$. Since

$$(1) \qquad \sum_{n=N}^{\infty} f_n(x)$$

was assumed convergent for an x between a and b, (1) converges for all x between a and b.

Since (3) converges uniformly, and since

$$|h| < b - a,$$

we have, by Theorem 227 (with $g(h) = h$), that the series (4) converges uniformly for fixed ξ in $a < \xi < b$ and for $h \neq 0$, $a < \xi + h < b$. Therefore (1) converges uniformly for $a < x < b$.

Now for fixed ξ with $a < \xi < b$, and for $n \geqq N$, we set

$$\psi_n(h) = \begin{cases} \dfrac{f_n(\xi + h) - f_n(\xi)}{h} & \text{for } h \neq 0,\ a < \xi + h < b, \\[2mm] f_n'(\xi) & \text{for } h = 0. \end{cases}$$

Then $\psi_n(h)$ is continuous at $h = 0$. By what has been proved concerning (3) and by Theorem 226, we have that

$$(5) \qquad \sum_{n=N}^{\infty} \psi_n(h)$$

converges uniformly for $a - \xi < h < b - \xi$. By Theorem 231 (with $p = \text{Min}\,(b - \xi, \xi - a)$, and h in place of x), the function (5) is continuous at $h = 0$, so that

$$g(\xi) = \sum_{n=N}^{\infty} f_n'(\xi) = \sum_{n=N}^{\infty} \psi_n(0) = \lim_{h=0} \sum_{n=N}^{\infty} \psi_n(h)$$

$$= \lim_{h=0} \sum_{n=N}^{\infty} \frac{f_n(\xi + h) - f_n(\xi)}{h} = \lim_{h=0} \frac{f(\xi + h) - f(\xi)}{h} = f'(\xi).$$

Example: $\qquad\qquad f_n(x) = \dfrac{x^n}{n} \ \text{for } n \geq 1,$

$$a = -\Theta, \qquad b = \Theta,$$

where

$$0 < \Theta < 1.$$

$$\sum_{n=1}^{\infty} f_n(x)$$

converges at $x = 0$ (since every $f_n(0) = 0$).

$$\sum_{n=1}^{\infty} f_n'(x) = \sum_{n=1}^{\infty} x^{n-1}$$

converges uniformly for $a < x < b$, by Theorem 228 with

$$N = 1, \ p_n = \Theta^{n-1}.$$

Since

$$\sum_{n=1}^{\infty} f_n'(x) = \frac{1}{1-x},$$

we have by Theorem 233 that

$$\sum_{n=1}^{\infty} \frac{x^n}{n} = f(x)$$

converges for $a < x < b$ and that

$$f'(x) = \frac{1}{1-x}.$$

Since for every x with $|x| < 1$ we may choose a Θ with $|x| < \Theta < 1$, we have that

$$\sum_{n=1}^{\infty} \frac{x^n}{n}$$

converges for $|x| < 1$ and that

$$\left(\sum_{n=1}^{\infty} \frac{x^n}{n} \right)' = \frac{1}{1-x}.$$

Now, we have for $|x| < 1$ that

$$(- \log (1 - x))' = - \frac{1}{1-x} (-1) = \frac{1}{1-x}.$$

By Theorem 162 (to be applied for suitable a, b with $-1 < a < x < b < 1$), we have for $|x| < 1$ that

$$\sum_{n=1}^{\infty} \frac{x^n}{n} = - \log (1 - x) + c,$$

and $x = 0$ yields

$$0 = 0 + c,$$

$$c = 0,$$

$$\sum_{n=1}^{\infty} \frac{x^n}{n} = - \log (1 - x),$$

so that

$$\log (1 + x) = \sum_{n=1}^{\infty} \frac{(-1)^{n-1}}{n} x^n.$$

for $|x| < 1$, which was known to us in part from Theorem 184. (However, our present proof does not include the case $x = 1$.)

Theorem 234: *If $f(x)$ is continuous on $[a, b]$, then there exist entire rational functions $f_n(x)$ such that*

$$\sum_{n=1}^{\infty} f_n(x)$$

converges uniformly on $[a, b]$ and is equal to $f(x)$.

Proof: By Theorem 155, we choose for every $n > 0$ an entire rational function $P_n(x)$ with

$$|f(x) - P_n(x)| < \frac{1}{n} \quad \text{on } [a, b]$$

and we set

$$f_1(x) = P_1(x),$$

$$f_n(x) = P_n(x) - P_{n-1}(x) \quad \text{for } n > 1.$$

Then for every $\delta > 0$ we have for $m \geq \dfrac{1}{\delta}$ that

$$\left| \sum_{n=1}^{m} f_n(x) - f(x) \right| = |P_m(x) - f(x)| < \frac{1}{m} \leq \delta.$$

CHAPTER 14

POWER SERIES

Definition 57:
$$\sum_{n=0}^{\infty} c_n (x - a)^n,$$

where the c_n and a are fixed, is called (without regard to convergence) *a power series.*

This series must converge at $x = a$, since

$$c_n (x - a)^n = 0 \quad \text{for} \quad n \geqq 1.$$

We shall restrict ourselves to the case $a = 0$ until near the end of this chapter, when the corresponding theorems with arbitrary a will follow at one stroke from those with $a = 0$.

Theorem 235: *There exists a power series*

$$\sum_{n=0}^{\infty} c_n x^n$$

which converges only at $x = 0$.

Proof:
$$\sum_{n=0}^{\infty} n^n x^n$$

is of the required kind. For if the series were convergent for an $x \neq 0$, then we would have, by Theorem 204, that

$$\lim_{n=\infty} n^n x^n = 0;$$

but if $n > \dfrac{1}{|x|}$, we have

$$n \, |x| > 1,$$

$$|n^n x^n| > 1.$$

Theorem 236: *There exists a power series which converges for all x.*

Proof:
$$\sum_{n=0}^{\infty} \frac{x^n}{n!}$$

is of the required kind. For if $x \neq 0$ and $n \geqq 0$, we have that

$$\frac{\dfrac{x^{n+1}}{(n+1)!}}{\dfrac{x^n}{n!}} = \frac{x}{n+1} \to 0,$$

so that the convergence follows by Theorem 222 (with $N = 0$ and $\Theta = 0$).

Definition 58: *The sum of an everywhere convergent power series*

$$\sum_{n=0}^{\infty} c_n x^n$$

is called an entire function of x.

Example: Every entire rational function

$$\sum_{n=0}^{m} c_n x^n$$

is an entire function, since we may define

$$c_n = 0 \text{ for integral } n > m.$$

Theorem 237: *Let*

$$\xi \neq 0,$$

$$\sum_{n=0}^{\infty} c_n \xi^n \quad be \ convergent.$$

1) *Then*

(1)
$$\sum_{n=0}^{\infty} c_n x^n$$

converges absolutely for $|x| < |\xi|$.

2) *For every ϑ such that $0 \leqq \vartheta < 1$, (1) converges uniformly for $|x| \leqq \vartheta |\xi|$.*

Proof: It suffices to show that, for every ϑ such that $0 \leqq \vartheta < 1$, (1) is uniformly and absolutely convergent for $|x| \leqq \vartheta |\xi|$. For if we set

$$\vartheta = \left| \frac{y}{\xi} \right|,$$

then every fixed y such that $|y| < |\xi|$ belongs to the set of x for which $|x| \leqq \vartheta |\xi|$.

Since

$$\sum_{n=0}^{\infty} c_n \xi^n$$

converges, we have that, by Theorems 204 and 26,

$$|c_n \xi^n| < p,$$

where p is independent of n. Therefore if $|x| \leqq \vartheta |\xi|$, then

$$|c_n x^n| \leqq |c_n \xi^n| \vartheta^n \leqq p \vartheta^n,$$

and moreover

$$\sum_{n=0}^{\infty} p \vartheta^n$$

converges. From this follows the absolute convergence of the given series for $|x| \leqq \vartheta |\xi|$ and, by Theorem 228 (with $N = 0$, $p_n = p \vartheta^n$), so does its uniform convergence.

Theorem 238: *Let*

$$\sum_{n=0}^{\infty} c_n x^n$$

converge neither for $x = 0$ alone nor everywhere. Then there exists exactly one $r > 0$ such that the series

$$\text{converges for } |x| < r,$$

$$\text{diverges for } |x| > r.$$

Proof: 1) There is at most one such r. For if r_1 and r_2 were two such numbers and if $r_1 \neq r_2$, then the series would be both divergent and convergent at $\dfrac{r_1 + r_2}{2}$.

2) We place α in

Class I if $\alpha > 0$ and if the series converges at α, or if $\alpha \leqq 0$;

Class II if $\alpha > 0$ and if the series diverges at α.

There is a positive α in class I. For, by hypothesis, the series converges for some $\xi \neq 0$. The number $\alpha = \dfrac{|\xi|}{2}$, by Theorem 237, 1), is of the required kind.

There is an α in class II. For, by hypothesis, the series diverges for some $\eta \neq 0$. The number $\alpha = 2|\eta|$ is then of the required kind, by Theorem 237, 1).

If α is in class II and $\beta > \alpha$, then the series diverges at α, and therefore, by Theorem 237, 1), diverges at β. Hence β is in class II.

Therefore there exists an $r > 0$ such that every $\alpha < r$ is in class I, and every $\alpha > r$ is in class II.

If

$$|x| < r,$$

then

$$|x| < \frac{|x| + r}{2} < r.$$

$\dfrac{|x| + r}{2}$ is in class I, and the series converges at $\dfrac{|x| + r}{2}$, and hence, by Theorem 237, 1), at x.

If

$$|x| > r,$$

then

$$|x| > \frac{|x| + r}{2} > r.$$

$\dfrac{|x| + r}{2}$ is therefore in class II and the series diverges at $\dfrac{|x| + r}{2}$, and

therefore, by Theorem 237, 1), at x.

Examples: 1) $r = 1$ for the power series

$$\sum_{n=0}^{\infty} x^n.$$

For we know that it converges for $|x| < 1$ and that it diverges at 1, since 1^n does not approach 0. It also diverges at -1, since $(-1)^n$ does not approach 0.

2) For

$$\sum_{n=1}^{\infty} \frac{x^n}{n^2}$$

we also have $r = 1$. For, this series converges for $|x| \leqq 1$, since

$$\left| \frac{x^n}{n^2} \right| \leqq \frac{1}{n^2},$$

and diverges for $x > 1$ since we have, ultimately,

$$\frac{\dfrac{x^{n+1}}{(n+1)^2}}{\dfrac{x^n}{n^2}} = x \left(\frac{n}{n+1} \right)^2 > 1,$$

so that the (positive) terms ultimately increase. As already mentioned, the series converges at 1 and -1.

3) We know that the series

$$\sum_{n=1}^{\infty} \frac{x^n}{n}$$

is divergent at 1 and convergent at -1. From this it follows that $r = 1$.

4) The series

$$\sum_{n=1}^{\infty} \frac{(-1)^n}{n} x^n$$

converges at 1 and diverges at -1. Hence $r = 1$.

These four examples demonstrate that we cannot make a general statement about convergence or divergence at r or at $-r$. All four possibilities may occur.

Theorem 239: *Let* $R > 0$, *and let*

$$\sum_{n=0}^{\infty} c_n \, x^n$$

converge for $|x| < R$. *Then the series converges absolutely for* $|x| < R$ *and uniformly for* $|x| \leqq \vartheta R$ *for any* ϑ *such that* $0 \leqq \vartheta < 1$.

Proof: It suffices to show uniform and absolute convergence for $|x| \leqq \vartheta R$. The series converges at $\dfrac{1 + \vartheta}{2} R$, since

$$\left| \frac{1 + \vartheta}{2} R \right| < R ,$$

and so, by Theorem 237 (with $\dfrac{2\vartheta}{1 + \vartheta}$ for ϑ), uniformly and absolutely for

$$|x| \leqq \frac{2\vartheta}{1 + \vartheta} \; \frac{1 + \vartheta}{2} R = \vartheta R .$$

Theorem 240: *If*

$$f(x) = \sum_{n=0}^{\infty} c_n \, x^n$$

converges only at 0, *or is convergent everywhere, or if neither of these cases holds* (so that there exists an r in the sense of Theorem 238), *then the series*

$$g(x) = \sum_{n=0}^{\infty} (n + 1)c_{n+1} \, x^n$$

converges only at 0, *or converges everywhere, or belongs to the same* r, *respectively.*

Proof: It evidently suffices to show the following:

1) If $\xi \neq 0$ and if the first series converges at ξ, then the second converges for $|x| < |\xi|$.

2) If $\xi \neq 0$ and if the second series converges at ξ, then the first converges for $|x| < |\xi|$.

This suffices for the following reasons:

a) If the f-series converges only at 0, then by 2), the g-series converges only at 0.

b) If the f-series converges everywhere, then by 1), the g-series converges everywhere.

c) If the f-series belongs to r, then the g-series converges, by 1), for $|x| < r \left(\text{setting } \xi = \dfrac{|x| + r}{2} \right)$ and diverges, by 2), for $|x| > r \left(\text{setting } \xi = \dfrac{|x| + r}{2} \right).$

As regards 1):
$$\left|\, c_{n+1}\, \xi^{n+1}\,\right| < g\,,$$

$$\left|\, c_{n+1}\,\right|\left|\,\xi\,\right|^n < \frac{g}{\left|\,\xi\,\right|} = g_1\,,$$

$$\left|\,(n+1)c_{n+1}\, x^n\,\right| = (n+1)\left|\, c_{n+1}\,\right|\left|\,\xi\,\right|^n\left|\,\frac{x}{\xi}\,\right|^n \leq (n+1)g_1\left|\,\frac{x}{\xi}\,\right|^n.$$

The series

$$\sum_{n=0}^{\infty} (n+1)\left|\,\frac{x}{\xi}\,\right|^n$$

converges for $\left|\, x\,\right| < \left|\,\xi\,\right|$, by the example to Theorem 220. Therefore, so does

$$\sum_{n=0}^{\infty} (n+1)c_{n+1}\, x^n.$$

As regards 2): $\left|\,(n+1)c_{n+1}\xi^n\,\right| < k$ for $n \geqq 0$,

and therefore, for $n \geqq 1$,

$$\left|\, c_n x^n\,\right| = \left|\,\xi\,\right|\left|\, c_n\,\xi^{n-1}\,\right|\left|\,\frac{x}{\xi}\,\right|^n \leqq \left|\,\xi\,\right| k\left|\,\frac{x}{\xi}\,\right|^n.$$

The series

$$\sum_{n=1}^{\infty} \left|\,\frac{x}{\xi}\,\right|^n$$

converges, and hence so does the series

$$\sum_{n=0}^{\infty} c_n\, x^n.$$

Theorem 241: *If*

$$f(x) = \sum_{n=0}^{\infty} c_n\, x^n$$

is everywhere convergent (or if there is an r in the sense of Theorem 238), then $f(x)$ is differentiable (and thus continuous) everywhere (or for $\left|\, x\,\right| < r$), and

$$f'(x) = \sum_{n=0}^{\infty} (n+1)c_{n+1}\, x^n.$$

Proof: Let ξ be arbitrary (or let $\left|\,\xi\,\right| < r$). Then we set $\eta = \left|\,\xi\,\right| + 1$ (or $\eta = \dfrac{\left|\,\xi\,\right| + r}{2}$). By Theorems 240 and 239,

$$\sum_{n=0}^{\infty} (n+1)c_{n+1}\, x^n$$

converges uniformly for $\left|\, x\,\right| < \eta$. The assertion at $x = \xi$ thus follows from Theorem 233, since

$$(c_{n+1}\, x^{n+1})' = (n+1)c_{n+1}\, x^n.$$

Theorem 242: *If* $R > 0$ *and if*

$$\sum_{n=0}^{\infty} a_n x^n = \sum_{n=0}^{\infty} b_n x^n \text{ for } |x| < R,$$

then

$$a_n = b_n \text{ for } n \geq 0.$$

Proof: Otherwise, let m be the smallest n such that

$$a_n \neq b_n.$$

Then we would have for $|x| < R$ that

$$0 = \sum_{n=0}^{\infty} (a_n - b_n)x^n = \sum_{n=m}^{\infty} (a_n - b_n)x^n = \sum_{n=0}^{\infty} (a_{n+m} - b_{n+m})x^{n+m},$$

and therefore, for $0 < |x| < R$,

$$0 = \sum_{n=0}^{\infty} (a_{n+m} - b_{n+m})x^n.$$

If

$$\sum_{n=0}^{\infty} (a_{n+m} - b_{n+m})x^n$$

belongs to an r in the sense of Theorem 238, then $R \leq r$. Otherwise, this series converges everywhere. In any case, by Theorem 241 (continuity), we would have

$$a_m - b_m = \lim_{x=0} \sum_{n=0}^{\infty} (a_{n+m} - b_{n+m})x^n = \lim_{x=0} 0 = 0.$$

Theorem 243 (Abel's continuity theorem): *Let* $\xi > 0$ *(or* $\xi < 0$*) and let*

$$\sum_{n=0}^{\infty} c_n \xi^n$$

converge. If we set

$$f(x) = \sum_{n=0}^{\infty} c_n x^n \text{ for } |x| < \xi \text{ and } x = \xi,$$

then $f(x)$ *is continuous at* ξ *on the left (or on the right).*

Preliminary Remarks: 1) Do we not yet have this result? If the power series converges everywhere, then we do, by Theorem 241 (continuity). If there corresponds to the power series an r in the sense of Theorem 238 (in this case we must have $|r| \geq |\xi|$), then we do if $r > |\xi|$; we do not if $r = |\xi|$. But this last case is the important one here.

2) From Theorem 243 we learn once more that

$$\log(1 + x) = \sum_{n=1}^{\infty} \frac{(-1)^{n-1}}{n} x^n$$

not only for $|x| < 1$, but also, as a consequence, for $x = 1$. Cf. the example to Theorem 233, where the case $x = 1$ had to be omitted.

Proof: W.l.g. let $\xi > 0$, for otherwise consider

$$f(-x) = \sum_{n=0}^{\infty} (-1)^n c_n x^n.$$

W.l.g. let $\xi = 1$, for otherwise consider

$$f(\xi x) = \sum_{n=0}^{\infty} c_n \xi^n x^n.$$

W.l.g. let

$$\sum_{n=0}^{\infty} c_n = 0;$$

for otherwise consider

$$f(x) - f(1) = (c_0 - f(1)) + \sum_{n=1}^{\infty} c_n x^n.$$

By Theorem 230, it suffices to prove the uniform convergence of

$$\sum_{n=0}^{\infty} c_n x^n$$

for $0 < x < 1$. Setting

$$s_m = \sum_{n=0}^{m} c_n \text{ for integral } m \geqq 0,$$

we obtain, for integral u, v, with $v \geqq u \geqq 1$, that

$$\sum_{n=u}^{v} c_n x^n = \sum_{n=u}^{v} (s_n - s_{n-1}) x^n = \sum_{n=u}^{v} s_n x^n - \sum_{n=u}^{v} s_{n-1} x^n$$

$$= \sum_{n=u}^{v} s_n x^n - \sum_{n=u-1}^{v-1} s_n x^{n+1} = -s_{u-1} x^u + \sum_{n=u}^{v} s_n (x^n - x^{n+1}) + s_v x^{v+1}$$

$$= (1 - x) \sum_{n=u}^{v} s_n x^n - s_{u-1} x^u + s_v x^{v+1}.$$

Let $\delta > 0$ be given. Since

$$s_m \to 0,$$

there exists an integral $\mu \geqq 0$ such that

$$|s_n| < \frac{\delta}{2} \text{ for } n \geqq \mu.$$

Therefore, for $0 < x < 1$ and for integral u, v such that $v \geqq u > \mu$, we have

$$\left| \sum_{n=u}^{v} c_n x^n \right| < (1 - x) \frac{\delta}{2} \sum_{n=u}^{v} x^n + \frac{\delta}{2} x^u + \frac{\delta}{2} x^{v+1}$$

$$= \frac{\delta}{2} (x^u - x^{v+1}) + \frac{\delta}{2} x^u + \frac{\delta}{2} x^{v+1} = \delta x^u < \delta,$$

so that

$$\sum_{n=0}^{\infty} c_n x^n$$

is, by Theorem 225, uniformly convergent for $0 < x < 1$.

Theorem 244: *If* $R > 0$ *and if*

$$f(x) = \sum_{n=0}^{\infty} c_n x^n \text{ for } |x| < R,$$

then for every integral $m \geq 0$ *and for* $|x| < R$, *we have*

$$f^{(m)}(x) = \sum_{n=m}^{\infty} c_n m! \binom{n}{m} x^{n-m},$$

and, in particular,

$$c_m = \frac{f^{(m)}(0)}{m!}.$$

Proof: $m = 0$: Obvious. To proceed from m to $m + 1$: By Theorem 241, we have

$$\left(\sum_{n=m}^{\infty} c_n m! \binom{n}{m} x^{n-m} \right)' = \left(\sum_{k=0}^{\infty} c_{k+m} m! \binom{k+m}{m} x^k \right)'$$

$$= \sum_{k=0}^{\infty} c_{k+m+1} m! \binom{k+m+1}{m} (k+1) x^k = \sum_{n=m+1}^{\infty} c_n m! \binom{n}{m} (n-m) x^{n-m-1}$$

$$= \sum_{n=m+1}^{\infty} c_n (m+1)! \binom{n}{m+1} x^{n-(m+1)}.$$

By the trivial transformation

$$x = y - a,$$

the preceding theorems imply

Theorem 245: *Let*

$$\sum_{n=0}^{\infty} c_n (x-a)^n$$

converge, and not only at $x = a$. *Then either the series is everywhere convergent, or there exists exactly one* $r > 0$ *such that the series*

converges for $|x-a| < r$,

diverges for $|x-a| > r$.

The series is absolutely convergent everywhere, or for $|x-a| < r$, *respectively. The series is uniformly convergent for* $|x-a| \leq \varrho$ *for every* $\varrho \geq 0$, *or for any* ϱ *such that* $0 \leq \varrho < r$, *respectively.*

If $f(x)$ is the sum of the series, then it is arbitrarily often differentiable everywhere, or for $|x - a| < r$ respectively. Moreover (m an integer $\geqq 0$),

$$f^{(m)}(x) = \sum_{n=m}^{\infty} c_n \, m! \binom{n}{m} (x - a)^{n-m},$$

so that, in particular,

$$c_m = \frac{f^{(m)}(a)}{m!},$$

$$f(x) = \sum_{n=0}^{\infty} \frac{f^{(n)}(a)}{n!} (x - a)^n.$$

(Can this be [cf. Theorem 185] ? Yes, if we already know that $f(x)$ is a power series.)

If there is an $r > 0$ in the above sense, and if the given series converges at $a - r$ (or at $a + r$), then the sum of the series is continuous on the right (or on the left).

CHAPTER 15

THE EXPONENTIAL AND BINOMIAL SERIES

Theorem 246:
$$e^x = \sum_{n=0}^{\infty} \frac{x^n}{n!}.$$

Preliminary Remark: The series on the right is called the exponential series.

Proof: By the proof of Theorem 236, we know that the power series $f(x)$ on the right is convergent everywhere. By Theorem 241, we have

$$f'(x) = \sum_{n=0}^{\infty} (n+1) \frac{1}{(n+1)!} x^n = \sum_{n=0}^{\infty} \frac{x^n}{n!} = f(x),$$

everywhere, so that

$$\left(e^{-x} f(x)\right)' = - e^{-x} f(x) + e^{-x} f'(x) = 0,$$

so that we have by Theorem 163 that

$$e^{-x} f(x) = e^{-0} f(0) = 1 \cdot 1 = 1,$$

$$f(x) = e^x.$$

Theorem 247: *For $|x| < 1$ and for every α, we have*

$$(1 + x)^\alpha = \sum_{n=0}^{\infty} \binom{\alpha}{n} x^n.$$

Preliminary Remark: The series on the right is called the binomial series.

Proof: 1) The series on the right converges, since for integral $\alpha \geqq 0$ we have that, ultimately (for $n > \alpha$),

$$\binom{\alpha}{n} = 0,$$

and for the other α, if w.l.g. $x \neq 0$, that

$$\frac{\binom{\alpha}{n+1} x^{n+1}}{\binom{\alpha}{n} x^n} = \frac{\alpha - n}{n+1} x = \frac{\frac{\alpha}{n} - 1}{1 + \frac{1}{n}} x \to - x,$$

so that the series converges, by Theorem 222, since $|x| < 1$.

2) For $|x| < 1$, I set

$$f(x) = (1 + x)^\alpha,$$

$$g(x) = \sum_{n=0}^{\infty} \binom{\alpha}{n} x^n$$

and must prove that

$$f(x) = g(x).$$

By Theorem 241, we have

$$g'(x) = \sum_{n=0}^{\infty} \binom{\alpha}{n+1} (n+1)x^n = \alpha \sum_{n=0}^{\infty} \binom{\alpha-1}{n} x^n,$$

$$(1 + x)g'(x) = \alpha \left(\sum_{n=0}^{\infty} \binom{\alpha-1}{n} x^n + \sum_{n=0}^{\infty} \binom{\alpha-1}{n} x^{n+1} \right)$$

$$= \alpha \left(1 + \sum_{n=1}^{\infty} \binom{\alpha-1}{n} x^n + \sum_{n=1}^{\infty} \binom{\alpha-1}{n-1} x^n \right)$$

$$= \alpha \left(1 + \sum_{n=1}^{\infty} \binom{\alpha}{n} x^n \right) = \alpha g(x).$$

On the other hand, we have

$$f'(x) = \alpha(1 + x)^{\alpha-1},$$

$$(1 + x)f'(x) = \alpha (1 + x)^\alpha = \alpha f(x).$$

Thus we have

$$(1 + x)g(x)f'(x) = \alpha g(x)f(x) = (1 + x)f(x)g'(x),$$

$$g(x)f'(x) = f(x)g'(x),$$

$$f(x) \neq 0,$$

so that

$$\left(\frac{g(x)}{f(x)} \right)' = \frac{f(x)g'(x) - g(x)f'(x)}{f^2(x)} = 0,$$

so that, by Theorem 163,

$$\frac{g(x)}{f(x)} = \frac{g(0)}{f(0)} = \frac{1}{1} = 1,$$

$$f(x) = g(x).$$

CHAPTER 16

THE TRIGONOMETRIC FUNCTIONS

We shall consider four functions, called sine, cosine, tangent, and cotangent.

Theorem 248: $$\sum_{m=0}^{\infty} \frac{(-1)^m}{(2m+1)!} x^{2m+1}$$

converges everywhere, and is therefore an integral function

$$\sum_{n=0}^{\infty} c_n x^n$$

with

$$c_n = \begin{cases} \dfrac{(-1)^{\frac{n-1}{2}}}{n!} & \text{for odd } n \geqq 0, \\ 0 & \text{for even } n \geqq 0. \end{cases}$$

Proof: $$\left| c_n x^n \right| \leqq \frac{|x|^n}{n!},$$

so that

$$\sum_{n=0}^{\infty} \frac{|x|^n}{n!}$$

converges.

Definition 59: $\quad \sin x = \sum_{m=0}^{\infty} \dfrac{(-1)^m}{(2m+1)!} x^{2m+1}.$

sin is to be read "sine."

Theorem 249: $\quad \sin(-x) = -\sin x.$

Proof: Definition 59.

Theorem 250: $\quad \sin 0 = 0.$

Proof: Definition 59.

Theorem 251: $$\sum_{m=0}^{\infty} \frac{(-1)^m}{(2m)!} x^{2m}$$

converges everywhere, and is therefore an integral function

$$\sum_{n=0}^{\infty} c_n x^n$$

with

$$c_n = \begin{cases} \dfrac{(-1)^{\frac{n}{2}}}{n!} & \text{for even } n \geq 0, \\[2mm] 0 & \text{for odd } n \geq 0. \end{cases}$$

Proof: As that of Theorem 248.

Definition 60: $\qquad \cos x = \sum\limits_{m=0}^{\infty} \dfrac{(-1)^m}{(2m)!} x^{2m}.$

cos is to be read "cosine."

Theorem 252: $\qquad \cos(-x) = \cos x.$

Proof: Definition 60.

Theorem 253: $\qquad \cos 0 = 1.$

Proof: Definition 60.

Theorem 254: $\qquad \dfrac{d \sin x}{dx} = \cos x.$

Proof: By Theorem 241, we may differentiate an everywhere convergent power series term by term. We have

$$\left(\frac{(-1)^m}{(2m+1)!} x^{2m+1}\right)' = \frac{(-1)^m}{(2m+1)!}(2m+1)x^{2m} = \frac{(-1)^m}{(2m)!} x^{2m}.$$

Theorem 255: $\qquad \dfrac{d \cos x}{dx} = -\sin x.$

Proof: $\qquad \cos x = 1 + \sum\limits_{m=0}^{\infty} \dfrac{(-1)^{m+1}}{(2m+2)!} x^{2m+2}.$

By Theorem 241, we may differentiate term by term. We have

$$\left(\frac{(-1)^{m+1}}{(2m+2)!} x^{2m+2}\right)' = \frac{(-1)^{m+1}}{(2m+2)!}(2m+2)x^{2m+1} = -\frac{(-1)^m}{(2m+1)!} x^{2m+1}.$$

Theorem 256: $\sin(x+y) = \sin x \cos y + \cos x \sin y,$

$\qquad\qquad\qquad \cos(x+y) = \cos x \cos y - \sin x \sin y.$

Proof: For fixed y, we set

$$f(x) = \sin(x+y) - \sin x \cos y - \cos x \sin y,$$

$$g(x) = \cos(x+y) - \cos x \cos y + \sin x \sin y.$$

Then, by Theorems 254 and 255, we have that

$$f'(x) = \cos (x + y) - \cos x \cos y + \sin x \sin y = g(x),$$

$$g'(x) = - \sin (x + y) + \sin x \cos y + \cos x \sin y = -f(x),$$

$$\left(f^2(x) + g^2(x)\right)' = 2f(x)f'(x) + 2g(x)g'(x) = 2f(x)g(x) - 2g(x)f(x) = 0,$$

so that, by Theorem 163,

$$f^2(x) + g^2(x) = f^2(0) + g^2(0) = (\sin y - \sin y)^2 + (\cos y - \cos y)^2 = 0,$$

$$f(x) = g(x) = 0.$$

Theorem 257: $\qquad \sin 2x = 2 \sin x \cos x.$

Proof: $\qquad \sin 2x = \sin (x + x) = \sin x \cos x + \cos x \sin x$

$$= 2 \sin x \cos x.$$

Theorem 258: $\qquad \sin^2 x + \cos^2 x = 1.$

Proof: $\quad 1 = \cos 0 = \cos (x - x) = \cos x \cos (- x) - \sin x \sin (-x)$

$$= \cos^2 x + \sin^2 x.$$

Theorem 259: $\qquad \cos 2x = 2 \cos^2 x - 1.$

Proof: $\qquad \cos 2x = \cos (x+x) = \cos x \cos x - \sin x \sin x$

$$= \cos^2 x - \sin^2 x = \cos^2 x - (1 - \cos^2 x) = 2\cos^2 x - 1.$$

Theorem 260: $\qquad | \sin x | \leqq 1.$
Proof: Theorem 258.
Theorem 261: $\qquad | \cos x | \leqq 1.$
Proof: Theorem 258.
Theorem 262: *There exists exactly one $\pi > 0$ such that*

$$\cos \frac{\pi}{2} = 0,$$

$$\cos x > 0 \ \textit{for} \ 0 \leqq x < \frac{\pi}{2}.$$

In other words,

$$\cos y = 0$$

has a positive solution, and in fact a smallest one.

Proof: 1) It is obvious that there is at most one such π.
2) By Theorem 159 (with

$$f(x) = \sin x, a = 0, b = 2)$$

and Theorem 254, there exists a ξ such that

$$0 < \xi < 2, \quad \frac{\sin 2 - \sin 0}{2} = \cos \xi \,;$$

by Theorems 250 and 260, we have that

$$|\cos \xi| = \frac{|\sin 2|}{2} \leqq \frac{1}{2} \,;$$

so that if we set

$$2\xi = b,$$

then we have by Theorem 259 that

$$\cos b = 2 \cos^2 \xi - 1 \leqq 2 \cdot \frac{1}{4} - 1 = -\frac{1}{2} < 0 \,.$$

By Theorem 149 (with

$$f(x) = \cos x, \quad a = 0)$$

there exists a $\pi > 0$ such that

$$\cos \frac{\pi}{2} = 0 \,,$$

$$\cos x > 0 \text{ for } 0 \leqq x < \frac{\pi}{2} \,.$$

Definition 61: *The "universal constant" of Theorem 262 will be denoted henceforth by π.*

Theorem 263: $\qquad \sin \dfrac{\pi}{2} = 1 \,.$

Proof: By Theorems 258 and 262, we have

$$\sin^2 \frac{\pi}{2} = 1 - \cos^2 \frac{\pi}{2} = 1 \,,$$

$$\sin \frac{\pi}{2} = 1 \text{ or } -1 \,.$$

The first equality holds, since by Theorems 159, 254, and 262, we have for a suitable ξ that

$$0 < \xi < \frac{\pi}{2}, \quad \sin \frac{\pi}{2} = \sin \frac{\pi}{2} - \sin 0 = \frac{\pi}{2} \cos \xi > 0 \,.$$

Theorem 264: $\qquad \cos \dfrac{\pi}{4} = \dfrac{1}{\sqrt{2}} \,.$

Proof: By Theorem 259, we have

$$0 = \cos \frac{\pi}{2} = 2 \cos^2 \frac{\pi}{4} - 1 \,,$$

$$\cos^2 \frac{\pi}{4} = \tfrac{1}{2} \,;$$

and since

$$\cos \frac{\pi}{4} > 0,$$

we therefore have

$$\cos \frac{\pi}{4} = \frac{1}{\sqrt{2}}.$$

Theorem 265: $\qquad \sin \frac{\pi}{4} = \frac{1}{\sqrt{2}}.$

Proof: By Theorems 263, 257, and 264, we have

$$1 = \sin \frac{\pi}{2} = 2 \sin \frac{\pi}{4} \cos \frac{\pi}{4} = \sqrt{2} \sin \frac{\pi}{4}.$$

Theorem 266: $\qquad \cos \pi = -1.$

Proof: $\qquad \cos \pi = 2 \cos^2 \frac{\pi}{2} - 1 = -1.$

Theorem 267: $\qquad \sin \pi = 0.$

Proof: $\qquad \sin \pi = 2 \sin \frac{\pi}{2} \cos \frac{\pi}{2} = 0.$

Theorem 268: $\qquad \cos 2\pi = 1.$

Proof: $\qquad \cos 2\pi = 2 \cos^2 \pi - 1 = 1.$

Theorem 269: $\qquad \sin 2\pi = 0.$

Proof: $\qquad \sin 2\pi = 2 \sin \pi \cos \pi = 0.$

Theorem 270: $\qquad \sin \left(\frac{\pi}{2} - x \right) = \cos x.$

Proof: $\qquad \sin \left(\frac{\pi}{2} - x \right) = \sin \frac{\pi}{2} \cos x + \cos \frac{\pi}{2} \sin (-x).$

Theorem 271: $\qquad \sin (\pi - x) = \sin x.$

Proof: $\qquad \sin (\pi - x) = \sin \pi \cos x + \cos \pi \sin (-x).$

Theorem 272: $\qquad \cos (\pi - x) = -\cos x.$

Proof: $\qquad \cos (\pi - x) = \cos \pi \cos x - \sin \pi \sin (-x).$

Theorem 273: $\qquad \sin (x + 2\pi) = \sin x.$

In other words, "sin x has the period 2π."

Proof: $\quad \sin (x + 2\pi) = \sin x \cos 2\pi + \cos x \sin 2\pi$.

Theorem 274: *For $0 < x < \pi$ and for $\pi < x < 2\pi$, we have that*

$$\sin x \neq 0.$$

Proof: We have that

$$\sin 0 = \sin \pi = 0.$$

If there existed a ξ such that

$$0 < \xi < \pi, \ \sin \xi = 0,$$

then by Theorem 156, there would exist a ξ_1 and a ξ_2 such that

$$0 < \xi_1 < \xi < \xi_2 < \pi, \ \cos \xi_1 = \cos \xi_2 = 0.$$

One of the numbers ξ_1 or ξ_2 would be $\neq \dfrac{\pi}{2}$. However, we have by Theorem 262 that

$$\cos x \neq 0 \ \text{ for } \ 0 < x < \frac{\pi}{2},$$

so that, by Theorem 272,

$$\cos x = - \cos (\pi - x) \neq 0 \ \text{ for } \ \frac{\pi}{2} < x < \pi.$$

Hence we have for $0 < x < \pi$ that

$$\sin x \neq 0;$$

and for $\pi < x < 2\pi$ that

$$\sin x = \sin (\pi - x) = - \sin (x - \pi) \neq 0.$$

Theorem 275: *The equation*

$$\sin (x + c) = \sin x$$

holds for all x if and only if

$$c = 2n\pi, \ n \ \text{an integer.}$$

Proof: 1) Let n be an integer.

$$\sin (x + 2n\pi) = \sin x$$

is obvious for $n = 0$ and follows for $n \geqq 0$ by proceeding from n to $n + 1$ since

$$\sin \left(x + 2(n + 1)\pi\right) = \sin \left((x + 2n\pi) + 2\pi\right) = \sin (x + 2n\pi)$$

by Theorem 273. Hence we have for $n < 0$ that

$$\sin (x + 2n\pi) = \sin (x + 2n\pi + 2 \left| n \right| \pi) = \sin x.$$

2) It suffices to show that

(1) $$\sin (x + c) = \sin x, 0 \leqq c < 2\pi,$$

is an identify in x only for $c = 0$. This suffices, for if (1) is true, then, by 1),

$$\sin \left(x + c - 2\pi \left[\frac{c}{2\pi}\right]\right) = \sin x,$$

and if $\dfrac{c}{2\pi}$ is not an integer, we have

$$c - 2\pi \left[\dfrac{c}{2\pi}\right] \begin{cases} > c - 2\pi\,\dfrac{c}{2\pi} = 0, \\[2mm] < c - 2\pi\left(\dfrac{c}{2\pi} - 1\right) = 2\pi. \end{cases}$$

Substituting $x = 0$ in (1) gives

$$\sin c = 0, \quad 0 \leqq c < 2\pi.$$

By Theorem 274,

$$c = 0 \ \text{ or } \ c = \pi.$$

But we cannot have $c = \pi$, for if we substitute $x = -\dfrac{\pi}{2}$ in (1), then

$$1 = \sin \dfrac{\pi}{2} = \sin (x + c) = \sin x = -\sin \dfrac{\pi}{2} = -1$$

would be true.

Theorem 276: $\qquad \cos (x + 2\pi) = \cos x.$

In other words, "cos x has the period 2π."

Proof: $\qquad \cos (x + 2\pi) = \cos x \cos 2\pi - \sin x \sin 2\pi.$

Theorem 277: *The equation*

$$\cos (x + c) = \cos x$$

holds for all x if and only if

$$c = 2n\pi, \ n \ \text{an integer.}$$

Proof: By Theorem 270, the first of the above equations is equivalent to

$$\sin \left(\dfrac{\pi}{2} - x - c\right) = \sin \left(\dfrac{\pi}{2} - x\right)$$

for all x, or, setting

$$\dfrac{\pi}{2} - x - c = y,$$

to

$$\sin y = \sin (y + c)$$

for all y. Hence Theorem 277 follows from Theorem 275.

Theorem 278: *If m is an integer, and if*

$$2m\pi - \dfrac{\pi}{2} \leqq x < y \leqq 2m\pi + \dfrac{\pi}{2},$$

then

$$\sin x < \sin y.$$

Proof: We have for $2m\pi - \dfrac{\pi}{2} < z < 2m\pi + \dfrac{\pi}{2}$ that

$$\cos z = \cos (z - 2m\pi) > 0.$$

By Theorem 159, there exists a ξ such that

$$x < \xi < y, \quad \sin y - \sin x = (y - x) \cos \xi > 0.$$

Theorem 279: $\qquad\qquad \sin x = 0$

holds for the numbers

$$x = n\pi, \ n \ \text{an integer,}$$

and only for these numbers.

Proof: Theorem 274 and

$$\sin (x + 2n\pi) = \sin x \ \text{ for integral } n.$$

Theorem 280: $\qquad\qquad \cos x = 0$

holds for the numbers

$$x = (n + \tfrac{1}{2})\pi, \ n \ \text{an integer,}$$

and only for these numbers.

Proof: $\qquad \cos \left(x - \dfrac{\pi}{2} \right) = \cos \left(\dfrac{\pi}{2} - x \right) = \sin x \ ;$

hence Theorem 279 proves our assertion.

Theorem 281: *If n is an integer, then*

$$\cos n\pi = (-1)^n.$$

Proof: $n = 0$ follows from

$$\cos n\pi = \cos 0 = 1 = (-1)^n.$$

$n + 1$ follows from n, since

$$\cos (n + 1)\pi = \cos (n\pi + \pi) = \cos n\pi \cos \pi - \sin n\pi \sin \pi$$

$$= - (-1)^n = (-1)^{n+1}.$$

This proves Theorem 281 for $n \geqq 0$. The theorem follows for $n < 0$ since

$$\cos n\pi = \cos \big((-n)\pi\big) = (-1)^{-n} = (-1)^n.$$

Definition 62: $\qquad \displaystyle\prod_{n=1}^{\infty} a_n = \lim_{m=\infty} \ \prod_{n=1}^{m} a_n \ ,$

if this limit exists. We then call

$$\prod_{n=1}^{\infty} a_n$$

a convergent infinite product.

Examples: 1) If one $a_n = 0$ and if the others are arbitrary, then we have that, ultimately,

$$\prod_{n=1}^{m} a_n = 0 ,$$

so that

$$\prod_{n=1}^{\infty} a_n = 0 .$$

2) If all $a_n = \frac{1}{2}$, then we have

$$\prod_{n=1}^{\infty} a_n = \lim_{m=\infty} \left(\tfrac{1}{2}\right)^m = 0 .$$

Theorem 282: *If*

$$a_n > 0$$

for all integers $n \geq 1$, *then*

$$\sum_{n=1}^{\infty} \log a_n = b$$

converges if and only if

$$\prod_{n=1}^{\infty} a_n = a$$

converges and if

$$a > 0.$$

Moreover, we then have

$$b = \log a.$$

Proof: 1) Let

$$\prod_{n=1}^{m} a_n \to a, \quad a > 0 .$$

Since $\log y$ is continuous for $y > 0$, we have

$$\sum_{n=1}^{m} \log a_n = \log \prod_{n=1}^{m} a_n \to \log a.$$

2) Let

$$\sum_{n=1}^{m} \log a_n \to b.$$

Since e^y is continuous for all y, we have

$$\prod_{n=1}^{m} a_n = e^{\sum_{n=1}^{m} \log a_n} \to e^b,$$

$$e^b > 0.$$

Theorem 283: *We have for all x that*

$$\sin \pi x = \pi x \prod_{n=1}^{\infty} \left(1 - \frac{x^2}{n^2}\right) ;$$

hence, for all x, that

$$\sin x = x \prod_{n=1}^{\infty} \left(1 - \frac{x^2}{\pi^2 n^2}\right) .$$

Proof: The power series

$$g(x) = \sum_{\nu=1}^{\infty} \left(\frac{x^{2\nu}}{\nu} \sum_{n=1}^{\infty} \frac{1}{n^{2\nu}}\right)$$

converges for $|x| < 1$, since

$$\frac{1}{\nu} \sum_{n=1}^{\infty} \frac{1}{n^{2\nu}} \leq \sum_{n=1}^{\infty} \frac{1}{n^2} .$$

Hence $g'(x)$ exists and is continuous for $|x| < 1$. Furthermore, by Theorem 219, we have for $|x| < 1$ that

$$g(x) = \sum_{\nu=1}^{\infty} \sum_{n=1}^{\infty} \frac{x^{2\nu}}{\nu} \frac{1}{n^{2\nu}} = \sum_{n=1}^{\infty} \sum_{\nu=1}^{\infty} \frac{x^{2\nu}}{\nu} \frac{1}{n^{2\nu}}$$

$$= \sum_{n=1}^{\infty} \sum_{\nu=1}^{\infty} \frac{1}{\nu} \left(\frac{x^2}{n^2}\right)^{\nu} ,$$

so that, by the example to Theorem 233,

$$- g(x) = \sum_{n=1}^{\infty} \log \left(1 - \frac{x^2}{n^2}\right) ;$$

and so we have by Theorem 282 that

$$e^{-g(x)} = \prod_{n=1}^{\infty} \left(1 - \frac{x^2}{n^2}\right).$$

If for all x for which the product converges we set

$$\prod_{n=1}^{\infty} \left(1 - \frac{x^2}{n^2}\right) = F(x) ,$$

then $F(x)$ exists for $|x| < 1$, and here we have

$$F(x) = e^{-g(x)} > 0,$$
$$F'(x) = - g'(x)e^{-g(x)},$$

so that $F'(x)$ is continuous.

We now show that $F(x)$ converges for all x, and that if we set

$$f(x) = \pi x F(x),$$

then we have

(1) $$f(x + 1) = - f(x).$$

This is obvious for integral x, since x or some $1 - \dfrac{x^2}{n^2}$ is 0, as are also $x + 1$ or some $1 - \left(\dfrac{x+1}{n}\right)^2$. Since we know the convergence for $|x| < 1$, it suffices to show that, for non-integral x, convergence for x implies convergence for $x + 1$ and (1), and that convergence for $x + 1$ implies convergence for x. All of this will be established if we can show that

$$\lim_{m=\infty} \frac{(x+1) \displaystyle\prod_{\substack{n=-m \\ n \neq 0}}^{m} \left(1 + \frac{x+1}{n}\right)}{x \displaystyle\prod_{\substack{n=-m \\ n \neq 0}}^{m} \left(1 + \frac{x}{n}\right)} = -1.$$

Now, the expression following the limit sign is equal to

$$\frac{\displaystyle\prod_{n=-m}^{m} (n+1+x)}{\displaystyle\prod_{n=-m}^{m} (n+x)} = \frac{\displaystyle\prod_{n=-m+1}^{m+1} (n+x)}{\displaystyle\prod_{n=-m}^{m} (n+x)} = \frac{m+1+x}{-m+x} \to -1.$$

Thus the above assertions are proved.

We now show that

$$(2) \qquad\qquad f(x)f(x + \tfrac{1}{2}) = \tfrac{1}{2} f(\tfrac{1}{2}) f(2x).$$

In fact, we have

$$f(x)f(x+\tfrac{1}{2}) = \pi^2 x(x + \tfrac{1}{2}) \lim_{m=\infty} \prod_{\substack{n=-m \\ n\neq 0}}^{m} \left(1 + \frac{x}{n}\right)\left(1 + \frac{x + \frac{1}{2}}{n}\right)$$

$$= \pi^2 x(x + \tfrac{1}{2}) \lim_{m=\infty} \prod_{\substack{n=-m \\ n\neq 0}}^{m} \frac{2x+2n}{2n} \cdot \frac{2x+2n+1}{2n+1} \cdot \frac{2n+1}{2n}$$

$$= \pi^2 x(x + \tfrac{1}{2}) \lim_{m=\infty} \left(\prod_{\substack{n=-2m \\ n\neq 0,\, n\neq 1}}^{2m+1} \frac{2x+n}{n} \cdot \prod_{\substack{n=-m \\ n\neq 0}}^{m} \frac{2n+1}{2n} \right)$$

$$= \tfrac{1}{2}\pi \cdot 2x \lim_{m=\infty} \left(\prod_{\substack{n=-2m \\ n\neq 0}}^{2m+1} \left(1 + \frac{2x}{n}\right) \cdot \pi \cdot \tfrac{1}{2} \prod_{\substack{n=-m \\ n\neq 0}}^{m} \left(1 + \frac{\frac{1}{2}}{n}\right) \right)$$

$$= \tfrac{1}{2} f(2x) f(\tfrac{1}{2}).$$

Now we show that $\sin \pi x$ has the properties (1) and (2) for $f(x)$. We have

(3) $$\sin (\pi(x + 1)) = \sin (\pi x + \pi) = - \sin \pi x \ ,$$

$$\sin \pi x \sin (\pi(x + \tfrac{1}{2})) = \sin \pi x \cos \pi x = \tfrac{1}{2} \sin 2\pi x$$

(4) $$= \tfrac{1}{2} \sin \frac{\pi}{2} \sin 2\pi x.$$

Now we set

$$G(x) = \begin{cases} \dfrac{f(x)}{\sin \pi x} & \text{for non-integral } x. \\ 1 & \text{for integral } x. \end{cases}$$

Then, by (1), (2), (3), (4), we have that

(5) $$G(x + 1) = G(x),$$

$$G(\tfrac{1}{2}) G(2x) = G(x) G(x + \tfrac{1}{2}).$$

Furthermore, we have for $0 \leqq x < 1$ (and hence, by (5), for all x) that

$$G(x) > 0.$$

$$\varphi(x) = \begin{cases} \dfrac{\sin \pi x}{\pi x} & \text{for } x \neq 0, \\ 1 & \text{for } x = 0 \end{cases}$$

is an integral function, so that $\varphi'(x)$ exists and is continuous for all x. If $|x| < 1$, then

$$\varphi(x) \neq 0 .$$

Hence

$$G(x) = \frac{F(x)}{\varphi(x)}$$

has a continuous derivative for $|x| < 1$. Therefore, by (5), $G'(x)$ exists everywhere, and is continuous everywhere.

Setting

$$H(x) = \log \frac{G(x)}{G(\tfrac{1}{2})} \ ,$$

we have that

(6) $$H(x + 1) = H(x),$$

(7) $$H(2x) = H(x) + H(x + \tfrac{1}{2}),$$

$$H'(x) \text{ is continuous,}$$

(8) $$H'(x + 1) = H'(x).$$

From (7), we obtain for integral $n > 0$ that

$$H(2^n x) = \sum_{\nu=0}^{2^n - 1} H\left(x + \frac{\nu}{2^n}\right) ;$$

for, this is (7) for $n = 1$, and $n + 1$ follows from n because

$$H\left(2^{n+1}x\right) = H\left(2^n \cdot 2x\right) = \sum_{\nu=0}^{2^n-1} H\left(2x + \frac{\nu}{2^n}\right)$$

$$= \sum_{\nu=0}^{2^n-1} \left(H\left(x + \frac{\nu}{2^{n+1}}\right) + H\left(x + \frac{\nu+2^n}{2^{n+1}}\right)\right) = \sum_{\nu=0}^{2^{n+1}-1} H\left(x + \frac{\nu}{2^{n+1}}\right).$$

Hence we have

$$H(x) = \sum_{\nu=0}^{2^n-1} H\left(\frac{x+\nu}{2^n}\right),$$

(9)
$$H'(x) = \frac{1}{2^n} \sum_{\nu=0}^{2^n-1} H'\left(\frac{x+\nu}{2^n}\right).$$

Since $H'(x)$ is continuous and (8) is true, $H'(x)$ has a largest value M. Choose a ξ such that

$$H'(\xi) = M.$$

Then we have, for integral $n > 0$ and integral ν with $0 \leqq \nu < 2^n$, that

$$H'\left(\frac{\xi+\nu}{2^n}\right) \leq M,$$

so that

$$H'\left(\frac{\xi+\nu}{2^n}\right) = M,$$

since otherwise, we would have by (9) (with $x = \xi$) that

$$H'(\xi) < M.$$

For $0 \leqq x < 1$, integral $n > 0$, $\nu = [2^n x]$, we have $0 \leqq \nu < 2^n$, and

$$\lim_{n=\infty} \frac{\xi+\nu}{2^n} = x\,;$$

and therefore, since $H'(x)$ is continuous, we have

$$H'(x) = M \quad \text{for} \quad 0 \leqq x < 1,$$

and, because of (8), for all x. Hence we have

$$H(x) = Mx + c,$$

so that, by (6),

$$M = 0,$$

$$H(x) = c.$$

From (7), we have

$$c = c + c,$$

$$c = 0,$$

$$H(x) = 0,$$

$$G(x) = G(\tfrac{1}{2}),$$

$$1 = \tfrac{1}{1} = \frac{F(0)}{\varphi(0)} = G(0) = G(\tfrac{1}{2}),$$

$$G(x) = 1,$$

$$f(x) = \sin \pi x.$$

Definition 63: $\quad \mathrm{tg}\, x = \dfrac{\sin x}{\cos x}$ *for non-integral* $\dfrac{x}{\pi} - \dfrac{1}{2}$.

tg is to be read "tangent."

Definition 64: $\quad \mathrm{ctg}\, x = \dfrac{\cos x}{\sin x}$ *for non-integral* $\dfrac{x}{\pi}$.

ctg is to be read "cotangent."

Theorems 284, 286, 289 - 292, 294 are meant in the following sense: "If one of the sides is meaningful," i.e. either the numbers $x = (n + \tfrac{1}{2})\pi$ (n integral) or the numbers $x = n\pi$ (n integral) are to be excluded.

Theorem 284: $\qquad \mathrm{tg}\,(-x) = -\,\mathrm{tg}\, x.$

Proof: Definition 63.

Theorem 285: $\qquad \mathrm{tg}\, 0 = 0.$

Proof: Definition 63.

Theorem 286: $\qquad \mathrm{ctg}\,(-x) = -\,\mathrm{ctg}\, x.$

Proof: Definition 64.

Theorem 287: $\qquad \mathrm{ctg}\, \dfrac{\pi}{2} = 0.$

Proof: Definition 64.

Theorem 288: $\qquad \mathrm{tg}\, \dfrac{\pi}{4} = 1.$

Proof: By Theorems 265 and 264, we have

$$\mathrm{tg}\, \frac{\pi}{4} = \frac{\sin \dfrac{\pi}{4}}{\cos \dfrac{\pi}{4}} = \frac{\dfrac{1}{\sqrt{2}}}{\dfrac{1}{\sqrt{2}}} = 1.$$

Theorem 289:
$$\frac{d\,\text{tg}\,x}{dx} = \frac{1}{\cos^2 x}.$$

Proof:
$$\left(\frac{\sin x}{\cos x}\right)' = \frac{\cos x\,(\sin x)' - \sin x\,(\cos x)'}{\cos^2 x}$$

$$= \frac{\cos x \cos x + \sin x \sin x}{\cos^2 x} = \frac{1}{\cos^2 x}.$$

Theorem 290:
$$\frac{d\,\text{ctg}\,x}{dx} = -\frac{1}{\sin^2 x}.$$

Proof:
$$\left(\frac{\cos x}{\sin x}\right)' = \frac{\sin x\,(\cos x)' - \cos x\,(\sin x)'}{\sin^2 x}$$

$$= \frac{\sin x\,(-\sin x) - \cos x \cos x}{\sin^2 x} = -\frac{1}{\sin^2 x}.$$

Theorem 291:
$$\text{tg}\left(\frac{\pi}{2} - x\right) = \text{ctg}\,x.$$

Proof:
$$\frac{\sin\left(\dfrac{\pi}{2} - x\right)}{\cos\left(\dfrac{\pi}{2} - x\right)} = \frac{\cos x}{\sin x}.$$

Theorem 292:
$$\text{tg}\,(x + \pi) = \text{tg}\,x.$$

In other words, "tg x has the period π."

Proof: By Theorems 271 and 272, we have

$$\frac{\sin(x + \pi)}{\cos(x + \pi)} = \frac{\sin(-x)}{-\cos(-x)} = \frac{\sin x}{\cos x}.$$

Theorem 293:
$$\text{tg}\,(x + c) = \text{tg}\,x$$

holds for all x for which one of the sides is meaningful, if and only if

$$c = n\pi, \; n \; an \; integer.$$

Proof: 1) If one of the sides is meaningful, we have that

$$\text{tg}\,(x + n\pi) = \frac{\sin(x + n\pi)}{\cos(x + n\pi)} = \frac{\sin x \cos n\pi + \cos x \sin n\pi}{\cos x \cos n\pi - \sin x \sin n\pi} = \frac{\sin x}{\cos x} = \text{tg}\,x.$$

2) It suffices to show that

$$\operatorname{tg} c = 0$$

holds only for $c = n\pi$, n an integer. In fact, it follows that

$$\sin c = \cos c \operatorname{tg} c = 0,$$

and Theorem 279 proves our assertion.

Theorem 294: $\operatorname{ctg}(x + \pi) = \operatorname{ctg} x.$

In other words, "ctg x has the period π."

Proof: By Theorems 272 and 271, we have

$$\frac{\cos(x + \pi)}{\sin(x + \pi)} = \frac{-\cos(-x)}{\sin(-x)} = \frac{\cos x}{\sin x}.$$

Theorem 295: $\operatorname{ctg}(x + c) = \operatorname{ctg} x$

holds for all x for which one of the sides is meaningful, if and only if

$$c = n\pi, \ n \ \text{is an integer}.$$

Proof: By Theorem 291, our statement is equivalent with

$$\operatorname{tg}\left(\frac{\pi}{2} - x - c\right) = \operatorname{tg}\left(\frac{\pi}{2} - x\right),$$

if one of the sides is meaningful; and therefore with

$$\operatorname{tg} y = \operatorname{tg}(y + c)$$

if one of the sides is meaningful. Hence Theorem 293 proves our assertion.

For the conclusion of this chapter, I present a simpler example, now available, of a function $\varphi(z)$ which was needed for the proof of Theorem 165. Evidently, it was essential only that $\varphi(z)$ have a positive period and be everywhere differentiable (and hence bounded) without having $\varphi'(z)$ constant. Such a function is

$$\varphi(z) = \cos z.$$

We now condense the entire proof of Theorem 165, by means of our new function.

Let

$$f(x) = \begin{cases} 0 & \text{for } x = 0, \\ x^2 \cos \dfrac{1}{x} & \text{for } x \neq 0. \end{cases}$$

Then we have

$$f'(0) = \lim_{x=0} x \cos \frac{1}{x} = 0$$

and, for $x \neq 0$,

$$f'(x) = 2x \cos \frac{1}{x} - \sin \frac{1}{x}.$$

We have for integral $n > 0$ that

$$f'\left(\frac{1}{(2n + \frac{1}{2})\pi}\right) = -1,$$

so that $f(x)$ is not continuous on the right at 0.

CHAPTER 17

FUNCTIONS OF TWO VARIABLES; PARTIAL DIFFERENTIATION

Definition 65: *Let $\mathfrak{M}$ be a set of number-pairs (x, y). To every pair (x, y) of $\mathfrak{M}$ let a number z be assigned. Then z is said to be a function of the two variables x and y.*

Notation: $z = f(x, y)$, or something similar.

Examples: 1) $z = e^{x+y^2}$, $\mathfrak{M}$ arbitrary.

2) $$z = \frac{1}{x + y}$$

and $\mathfrak{M}$ the set of all (x, y) with $y \neq -x$.

3) $$z = \frac{1}{x + y}$$

and $\mathfrak{M}$ the set of all (x, y) with $x > 0$, $y > 0$.

Definition 66: *$f(x, y)$ is said to be continuous at (ξ, η), if for every $\delta > 0$ there exists an $\varepsilon > 0$ such that*

$$| f(x, y) - f(\xi, \eta) | < \delta \ \text{ for } \ | x - \xi | < \varepsilon, \ | y - \eta | < \varepsilon.$$

Thus, first of all, $f(x, y)$ must be defined for

$$| x - \xi | < p, | y - \eta | < p,$$

with a suitable $p > 0$.

Example: xy is continuous at $(0, 0)$. For if $| x | < \sqrt{\delta}, | y | < \sqrt{\delta}$, we have

$$| xy - 0 \cdot 0 | = | xy | < \delta.$$

Theorem 296: *If $f(x, y)$ is continuous at (ξ, η), and if $g(x)$ is continuous at ξ and $g(\xi) = \eta$, then $f(x, g(x))$, which is a function of one variable, is continuous at ξ.*

Proof: Let $\delta > 0$ be given. There exists an $\varepsilon > 0$ such that

$$| f(x, y) - f(\xi, \eta) | < \delta \ \text{ for } \ | x - \xi | < \varepsilon, \ | y - \eta | < \varepsilon.$$

There exists a ζ with $0 < \zeta \leqq \varepsilon$ such that

$$|g(x) - \eta| < \varepsilon \text{ for } |x - \xi| < \zeta.$$

Hence we have for $|x - \xi| < \zeta$ that

$$|x - \xi| < \varepsilon,$$

$$|f(x, g(x)) - f(\xi, g(\xi))| = |f(x, g(x)) - f(\xi, \eta)| < \delta.$$

Theorem 297: *If $f(x, y)$ is continuous at (ξ, η), then the function $f(x, \eta)$ of one variable is continuous at $x = \xi$, and the function $f(\xi, y)$ of one variable is continuous at $y = \eta$.*

Proof: The first part of the theorem follows from Theorem 296 with $g(x) = \eta$; the second, by applying the first part to the continuous function $f(y, x)$ which is continuous at (η, ξ).

The converse of Theorem 297, by the way, is not true. **Counter-example:**

$$\xi = \eta = 0, \quad f(x, y) = \begin{cases} 0 \text{ for all } (x, y) \text{ with } x = 0 \text{ or } y = 0 \\ 1 \text{ otherwise.} \end{cases}$$

Definition 67: *If y (or x) is considered fixed and if we differentiate $z = f(x, y)$ (where possible) with respect to x (or y), then we obtain the two partial derivatives of first order of $f(x, y)$.*

Notation: $\dfrac{\partial z}{\partial x}$ *or* $\dfrac{\partial f(x, y)}{\partial x}$ *or* $f_1(x, y)$, *and* $\dfrac{\partial z}{\partial y}$ *or* $\dfrac{\partial f(x, y)}{\partial y}$ *or* $f_2(x, y)$,

respectively.

Thus,

$$f_1(\xi, \eta) = \lim_{h=0} \frac{f(\xi + h, \eta) - f(\xi, \eta)}{h}, \text{ if it exists,}$$

$$f_2(\xi, \eta) = \lim_{k=0} \frac{f(\xi, \eta + k) - f(\xi, \eta)}{k}, \text{ if it exists.}$$

Definition 68:

$$\left.\begin{aligned}
\frac{\partial^2 z}{\partial x^2} \quad or \quad \frac{\partial^2 f(x, y)}{\partial x^2} \quad or \quad f_{11}(x, y) &= \frac{\partial f_1(x, y)}{\partial x}, \\
\frac{\partial^2 z}{\partial x \partial y} \quad or \quad \frac{\partial^2 f(x, y)}{\partial x \partial y} \quad or \quad f_{12}(x, y) &= \frac{\partial f_1(x, y)}{\partial y}, \\
\frac{\partial^2 z}{\partial y \partial x} \quad or \quad \frac{\partial^2 f(x, y)}{\partial y \partial x} \quad or \quad f_{21}(x, y) &= \frac{\partial f_2(x, y)}{\partial x}, \\
\frac{\partial^2 z}{\partial y^2} \quad or \quad \frac{\partial^2 f(x, y)}{\partial y^2} \quad or \quad f_{22}(x, y) &= \frac{\partial f_2(x, y)}{\partial y},
\end{aligned}\right\} \text{ if they exist,}$$

are the four partial derivatives of second order of $f(x, y)$.

Example: $\qquad\qquad f(x, y) = e^{x+y^2}$.

For all x and y, we have

$$f_1\ (x, y) = e^{x+y^2},$$

$$f_2\ (x, y) = 2y\,e^{x+y^2},$$

$$f_{11}(x, y) = e^{x+y^2},$$

$$f_{12}(x, y) = 2y\,e^{x+y^2},$$

$$f_{21}(x, y) = 2y\,e^{x+y^2},$$

$$f_{22}(x, y) = 2e^{x+y^2} + 4y^2 e^{x+y^2}.$$

We observe here that

$$f_{12}(x, y) = f_{21}(x, y).$$

What is the significance of this? Theorem 298 will frighten us and Theorem 299 will reassure us.

Theorem 298: *It may happen that* $f_{12}(\xi, \eta)$ *and* $f_{21}(\xi, \eta)$ *exist and that*

$$f_{12}(\xi, \eta) \neq f_{21}(\xi, \eta).$$

Proofs: 1) In the following example, $f(x, y)$ is even continuous at (ξ, η). Let

$$\xi = \eta = 0,$$

$$f(x, y) = \begin{cases} xy & \text{for } |y| \leq |x|, \\ -xy & \text{for } |y| > |x|. \end{cases}$$

We have, for $|x| < \sqrt{\delta}$, $|y| < \sqrt{\delta}$,

$$|f(x, y) - f(0, 0)| = |xy| < \delta.$$

Hence $f(x, y)$ is continuous at $(0, 0)$.

If $0 < |h| < |y|$, then

$$\frac{f(h, y) - f(0, y)}{h} = -y,$$

so that, for $y \neq 0$,

$$f_1(0, y) = -y.$$

If $|h| > 0$, then

$$\frac{f(h, 0) - f(0, 0)}{h} = \frac{0}{h} = 0$$

and hence

$$f_1(0, 0) = 0.$$

Therefore we have for all y that
$$f_1(0, y) = -y.$$
Consequently, we have
$$f_{12}(0, 0) = -1.$$
If $0 < |k| \leq |x|$, then
$$\frac{f(x, k) - f(x, 0)}{k} = x,$$
so that, for $x \neq 0$,
$$f_2(x, 0) = x.$$
If $|k| > 0$, then
$$\frac{f(0, k) - f(0, 0)}{k} = \frac{0}{k} = 0,$$
and hence
$$f_2(0, 0) = 0.$$
Therefore, we have for all x that
$$f_2(x, 0) = x.$$
Consequently, we have
$$f_{21}(0, 0) = 1,$$
$$f_{12}(0, 0) \neq f_{21}(0, 0).$$

Moreover, neither $f_1(x, y)$ nor $f_2(x, y)$ exists for $|x| < p, |y| < p$ for any $p > 0$, since $f(x, y)$ is not differentiable with respect to x at $x = y$ for any $y \neq 0$ and is not differentiable with respect to y at $y = x$ for any $x \neq 0$.

2) In the following example, it is even true that $f(x, y)$, $f_1(x, y)$, and $f_2(x, y)$, are continuous at (ξ, η) and that $f_{11}(x, y)$, $f_{12}(x, y)$, $f_{21}(x, y)$, $f_{22}(x, y)$ exist everywhere.

Let
$$\xi = \eta = 0,$$
$$f(x, y) = \begin{cases} 0 & \text{for } x = y = 0, \\ xy \dfrac{x^2 - y^2}{x^2 + y^2} & \text{otherwise (i.e. for } x^2 + y^2 > 0). \end{cases}$$

If $|x| < \sqrt{\delta}$, $|y| < \sqrt{\delta}$, then
$$|f(x, y) - f(0, 0)| \begin{cases} = 0 < \delta & \text{if } x = y = 0, \\ \leq |x| |y| \dfrac{x^2 + y^2}{x^2 + y^2} = |x| |y| < \delta & \text{otherwise.} \end{cases}$$

Hence $f(x, y)$ is continuous at $(0, 0)$.

For all (x, y) with $x^2 + y^2 > 0$, we have

$$f_1(x, y) = y \frac{x^2 - y^2}{x^2 + y^2} + xy \frac{(x^2 + y^2)2x - (x^2 - y^2)2x}{(x^2 + y^2)^2}$$

(1)
$$= y \frac{x^4 - y^4}{(x^2 + y^2)^2} + xy \frac{4xy^2}{(x^2 + y^2)^2} = y \frac{x^4 + 4x^2y^2 - y^4}{(x^2 + y^2)^2},$$

$$f_2(x, y) = x \frac{x^2 - y^2}{x^2 + y^2} + xy \frac{-(x^2 + y^2)2y - (x^2 - y^2)2y}{(x^2 + y^2)^2}$$

(2)
$$= x \frac{x^4 - y^4}{(x^2 + y^2)^2} - xy \frac{4x^2y}{(x^2 + y^2)^2} = x \frac{x^4 - 4x^2y^2 - y^4}{(x^2 + y^2)^2},$$

so that $f_{11}(x, y)$, $f_{12}(x, y)$, $f_{21}(x, y)$, $f_{22}(x, y)$ evidently exist.

If $h \neq 0$, we have

$$\frac{f(h, 0) - f(0, 0)}{h} = 0.$$

Hence we have

(3)
$$f_1(0, 0) = 0.$$

By (1), we have for $y \neq 0$ that

$$f_1(0, y) = y \frac{-y^4}{y^4} = -y.$$

Hence for all y

$$f_1(0, y) = -y,$$

so that

$$f_{12}(0, 0) = -1.$$

If $k \neq 0$, we have

$$\frac{f(0, k) - f(0, 0)}{k} = 0.$$

Hence we have

(4)
$$f_2(0, 0) = 0.$$

By (2), we have for $x \neq 0$ that

$$f_2(x, 0) = x \frac{x^4}{x^4} = x.$$

Therefore we have for all x that

$$f_2(x, 0) = x,$$

so that

$$f_{21}(0, 0) = 1,$$

$$f_{12}(0, 0) \neq f_{21}(0, 0).$$

Moreover, by (1), we have for $x \neq 0$ that

$$f_1(x, 0) = 0,$$

so that, by (3),

$$f_1(x, 0) = 0,$$

for all x, so that

$$f_{11}(0, 0) = 0.$$

Furthermore, by (2), we have for $y \neq 0$ that

$$f_2(0, y) = 0,$$

so that, by (4),

$$f_2(0, y) = 0$$

for all y, so that

$$f_{22}(0, 0) = 0.$$

Finally, the continuity of $f_1(x, y)$ and $f_2(x, y)$ at $(0, 0)$ follows from

$$f_1(0, 0) = f_2(0, 0) = 0$$

and from the fact that, for $x^2 + y^2 > 0$,

$$\left| \frac{x^4 \pm 4x^2y^2 - y^4}{(x^2 + y^2)^2} \right| \leq \frac{2x^4 + 4x^2y^2 + 2y^4}{(x^2 + y^2)^2} = 2,$$

so that, by (1) and (2), we have for $|x| < \dfrac{\delta}{2}$, $|y| < \dfrac{\delta}{2}$, $x^2 + y^2 > 0$ that

$$\left. \begin{array}{l} |f_1(x, y) - f_1(0, 0)| \leq 2|y| \\ |f_2(x, y) - f_2(0, 0)| \leq 2|x| \end{array} \right\} < \delta.$$

Theorem 299: *Let $f_{12}(x, y)$ be continuous at (ξ, η) and let $f_2(x, \eta)$ exist in a neighborhood of $x = \xi$. Then $f_{21}(\xi, \eta)$ exists, and*

$$f_{12}(\xi, \eta) = f_{21}(\xi, \eta).$$

Preliminary Remark: Thus in the second example to Theorem 298, $f_{12}(x, y)$ cannot be continuous at $(0, 0)$.

Proof: By hypothesis, there exists a $p > 0$ such that $f_{12}(x, y)$ (and hence $f_1(x, y)$ and $f(x, y)$) exists for the x, y with

$$|x - \xi| < p, \quad |y - \eta| < p,$$

and such that $f_2(x, \eta)$ exists for

$$|x - \xi| < p.$$

Let

$$0 < |h| < p, \quad 0 < |k| < p.$$

If x is in the interval $[\xi, \xi + h]$ (or the interval $[\xi + h, \xi]$), then we set

$$g(x) = f(x, \eta + k) - f(x, \eta).$$

$$g'(x) = f_1(x, \eta + k) - f_1(x, \eta)$$

exists for the x in that interval. Hence, by Theorem 159, there exists an x between ξ and $\xi + h$ such that

$$g(\xi + h) - g(\xi) = hg'(x),$$

so that

$$f(\xi+h, \eta+k) - f(\xi+h, \eta) - f(\xi, \eta+k) + f(\xi, \eta) = h(f_1(x, \eta+k) - f_1(x, \eta)).$$

Our x depends on h and k.

Now $f_1(x, y)$, as a function of y in the interval $[\eta, \eta + k]$ ($[\eta + k, \eta]$), is differentiable, with derivative $f_{12}(x, y)$. Hence by Theorem 159, there exists a y between η and $\eta + k$ such that

$$f_1(x, \eta + k) - f_1(x, \eta) = kf_{12}(x, y),$$

so that

(1) $f(\xi+h, \eta+k) - f(\xi+h, \eta) - f(\xi, \eta+k) + f(\xi, \eta) = hkf_{12}(x, y).$

Our y depends on x and k, and hence on h and k.

By hypothesis,

$$\lim_{k=0} \frac{f(\xi + h, \eta + k) - f(\xi + h, \eta)}{k} = f_2(\xi + h, \eta)$$

exists for $0 < |h| < p$, and so does

$$\lim_{k=0} \frac{f(\xi, \eta + k) - f(\xi, \eta)}{k} = f_2(\xi, \eta).$$

Therefore, by (1),

$$\lim_{k=0} hf_{12}(x, y) = f_2(\xi + h, \eta) - f_2(\xi, \eta)$$

exists for $0 < |h| < p$, and so does

$$\lim_{k=0} f_{12}(x, y) = \frac{f_2(\xi + h, \eta) - f_2(\xi, \eta)}{h}.$$

Therefore we have shown existence of

(2) $\displaystyle\lim_{k=0} (f_{12}(x, y) - f_{12}(\xi, \eta)) = \frac{f_2(\xi + h, \eta) - f_2(\xi, \eta)}{h} - f_{12}(\xi, \eta).$

Since $f_{12}(x, y)$ is continuous at (ξ, η) (for the free variables x, y), there exists, for every $\delta > 0$, a positive $\varepsilon < p$ such that

(3) $\displaystyle |f_{12}(x, y) - f_{12}(\xi, \eta)| < \frac{\delta}{2}$ for $|x - \xi| < \varepsilon$, $|y - \eta| < \varepsilon$.

Now if

$$0 < |h| < \varepsilon, \quad 0 < |k| < \varepsilon,$$

then

$$0 < |h| < p, 0 < |k| < p,$$

so that (3) holds for our x and y which are dependent on h and k. (Indeed, we had $|x - \xi| \leqq |h|$, $|y - \eta| \leqq |k|$). From (2), we obtain for $0 < |h| < \varepsilon$ that

$$\left| \frac{f_2(\xi + h, \eta) - f_2(\xi, \eta)}{h} - f_{12}(\xi, \eta) \right| \leqq \frac{\delta}{2} < \delta.$$

Therefore $f_{21}(\xi, \eta)$ exists and $= f_{12}(\xi, \eta)$.

Definition 69: $f(x, y)$ *has a total differential at* (ξ, η) *if there are two numbers* t_1 *and* t_2 *and two functions* $\varphi(h, k)$ *and* $\psi(h, k)$ *continuous at* $(0, 0)$ *with*

$$\varphi(0, 0) = \psi(0, 0) = 0,$$

such that, for suitable $p > 0$, *we have for* $|h| < p$ *and for* $|k| < p$ *that*

$$f(\xi + h, \eta + k) - f(\xi, \eta) = t_1 h + t_2 k + h\varphi(h, k) + k\psi(h, k).$$

Theorem 300: *If* $f(x, y)$ *has a total differential at* (ξ, η), *then* t_1 *and* t_2 *are uniquely determined, in fact by*

$$t_1 = f_1(\xi, \eta),$$

$$t_2 = f_2(\xi, \eta).$$

Proof: By Definition 69 with $k = 0$, we have for $|h| < p$ that

$$f(\xi + h, \eta) - f(\xi, \eta) = t_1 h + h\varphi(h, 0) = t_1 h + h\varphi(h),$$

where $\varphi(h)$ is continuous at $h = 0$ and is 0 there. Hence we have

$$\lim_{h=0} \frac{f(\xi + h, \eta) - f(\xi, \eta)}{h} = t_1,$$

$$f_1(\xi, \eta) = t_1.$$

By considerations of symmetry, we have

$$f_2(\xi, \eta) = t_2.$$

Theorem 301: *If* $f(x, y)$ *has a total differential at* (ξ, η), *then* $f(x, y)$ *is continuous at* (ξ, η).

Proof: Using the notation of Definition 69, we have for suitable q with $0 < q < p$ that

$$|\varphi(h, k)| < 1, \quad |\psi(h, k)| < 1 \text{ for } |h| < q, \quad |k| < q.$$

Therefore, for these h, k we have

$$|f(\xi + h, \eta + k) - f(\xi, \eta)| \leqq |t_1||h| + |t_2||k| + |h| + |k|.$$

For a given $\delta > 0$, this is $< \delta$ if

$$\left. \begin{array}{c} |\,h\,| \\ |\,k\,| \end{array} \right\} < \operatorname{Min}\left(q, \ \frac{\delta}{2 + |\,t_1\,| + |\,t_2\,|}\right).$$

Theorem 302: *Let $p > 0$ and let $f_1(x, y)$ and $f_2(x, y)$ be continuous at (ξ, η). Then $f(x, y)$ has a total differential at (ξ, η)* (and hence is continuous there, by Theorem 301).

Proof: By hypothesis, $f_1(x, y)$ and $f_2(x, y)$ exist for $|\,x - \xi\,| < p$, $|\,y - \eta\,| < p$, with a suitable $p > 0$.

Therefore if $|\,h\,| < p, |\,k\,| < p$, and if we set

$$\eta + k = \mu,$$

then there exists a ϑ with

$$0 < \vartheta < 1,$$

$$f(\xi+h, \mu) = f(\xi, \mu) + hf_1(\xi+\vartheta h, \mu) = f(\xi, \mu)+hf_1(\xi, \eta) + h\varphi(h, k)$$

where

$$\varphi(h, k) = f_1(\xi + \vartheta h, \eta + k) - f_1(\xi, \eta).$$

(This follows from Theorem 159 if $h \neq 0$, and if $h = 0$ this is trivial, for we may choose $\vartheta = \frac{1}{2}$.) $\varphi(h, k)$ is continuous and equal to zero at $(0, 0)$, since $f_1(x, y)$ is continuous at (ξ, η).

By Theorem 159, there exists for $0 < |\,k\,| < p$ a Θ, and for $k = 0$ a Θ $(\Theta = \frac{1}{2})$ with

$$0 < \Theta < 1,$$

$$f(\xi, \mu) = f(\xi, \eta+k) = f(\xi, \eta) + kf_2(\xi, \eta + \Theta k)$$

$$= f(\xi, \eta) + kf_2(\xi, \eta) + k\psi(h, k)$$

where

$$\psi(h, k) = f_2(\xi, \eta + \Theta k) - f_2(\xi, \eta).$$

(ψ actually does not depend on h.) $\psi(h, k)$ is continuous and equal to zero at $(0, 0)$, since $f_2(x, y)$ is continuous at (ξ, η).

Combining these results, we have for $|\,h\,| < p, |\,k\,| < p$, that

$$f(\xi+h, \eta+k) = f(\xi, \eta) + hf_1(\xi, \eta) + kf_2(\xi, \eta) + h\varphi(h, k) + k\psi(h, k).$$

Theorem 303: *Let*

$$F(\tau) = \xi, \quad G(\tau) = \eta,$$

$$F'(\tau) = \alpha, \quad G'(\tau) = \beta.$$

Let $f(x, y)$ have a total differential at (ξ, η). Let

$$g(t) = f(F(t), G(t)).$$

Then we have

$$g'(\tau) = f_1(\xi, \eta)\alpha + f_2(\xi, \eta)\beta.$$

Briefly written,

$$\frac{d\dot{f}}{dt} = \frac{\partial f}{\partial x} \frac{dx}{dt} + \frac{\partial f}{\partial y} \frac{dy}{dt} \, .$$

Proof: For suitable $p > 0$, we have for $|h| < p, |k| < p$, that

$$f(\xi + h, \eta + k) - f(\xi, \eta) = f_1(\xi, \eta)h + f_2(\xi, \eta)k + h\varphi(h, k) + k\psi(h, k),$$

where $\varphi(h, k)$ and $\psi(h, k)$ are continuous and equal to zero at $(0, 0)$.
For suitable $\varepsilon > 0$, if we set

$$h = h(l) = F(\tau + l) - F(\tau),$$
$$k = k(l) = G(\tau + l) - G(\tau),$$

then we have for $|l| < \varepsilon$ that

$$|h| < p, \quad |k| < p,$$
$$g(\tau + l) - g(\tau) = f(F(\tau + l), G(\tau + l)) - f(F(\tau), G(\tau))$$
$$= f(\xi + h, \eta + k) - f(\xi, \eta).$$

Therefore if $0 < |l| < \varepsilon$, then

$$\frac{g(\tau + l) - g(\tau)}{l}$$

$$= f_1(\xi, \eta)\frac{h(l)}{l} + f_2(\xi, \eta)\frac{k(l)}{l} + \frac{h(l)}{l}\varphi(h(l), k(l)) + \frac{k(l)}{l}\psi(h(l), k(l)).$$

Now we have

$$\lim_{l=0} \frac{h(l)}{l} = \alpha \, ,$$

$$\lim_{l=0} \frac{k(l)}{l} = \beta \, ,$$

$$\lim_{l=0} h(l) = 0 \, ,$$

$$\lim_{l=0} k(l) = 0 \, ,$$

$$\lim_{l=0} \varphi(h(l), k(l)) = 0 \, ,$$

$$\lim_{l=0} \psi(h(l), k(l)) = 0 \, .$$

Therefore we have

$$\lim_{l=0} \frac{g(\tau + l) - g(\tau)}{l} = f_1(\xi, \eta)\alpha + f_2(\xi, \eta)\beta + \alpha \cdot 0 + \beta \cdot 0$$
$$= f_1(\xi, \eta)\alpha + f_2(\xi, \eta)\beta.$$

Example: Appears in the proof of Theorem 304.

Theorem 304: *Let h and k be arbitrary. Let the interval $a_1 < x < b_1$ contain ξ and $\xi + h$, and let the interval $a_2 < y < b_2$ contain η and $\eta + k$. Let $f_1(x, y)$ and $f_2(x, y)$ be continuous for $a_1 < x < b_1, a_2 < y < b_2$. Then there exists a ϑ such that*

$$0 < \vartheta < 1,$$

$$f(\xi + h, \eta + k) = f(\xi, \eta) + hf_1(\xi + \vartheta h, y + \vartheta k) + kf_2(\xi + \vartheta h, \eta + \vartheta k).$$

Proof: By Theorem 302, $f(x, y)$ has a total differential for

$$a_1 < x < b_1, a_2 < y < b_2$$

(and so is continuous there). The functions

$$F(t) = \xi + th, \qquad G(t) = \eta + tk$$

satisfy, for $0 \leqq t = \tau \leqq 1$, the hypotheses of Theorem 303 (with $\xi + \tau h$ for $\xi, \eta + \tau k$ for $\eta, a = h, \beta = k$). Setting

$$g(t) = f(\xi + th, \quad \eta + tk)$$

then by Theorem 303 we have

$$g'(\tau) = hf_1(\xi + \tau h, \eta + \tau k) + kf_2(\xi + \tau h, \eta + \tau k).$$

By Theorem 159, we have for suitable ϑ that

$$0 < \vartheta < 1, g(1) = g(0) + g'(\vartheta).$$

This is the statement we wished to prove.

Theorem 305: *If $f(x, y)$ is continuous for all (x, y) and if*

$$f_1(\xi + th, \eta + tk), f_2(\xi + th, \eta + tk)$$

exist for $0 \leqq t \leqq 1$, then there need not exist a ϑ in the sense of the statement of Theorem 304.

Proof:
$$f(x, y) = \sqrt{|xy|}$$

is continuous everywhere, since

$$f(\xi + h, \eta + k) - f(\xi, \eta) = \sqrt{|\xi + h|}\, \sqrt{|\eta + k|} - \sqrt{|\xi|}\, \sqrt{|\eta|}$$

$$= \sqrt{|\xi + h|}\, \left(\sqrt{|\eta + k|} - \sqrt{|\eta|}\right) + \sqrt{|\eta|}\, \left(\sqrt{|\xi + h|} - \sqrt{|\xi|}\right),$$

and, since $\sqrt{|u|}$ is continuous for all u, we have for every $\delta > 0$ that each of the two terms on the right is $< \dfrac{\delta}{2}$ in absolute value for $|h| < \varepsilon, |k| < \varepsilon$ with suitable $\varepsilon > 0$.

If $x > 0$ (or $x < 0$), we have

$$f_1(x, y) = \sqrt{|y|}\, \frac{1 \text{ (or} - 1)}{2\sqrt{|x|}};$$

and if $y > 0$ (or $y < 0$), we have

$$f_2(x, y) = \sqrt{|x|} \frac{1 \ (\text{or} -1)}{2\sqrt{|y|}}.$$

Since $f(x, y)$ equals 0 for $y = 0$ and all x, and also for $x = 0$ and all y, we have

$$f_1(0, 0) = 0,$$

$$f_2(0, 0) = 0.$$

Therefore we have for all x that

$$f_1(x, x) + f_2(x, x) = 1 \quad \text{or} \quad -1 \quad \text{or} \quad 0.$$

Therefore, if the formula of Theorem 304 were true for

$$\xi = \eta = -1, h = k = 3,$$

then for suitable x we would have

$$f(2, 2) = f(-1, -1) + 3(f_1(x, x) + f_2(x, x)),$$

so that we would have

$$2 = 1 + 3 \quad \text{or } 1 - 3 \quad \text{or } 1 + 0,$$

neither of which is true.

Definition 70: *If n is an integer > 1, we define*

$$\left. \begin{array}{l} f_{\mu_1\mu_2\cdots\mu_{n-1}1}(x, y) = \dfrac{\partial f_{\mu_1\mu_2\cdots\mu_{n-1}}(x, y)}{\partial x}, \\[3mm] f_{\mu_1\mu_2\cdots\mu_{n-1}2}(x, y) = \dfrac{\partial f_{\mu_1\mu_2\cdots\mu_{n-1}}(x, y)}{\partial y}, \end{array} \right\} \text{if they exist,}$$

where, for $n - 1$, the 2^{n-1} functions

$$f_{\mu_1\mu_2\cdots\mu_{n-1}}(x, y) \quad (\text{where each } \mu = 1 \text{ or } 2)$$

are defined correspondingly.

If $z = f(x, y)$, we also write

$$\frac{\partial^n f(x, y)}{\partial x_{\mu_1} \partial x_{\mu_2} \cdots \partial x_{\mu_n}} \quad \text{or} \quad \frac{\partial^n z}{\partial x_{\mu_1} \partial x_{\mu_2} \cdots \partial x_{\mu_n}}$$

for the left-hand side, with $\mu_n = 1$ or 2.

These functions are the 2^n partial derivatives of order n.

Definition 68 is a special case of this definition; there, we combined consecutive "equal" "factors" ∂x_μ into "powers."

Theorem 306: *Let n be an integer $\geqq 1$. Let the 2^n partial derivatives of n-th order exist for $|x - \xi| < \varepsilon$, $|y - \eta| < \varepsilon$, and let them be continuous* (so that the same holds, by Theorem 302, for the partial derivatives of lower order and for $f(x, y)$). *Then we have*

$$f_{\mu_1 \ldots \mu_n}(x, y) = f_{\nu_1 \ldots \nu_n}(x, y)$$

there, if the number of ones (if any) *among the μ equals the number of ones* (if any) *among the ν.*

In this case, therefore, each of the 2^n partial derivatives of the n-th order is equal to one of the $n + 1$ partial derivatives of the n-th order with

$$\mu_1 \leqq \mu_2 \leqq \ldots \leqq \mu_n,$$

where the ones appear first (there are either 0 or 1 or 2 ... or n of them), and then the twos.

Proof: This is trivial for $n = 1$, and is a special case of Theorem 299 for $n = 2$.

To proceed from $n - 1$ to n for $n \geqq 3$:

If

$$\mu_n = \nu_n,$$

then, since

$$f_{\mu_1 \ldots \mu_{n-1}}(x, y) = f_{\nu_1 \ldots \nu_{n-1}}(x, y),$$

the assertion is obvious.

Suppose that

$$\mu_n \neq \nu_n,$$

so that w.l.g.,

$$\mu_n = 1, \quad \nu_n = 2,$$

If E is the number of ones among the μ (so that $1 \leqq E \leqq n - 1$) and if $\lambda_1, \ldots, \lambda_{n-2}$ starts with $E - 1$ ones (so that, in case $E = 1$, it contains none) and then (in case $E < n - 1$) contains only twos, then

$$f_{\mu_1 \ldots \mu_{n-1}}(x, y) = f_{\lambda_1 \ldots \lambda_{n-2}2}(x, y),$$

$$f_{\nu_1 \ldots \nu_{n-1}}(x, y) = f_{\lambda_1 \ldots \lambda_{n-2}1}(x, y),$$

and our assertion follows by applying Theorem 299 to the function $f_{\lambda_1 \ldots \lambda_{n-2}}(x, y)$ in place of $f(x, y)$.

Theorem 307: *Let n be an integer $\geqq 1$, and let h and k be arbitrary. Let the interval $a_1 < x < b_1$ contain ξ and $\xi + h$, and the interval $a_2 < y < b_2$ contain η and $\eta + k$. Let the partial derivatives of the n-th order exist and be continuous for $a_1 < x < b_1$, $a_2 < y < b_2$ (and so also, by Theorem 302, the partial derivatives of lower order and $f(x, y)$). Then there exists a ϑ such that*

$$0 < \vartheta < 1,$$

$$f(\xi + h, \eta + k) = \sum_{\nu=0}^{n-1} \frac{1}{\nu!} \sum_{\mu=0}^{\nu} \binom{\nu}{\mu} h^{\mu} k^{\nu-\mu} f_{\lambda_1\ldots\lambda_\nu} (\xi, \eta)$$

$$+ \frac{1}{n!} \sum_{\mu=0}^{n} \binom{n}{\mu} h^{\mu} k^{n-\mu} f_{\lambda_1\ldots\lambda_n} (\xi + \vartheta h, \eta + \vartheta k),$$

where $f_{\lambda_1\ldots\lambda_\nu} (\xi, \eta)$ is defined to be $f(\xi, \eta)$ for $\nu = 0$ and where among the numbers $\lambda_1, \ldots, \lambda_\nu$ for $1 \leqq \nu \leqq n$, the first μ are 1 and the last $\nu - \mu$ are 2 (thus all are 2 if $\mu = 0$, and all are 1 if $\mu = \nu$).

Proof: As in the proof of Theorem 304 (which is the special case $n = 1$ of our theorem), we set

$$g(t) = f(\xi + th, \eta + tk).$$

Then if $0 \leqq \tau \leqq 1$, $0 \leqq \nu \leqq n$ (ν an integer), we have

$$(1) \qquad g^{(\nu)}(\tau) = \sum_{\mu=0}^{\nu} \binom{\nu}{\mu} h^{\mu} k^{\nu-\mu} f_{\lambda_1\ldots\lambda_\nu} (\xi + \tau h, \eta + \tau k).$$

For, this is true for $\nu = 0$, and if (1) is true for a ν with $0 \leqq \nu < n$, then by Theorems 302, 303, and 306, we have

$$g^{(\nu+1)}(\tau) = h \sum_{\mu=0}^{\nu} \binom{\nu}{\mu} h^{\mu} k^{\nu-\mu} f_{\lambda_1\ldots\lambda_\nu 1} (\xi + \tau h, \eta + \tau k)$$

$$+ k \sum_{\mu=0}^{\nu} \binom{\nu}{\mu} h^{\mu} k^{\nu-\mu} f_{\lambda_1\ldots\lambda_\nu 2} (\xi + \tau h, \eta + \tau k)$$

$$= \sum_{\mu=0}^{\nu} \binom{\nu}{\mu} h^{\mu+1} k^{\nu-\mu} f_{\lambda_1\ldots\lambda_\nu 1} (\xi + \tau h, \eta + \tau k)$$

$$+ \sum_{\mu=0}^{\nu} \binom{\nu}{\mu} h^{\mu} k^{\nu+1-\mu} f_{\lambda_1\ldots\lambda_\nu 2} (\xi + \tau h, \eta + \tau k)$$

$$= \sum_{\mu=1}^{\nu+1} \binom{\nu}{\mu-1} h^{\mu} k^{\nu+1-\mu} f_{1 \underbrace{\lambda_1\ldots\lambda_\nu}_{\text{first, } \mu-1 \text{ ones}}} (\xi + \tau h, \eta + \tau k)$$

$$+ \sum_{\mu=0}^{\nu} \binom{\nu}{\mu} h^{\mu} k^{\nu+1-\mu} f_{\underbrace{\lambda_1\ldots\lambda_\nu}_{\text{first, } \mu \text{ ones}} 2} (\xi + \tau h, \eta + \tau k)$$

$$= \sum_{\mu=0}^{\nu+1} \binom{\nu+1}{\mu} h^{\mu} k^{\nu+1-\mu} f_{\lambda_1\ldots\lambda_\nu\lambda_{\nu+1}} (\xi + \tau h, \eta + \tau k).$$

By Theorem 177, there is a ϑ with

$$0 < \vartheta < 1 \,,$$

$$g(1) = \sum_{\nu=0}^{n-1} \frac{g^{(\nu)}(0)}{\nu!} + \frac{1}{n!} g^{(n)}(\vartheta) \,.$$

By (1), this is our assertion.

CHAPTER 18

INVERSE FUNCTIONS AND IMPLICIT FUNCTIONS

Definition 71: $f(x)$ *is said to be monotonically increasing on* $[a, b]$ *if*

$$f(\alpha) < f(\beta) \quad for \quad a \leqq \alpha < \beta \leqq b.$$

Definition 72: $f(x)$ *is said to be monotonically decreasing on* $[a, b]$ *if*

$$f(\alpha) > f(\beta) \quad for \quad a \leqq \alpha < \beta \leqq b.$$

Theorem 308: *If $f(x)$ is monotonically increasing on $[a, b]$, then $f(x)$ increases at every x such that $a < x < b$.*

Proof: Obvious, by Definitions 27 and 71.

Theorem 309: *If $f(x)$ is monotonically decreasing on $[a, b]$, then $f(x)$ decreases at every x such that $a < x < b$.*

Proof: Obvious, by Definitions 28 and 72.

Theorem 310: *Let $f(x)$ be continuous on $[a, b]$, and let it increase at every x with $a < x < b$. Then $f(x)$ is monotonically increasing on $[a, b]$.*

Preliminary Remark: This should not be considered self-evident.

Proof: Let

$$a \leqq \alpha < \beta \leqq b.$$

Since $f(x)$ is continuous on $[\alpha, \beta]$, it has there, by Theorem 146, a largest value l, and by Theorem 147, a least value λ.

1) Let $a < \alpha$. Then l is not attained at α nor for $\alpha < x < \beta$, since $f(x)$ increases at every one of these numbers. Thus it is attained at β, and only there. Hence

$$f(\alpha) < l = f(\beta).$$

2) Let $a = \alpha, \beta < b$. Then λ is not attained at β nor for $\alpha < x < \beta$, since $f(x)$ increases at every one of these numbers. Thus it is attained at α, and only there. Hence,

$$f(\alpha) = \lambda < f(\beta).$$

3) Let $a = \alpha, b = \beta$. By 2) and 1), we have

$$f(a) < f\left(\frac{a+b}{2}\right) < f(b).$$

Theorem 311: *Let $f(x)$ be continuous on $[a, b]$, and let it decrease at every x with $a < x < b$. Then $f(x)$ is monotonically decreasing on $[a, b]$.*

Proof: Theorem 310 with $-f(x)$ in place of $f(x)$.

Theorem 312: *Let $f(x)$ be continuous on $[a, b]$ and monotonically increasing (monotonically decreasing), so that if we set*

$$A = f(a), \quad B = f(b),$$

then

$$f(x) = y$$

has, by Theorems 150 and 151, exactly one solution

$$x = g(y)$$

on $[a, b]$ for y on $[A, B]$ ($[B, A]$). (This solution is called the "inverse function.") *Then $g(y)$ is continuous on $[A, B]$ ($[B, A]$).*

Proof: W.l.g., let $f(x)$ be monotonically increasing. (Otherwise, consider $-f(x)$.) Therefore we have

$$A < B$$

It suffices to prove the continuity of $g(y)$ at every η with

$$A < \eta < B.$$

For otherwise, extend (or change) the definition of $f(x)$ by setting

$$f(x) = \begin{cases} f(a) + x - a & \text{for } a - 1 \leq x < a, \\ f(b) + x - b & \text{for } b < x \leq b + 1 \end{cases}$$

so that $f(x)$ is continuous and monotonically increasing on $[a - 1, b + 1]$.

I set

$$g(\eta) = \xi,$$

so that

$$a < \xi < b.$$

Let $\delta > 0$ be given and, w.l.g., be so small that

$$a < \xi - \delta, \quad \xi + \delta < b.$$

I set

$$\eta_1 = f(\xi - \delta), \quad \eta_2 = f(\xi + \delta).$$

Then we have

$$\eta_1 < \eta < \eta_2.$$

Now we have

$$\xi - \delta < g(y) < \xi \qquad \text{for } \eta_1 < y < \eta,$$

$$g(y) = \xi \qquad \text{for } y = \eta,$$

$$\xi < g(y) < \xi + \delta \quad \text{for } \eta < y < \eta_2.$$

Thus if

$$|h| < \text{Min} \, (\eta - \eta_1, \, \eta_2 - \eta),$$

we have

$$|g(\eta + h) - g(\eta)| < \delta.$$

Examples (I purposely choose old ones, for which we already know the result) :

1) $\qquad\qquad a = 0, \quad b > 0, \quad f(x) = x^2.$

Here, we have

$$g(y) = \sqrt{y}.$$

2) $\qquad\qquad 0 < a < b, \quad f(x) = \log x.$

Here, we have

$$g(y) = e^y.$$

Theorem 313: *Under the hypotheses of Theorem 312, let $a < \xi < b$ (so that $A < \eta = f(\xi) < B$ or $A > \eta = f(\xi) > B$) and let*

$$f'(\xi) \neq 0.$$

Then $g(y)$ is differentiable at η, and we have

$$g'(\eta) = \frac{1}{f'(\xi)} \, .$$

Briefly,

$$\frac{dx}{dy} = \frac{1}{\dfrac{dy}{dx}} \, .$$

Proof: By hypothesis,

$$\lim_{h=0} \frac{f(\xi + h) - f(\xi)}{h} = t \neq 0,$$

so that

$$\lim_{h=0} \frac{h}{f(\xi + h) - f(\xi)} = \frac{1}{t} \, .$$

The function

$$\varphi(k) = g(\eta + k) - g(\eta),$$

which, by Theorem 312, is continuous at $k = 0$ and is $\neq 0$ for $0 < |k| < p$ for suitable $p > 0$. Hence by Theorem 98 we have

$$\frac{1}{t} = \lim_{k=0} \frac{\varphi(k)}{f(\xi + \varphi(k)) - f(\xi)} = \lim_{k=0} \frac{g(\eta + k) - g(\eta)}{f(g(\eta + k)) - \eta}$$

$$= \lim_{k=0} \frac{g(\eta + k) - g(\eta)}{k} = g'(\eta).$$

Examples (the old ones, following Theorem 312):

1) For $y > 0$, we have

$$\frac{d\sqrt{y}}{dy} = \frac{dg(y)}{dy} = \frac{1}{\dfrac{dx^2}{dx}} = \frac{1}{2x} = \frac{1}{2\sqrt{y}}.$$

2) For every y, we have

$$\frac{de^y}{dy} = \frac{dg(y)}{dy} = \frac{1}{\dfrac{d \log x}{dx}} = \frac{1}{\dfrac{1}{x}} = x = e^y.$$

Theorem 314: *Let $p > 0$, and let $f(x, y)$ be continuous for*

$$|x - \xi| \leqq p, |y - \eta| \leqq p.$$

Let

$$f(\xi, \eta) = 0.$$

For every fixed x on $[\xi - p, \xi + p]$, let $f(x, y)$, considered as a function of y, be monotonically increasing (or decreasing) on $[\eta - p, \eta + p]$. (I.e., we assume that the function increases for all x, or that it decreases for all x.)

Then there exists a q with $0 < q \leqq p$ such that

1) *for $|x - \xi| < q$, there exists a*

$$y = g(x)$$

(and thus exactly one) *such that*

$$|y - \eta| < p, \quad f(x, y) = 0;$$

2) *$g(x)$ is continuous for $|x - \xi| < q$.*

("Implicit function.")

Proof: W.l.g., let the hypothesis read "increasing." For otherwise, replace $f(x, y)$ by $-f(x, y)$.

1) $\qquad f(\xi, \eta + p) > f(\xi, \eta) = 0 > f(\xi, \eta - p).$

$f(x, \eta + p)$ and $f(x, \eta - p)$ are continuous at ξ. Hence there exists a q such that

$$0 < q \leqq p,$$

so that

$$f(x, \eta + p) > 0 > f(x, \eta - p) \text{ for } \xi - q < x < \xi + q.$$

By Theorem 148, and since $f(x,y)$ is continuous on the y-interval $[\eta-p,\eta+p]$, there exists, for $\xi-q < x < \xi+q$, a

$$y = g(x)$$

such that

$$|y-\eta| < p, \quad f(x,\ y) = 0.$$

2) Let x_0 be given with $|x_0-\xi| < q$, so that

$$\eta-p < g(x_0) < \eta+p.$$

If

$$0 < \delta < \text{Min}\ (\eta+p-g(x_0),\ g(x_0)-\eta+p)$$

then

$$\eta-p < g(x_0)-\delta, \quad g(x_0)+\delta < \eta+p,$$

$$f\big(x_0,\ g(x_0)+\delta\big) > f\big(x_0,\ g(x_0)\big) = 0 > f\big(x_0,\ g(x_0)-\delta\big).$$

Therefore for suitable ε with $0 < \varepsilon \leqq q-|x_0-\xi|$, we have for

$$|x-x_0| < \varepsilon$$

that

$$f(x,\ g(x_0)+\delta) > 0 = f(x,\ g(x)) > f(x,\ g(x_0)-\delta),$$

$$g(x_0)+\delta > g(x) > g(x_0)-\delta,$$

$$|g(x)-g(x_0)| < \delta.$$

Therefore $g(x)$ is continuous at x_0.

Theorem 315: *Under the hypotheses of Theorem 314, let $f(x,y)$ have a total differential for $|x-\xi| < p, |y-\eta| < p$. Furthermore, let*

$$f_2(x,y) \neq 0$$

there (therefore > 0 in the first case, < 0 in the second case of Theorem 314). Then in the notation of Theorem 314, the function $g(x)$ is differentiable for $|x-\xi| < q$, and

$$g'(x) = -\frac{f_1\big(x,\ g(x)\big)}{f_2\big(x,\ g(x)\big)}.$$

Briefly,

$$\frac{dy}{dx} = -\frac{\dfrac{\partial f}{\partial x}}{\dfrac{\partial f}{\partial y}}.$$

Proof: Let x with $|x-\xi| < q$ be fixed. The function

$$k = g(x+h)-g(x) = k(h)$$

is continuous at $h = 0$ by Theorem 314, 2), and

$$k(0) = 0.$$

For suitable $\varepsilon > 0$, if we set

$$y = g(x),$$

then by Theorem 296, we have for $0 < |h| < \varepsilon$ that

$$0 = 0 - 0 = f(x + h,\ g(x + h)) - f(x,\ g(x)) = f(x + h,\ y + k) - f(x,\ y)$$

$$= h f_1(x,\ g(x)) + k f_2(x,\ g(x)) + h\varphi(h) + k\psi(h),$$

where

$$\lim_{h=0}\ \varphi(h) = 0,\quad \lim_{h=0}\ \psi(h) = 0.$$

For suitable ε_1 with $0 < \varepsilon_1 < \varepsilon$, we have for $0 < |h| < \varepsilon_1$ that

$$f_2(x,\ g(x)) + \psi(h) \neq 0,$$

so that

$$\frac{k}{h} = -\frac{f_1(x,\ g(x)) + \varphi(h)}{f_2(x,\ g(x)) + \psi(h)}\ ;$$

and so

$$\lim_{h=0}\ \frac{k}{h} = -\frac{f_1(x,\ g(x))}{f_2(x,\ g(x))}.$$

Example (again, intentionally, an old one) :

$$f(x,\ y) = x^2 + y^2 - 1,\quad |x| < 1,\quad y > 0\ .$$

$$f_2(x,\ y) = 2y > 0,$$

$$f_1(x,\ y) = 2x.$$

$$g'(x) = -\frac{2x}{2y} = -\frac{x}{y} = -\frac{x}{g(x)}.$$

$\bigg($ In fact, we already know that

$$y = g(x) = \sqrt{1 - x^2},$$

$$g'(x) = -\frac{x}{\sqrt{1 - x^2}}.\bigg)$$

CHAPTER 19

THE INVERSE TRIGONOMETRIC FUNCTIONS

These, the inverse functions of the trigonometric functions, are sometimes called cyclometric functions.

Theorem 316: *For* $|x| \leqq 1$, *there exists exactly one* y *such that*

$$\sin y = x, \quad |y| \leq \frac{\pi}{2}.$$

Proof: By Theorem 278, $\sin y$ is monotonically increasing on $[-\frac{\pi}{2}, \frac{\pi}{2}]$. Since

$$\sin\left(-\frac{\pi}{2}\right) = -1, \ \sin\frac{\pi}{2} = 1,$$

the required y exists and is unique, by Theorem 148.

Definition 73: *For* $|x| \leqq 1$, arc sin x *is the* y *of Theorem* 316. arcsin is to be read "arc sine."

Theorem 317: $\dfrac{d \text{ arc sin } x}{dx} = \dfrac{1}{\sqrt{1-x^2}}$ *for* $|x| < 1$.

Proof: Setting

$$y = \text{arc sin } x,$$

we have

$$|y| < \frac{\pi}{2},$$

$$x = \sin y,$$

$$\frac{dx}{dy} = \cos y > 0,$$

so that, by Theorem 313,

$$\frac{dy}{dx} = \frac{1}{\dfrac{dx}{dy}} = \frac{1}{\cos y} = \frac{1}{\sqrt{1-\sin^2 y}} = \frac{1}{\sqrt{1-x^2}}.$$

Theorem 318: *For $|x| \leqq 1$, there exists exactly one y such that*

$$\cos y = x, \qquad 0 \leqq y \leqq \pi,$$

namely

$$y = \frac{\pi}{2} - \text{arc sin } x.$$

Proof: $\qquad \cos y = x, \qquad 0 \leqq y \leqq \pi$

is the same as

$$\sin\left(\frac{\pi}{2} - y\right) = x, \quad -\frac{\pi}{2} \leqq \frac{\pi}{2} - y \leqq \frac{\pi}{2},$$

and so, the same as

$$\frac{\pi}{2} - y = \text{arc sin } x.$$

Definition 74: *For $|x| \leqq 1$, arc cos x is the y of Theorem* 318. arccos to be read "arc cosine."

Theorem 319: $\dfrac{d \text{ arc cos } x}{dx} = -\dfrac{1}{\sqrt{1-x^2}}$ *for* $|x| < 1$.

Proof: By Theorems 318 and 317, we have

$$(\text{arc cos } x)' = \left(\frac{\pi}{2} - \text{arc sin } x\right)' = -(\text{arc sin } x)' = -\frac{1}{\sqrt{1-x^2}}.$$

Theorem 320: *For every x, there is exactly one y such that*

$$\text{tg } y = x, \quad -\frac{\pi}{2} < y < \frac{\pi}{2},$$

namely

$$y = \text{arc sin } \frac{x}{\sqrt{1+x^2}}.$$

Proof: 1) For $-\dfrac{\pi}{2} < y < \dfrac{\pi}{2}$, we have

$$(\text{tg } y)' = \frac{1}{\cos^2 y} > 0 ;$$

and so there exists at most one y of the desired sort.

2) $\qquad \left| \dfrac{x}{\sqrt{1+x^2}} \right| = \sqrt{\dfrac{x^2}{1+x^2}} < 1.$

Therefore if

$$y = \text{arc sin } \frac{x}{\sqrt{1+x^2}},$$

we have

$$|y| < \frac{\pi}{2},$$

$$\cos y > 0,$$

$$\sin y = \frac{x}{\sqrt{1 + x^2}},$$

$$\cos^2 y = 1 - \sin^2 y = 1 - \frac{x^2}{1 + x^2} = \frac{1}{1 + x^2},$$

$$\cos y = \frac{1}{\sqrt{1 + x^2}},$$

$$\operatorname{tg} y = \frac{\sin y}{\cos y} = x.$$

Definition 75: arctg x *is the* y *of Theorem* 320. arctg is to be read "arc tangent."

Theorem 321: $\dfrac{d \operatorname{arc\,tg} x}{dx} = \dfrac{1}{1 + x^2}.$

Proof: By Theorems 320 and 317, we have

$$(\operatorname{arc\,tg} x)' = \left(\operatorname{arc\,sin} \frac{x}{\sqrt{1 + x^2}}\right)' = \frac{1}{\sqrt{1 - \dfrac{x^2}{1 + x^2}}} \left(\frac{x}{\sqrt{1 + x^2}}\right)'$$

$$= \sqrt{1 + x^2} \, \frac{\sqrt{1 + x^2} - \dfrac{x^2}{\sqrt{1 + x^2}}}{1 + x^2} = \frac{1}{1 + x^2}.$$

Theorem 322: *For every* x, *there exists exactly one* y *such that*

$$\operatorname{ctg} y = x, \quad 0 < y < \pi,$$

namely

$$y = \frac{\pi}{2} - \operatorname{arc\,tg} x.$$

Proof: $\operatorname{ctg} y = x, \quad 0 < y < \pi$

is the same as

$$\operatorname{tg}\left(\frac{\pi}{2} - y\right) = x, \quad -\frac{\pi}{2} < \frac{\pi}{2} - y < \frac{\pi}{2},$$

i.e., the same as

$$\frac{\pi}{2} - y = \operatorname{arc\,tg} x.$$

Definition 76: arcctg x *is the* y *of Theorem* 322. arcctg is to be read "arc cotangent."

Theorem 323: $$\frac{d \text{ arc ctg } x}{dx} = -\frac{1}{1 + x^2}.$$

Proof: By Theorems 322 and 321, we have

$$(\text{arc ctg } x)' = \left(\frac{\pi}{2} - \text{arc tg } x\right)' = -(\text{arc tg } x)' = -\frac{1}{1 + x^2}.$$

Why the solemn proceedings of a special chapter for these examples? Because we have found a function having the simple derivative $\dfrac{1}{1 + x^2}$. More about this in Chap. 23.

CHAPTER 20

SOME NECESSARY ALGEBRAIC THEOREMS

This chapter, the last before we begin the integral calculus, will serve to prepare us for Chap. 23.

§ 1. The Fundamental Theorem of Algebra

Our aim is the proof of two theorems on real numbers (Theorems 335 and 336). In this section, however, all numbers will be complex unless otherwise stated. For, each of the two theorems can more easily be proved with the aid of complex numbers. Of the theorems of § 1, only these two will be used in the sequel, and then only in § 2, and in Chaps. 23 and 24.

Common hypotheses of Theorems 324-327 and 332-336: *Let*

$$x \text{ and } y \text{ be real,}$$

$$z = x + yi,$$

$$g(z) = \sum_{\nu=0}^{n} a_\nu z^\nu,$$

$$f(x, y) = |g(z)|.$$

Theorem 324: *For every $c > 0$ and every $\delta > 0$, there exists an $\varepsilon > 0$ which is independent of x, y, such that if $|x| \leq c, |y| \leq c, -\varepsilon < h < \varepsilon$, then*

(1)
$$|f(x + h, y) - f(x, y)| < \delta$$

and

(2)
$$|f(x, y + h) - f(x, y)| < \delta.$$

Proof: W.l.g., let $n > 0$. Let

$$|x| \leq c, \quad |y| \leq c$$

(so that $|z| \leq |x| + |y| \leq 2c$). If $-1 < h < 1$, then, setting $l = h$ or $l = hi$, we have

$$| f(x + h, y) - f(x, y) | \quad \text{or} \quad | f(x, y + h) - f(x, y) |$$

$$= || g(z + l)| - |g(z)| | \leq | g(z + l) - g(z) | = \left| \sum_{\nu=0}^{n} a_\nu (z + l)^\nu - \sum_{\nu=0}^{n} a_\nu z^\nu \right|$$

$$= \left| \sum_{\nu=0}^{n} a_\nu ((z + l)^\nu - z^\nu) \right| = \left| l \sum_{\nu=1}^{n} a_\nu \sum_{\mu=0}^{\nu-1} (z + l)^{\nu-1-\mu} z^\mu \right|$$

$$\leq | h | \sum_{\nu=1}^{n} | a_\nu | \sum_{\mu=0}^{\nu-1} (2c + 1)^{\nu-1-\mu} (2c)^\mu = | h | q,$$

respectively, where $q \geq 0$ is independent of h, x, y, so that it is

$$< \delta \text{ for } -\varepsilon < h < \varepsilon, \; \varepsilon = \text{Min} \left(1, \frac{\delta}{q + 1} \right).$$

Theorem 325: *Let $c > 0$. Then $| g(z) |$ attains a least value for*

$$| x | \leq c, | y | \leq c.$$

Proof: For fixed x on $[-c, c]$, $f(x, y)$ is, by (2), a continuous function of y on $[-c, c]$, and so attains a least value $\lambda(x)$, by Theorem 147.

It suffices to show that $\lambda(x)$ attains a least value on $[-c, c]$. And, by Theorem 147, it suffices to show that $\lambda(x)$ is continuous on $[-c, c]$.

Let ξ in $[-c, c]$ be given. Choose an η such that

$$-c \leq \eta \leq c, \quad f(\xi, \eta) = \lambda(\xi).$$

By (1), there exists for every $\delta > 0$ an $\varepsilon > 0$ such that

$$(3) \qquad | f(\xi + h, y) - f(\xi, y) | < \delta \text{ for } | y | \leq c, \; -\varepsilon < h < \varepsilon.$$

On the one hand, we have by (3) that if $| y | \leq c, -\varepsilon < h < \varepsilon$, then

$$f(\xi + h, y) > f(\xi, y) - \delta \geq \lambda(\xi) - \delta,$$

so that, if in addition $-c \leq \xi + h \leq c$, then

$$\lambda(\xi + h) > \lambda(\xi) - \delta \text{ for } -\varepsilon < h < \varepsilon;$$

on the other hand, if $-c \leq \xi + h \leq c$, then

$$\lambda(\xi + h) \leq f(\xi + h, \eta) < f(\xi, \eta) + \delta = \lambda(\xi) + \delta.$$

Hence if $-\varepsilon < h < \varepsilon, -c \leq \xi + h \leq c$, then

$$| \lambda(\xi + h) - \lambda(\xi) | < \delta.$$

But this is exactly what was to be proved.

Theorem 326: *Let $n > 0, a_n \neq 0$. Then there exists a $c > 0$ such that*

$$| g(z) | \geq | a_0 | \text{ for } | z | > c.$$

Proof: We set

$$c = 1 + \frac{|a_0| + \sum\limits_{\nu=0}^{n-1} |a_\nu|}{|a_n|}.$$

Then if $|z| > c$, we have

$$|z| \geqq 1,$$

$$|g(z)| \geqq |a_n z^n| - \left|\sum_{\nu=0}^{n-1} a_\nu z^\nu\right| \geqq |a_n| |z|^n - \sum_{\nu=0}^{n-1} |a_\nu| |z|^{n-1}$$

$$= |z|^{n-1}\left(|a_n| |z| - \sum_{\nu=0}^{n-1} |a_\nu|\right) \geqq |z|^{n-1}\left(|a_n| c - \sum_{\nu=0}^{n-1} |a_\nu|\right)$$

$$\geqq |z|^{n-1}\left(|a_n| (c-1) - \sum_{\nu=0}^{n-1} |a_\nu|\right) = |z|^{n-1} |a_0| \geqq |a_0|.$$

Theorem 327: *Let $n > 0$, $a_n \neq 0$. Then $|g(z)|$ attains a least value.*

Proof: Determine c as in Theorem 326. Therefore, by Theorem 325, we have for suitable ζ and for $|x| \leqq c, |y| \leqq c$, that

$$|g(z)| \geqq |g(\zeta)|.$$

By Theorem 326, we have for $|x| > c$ or for $|y| > c$ (so that $|z| > c$) that

$$|g(z)| \geqq |a_0| = |g(0)| \geqq |g(\zeta)|.$$

Therefore we have for all z that

$$|g(z)| \geqq |g(\zeta)|.$$

Theorem 328: *If α and β are real, then*

$$(\cos \alpha + i \sin \alpha)(\cos \beta + i \sin \beta) = \cos(\alpha + \beta) + i \sin(\alpha + \beta).$$

Proof: The left-hand side equals

$$(\cos \alpha \cos \beta - \sin \alpha \sin \beta) + i(\sin \alpha \cos \beta + \cos \alpha \sin \beta)$$

$$= \cos(\alpha + \beta) + i \sin(\alpha + \beta).$$

Theorem 329: *If γ is real, and if n is an integer > 0, then*

$$(\cos \gamma + i \sin \gamma)^n = \cos n\gamma + i \sin n\gamma.$$

Proof: $n = 1$: Obvious. To proceed from n to $n + 1$: By Theorem 328, we have

$$(\cos \gamma + i \sin \gamma)^{n+1} = (\cos \gamma + i \sin \gamma)^n (\cos \gamma + i \sin \gamma)$$

$$= (\cos n\gamma + i \sin n\gamma)(\cos \gamma + i \sin \gamma)$$

$$= \cos(n + 1)\gamma + i \sin(n + 1)\gamma.$$

Theorem 330: *Let n be an integer > 0, and let*

$$|a| = 1.$$

Then there exists a t such that

$$t^n = a.$$

Proof: We have

$$a = u + vi, \quad u \text{ and } v \text{ real}, \quad u^2 + v^2 = 1.$$

1) Suppose that

$$v \geqq 0.$$

Set

$$\varphi = \text{arc cos } u.$$

Then we have

$$0 \leqq \varphi \leqq \pi, \quad \cos \varphi = u,$$

so that

$$\sin \varphi \geqq 0,$$

$$\sin^2 \varphi = 1 - \cos^2 \varphi = 1 - u^2 = v^2,$$

$$\sin \varphi = v.$$

If

$$t = \cos \frac{\varphi}{n} + i \sin \frac{\varphi}{n},$$

then, by Theorem 329,

$$t^n = \left(\cos \frac{\varphi}{n} + i \sin \frac{\varphi}{n}\right)^n = \cos \varphi + i \sin \varphi = u + vi = a.$$

2) Let

$$v < 0.$$

By 1), choose w such that

$$w^n = u - vi.$$

Then we have

$$\bar{w}^n = \overline{w^n} = u + vi = a.$$

Theorem 331: *Let n be an integer > 0, and let*

$$b \neq 0.$$

Then there exists a u such that

$$u^n = b.$$

Proof: We set

$$a = \frac{b}{|b|}.$$

Then

$$|a| = \frac{|b|}{||b||} = \frac{|b|}{|b|} = 1.$$

By Theorem 330, we choose a t such that

$$t^n = a$$

and set

$$u = t\sqrt[n]{|b|}.$$

Then we have

$$u^n = t^n |b| = \frac{b}{|b|} |b| = b.$$

Theorem 332: *Let $n > 0$, let $a_n \neq 0$, and let*

$$g(\zeta) \neq 0.$$

Then there exists a z such that

$$|g(z)| < |g(\zeta)|.$$

Proof: 1) W.l.g., let $\zeta = 0$. For otherwise, we consider

$$g(\zeta + z) = \sum_{\nu=0}^{n} a_\nu (\zeta + z)^\nu = \sum_{\nu=0}^{n} a_\nu \sum_{\mu=0}^{\nu} \binom{\nu}{\mu} \zeta^{\nu-\mu} z^\mu = \sum_{\nu=0}^{n} b_\nu z^\nu = G(z),$$

where

$$b_n = a_n,$$

so that

$$b_n \neq 0,$$

$$G(0) = g(\zeta),$$

so that

$$G(0) \neq 0,$$

and observe that if

$$|G(z)| < |G(0)|,$$

then

$$|g(\zeta + z)| < |g(\zeta)|.$$

2) W.l.g., let

$$g(0) = 1.$$

For otherwise, we consider

$$\frac{g(z)}{g(0)} = 1 + \sum_{\nu=1}^{n} c_\nu z^\nu = H(z), \quad c_n \neq 0,$$

and observe that if

$$|H(z)| < 1,$$

then

$$|g(z)| < |g(0)|.$$

3) Therefore we assume that

$$g(z) = 1 + \sum_{\nu=1}^{n} a_\nu z^\nu, \quad a_n \neq 0.$$

Let m be the smallest $\nu \geqq 1$ such that

$$a_\nu \neq 0 \,;$$

then we have

$$g(z) = 1 + \sum_{\nu=m}^{n} a_\nu z^\nu, \quad 1 \leqq m \leqq n.$$

4) W.l.g., let

$$a_m = -1;$$

for otherwise, we choose a u by Theorem 331 such that

$$u^m = -\frac{1}{a_m},$$

$$g(uz) = 1 + \sum_{\nu=m}^{n} a_\nu (uz)^\nu = 1 + \sum_{\nu=m}^{n} e_\nu z^\nu = K(z), \quad e_m = -1, \, e_n \neq 0,$$

and observe that if

$$\mid K(z) \mid < 1,$$

then

$$\mid g(uz) \mid < 1.$$

5) We proceed with the proof for

$$g(z) = 1 + \sum_{\nu=m}^{n} a_\nu z^\nu, \quad 1 \leqq m \leqq n, \quad a_m = -1.$$

(We shall make no further use of the fact that $a_n \neq 0$.) Assuming that $\sum_{\nu=m+1}^{n}$ means 0 in case $m = n$, we have

$$g(z) = (1 - z^m) + \sum_{\nu=m+1}^{n} a_\nu z^\nu,$$

so that we have for $0 < z \leqq 1$ that

$$\mid g(z) \mid \leqq \mid 1 - z^m \mid + \left| \sum_{\nu=m+1}^{n} a_\nu z^\nu \right| \leqq (1 - z^m) + \sum_{\nu=m+1}^{n} \mid a_\nu \mid z^\nu$$

$$\leqq (1 - z^m) + z^{m+1} \sum_{\nu=m+1}^{n} \mid a_\nu \mid = 1 - z^m + z^{m+1}q,$$

where $q \geqq 0$ and is independent of z.

If

$$z = \frac{1}{q+1}$$

then

$$0 < z \leqq 1,$$

$$1 - qz = 1 - \frac{q}{q+1} = \frac{1}{q+1} > 0,$$

$$\mid g(z) \mid \leqq 1 - z^m(1 - qz) < 1.$$

Theorem 333 (Gauss' fundamental theorem of algebra): *If*

$$n > 0, a_n \neq 0,$$

then there exists a ζ such that

$$g(\zeta) = 0.$$

Proof: Let $|g(\zeta)|$ be the smallest value of $|g(z)|$, which exists by Theorem 327. If we had

$$g(\zeta) \neq 0,$$

then this would be in contradiction to Theorem 332.

Theorem 334: *If $n > 0, a_n \neq 0$, then we have for suitable ζ_ν that*

$$g(z) = a_n \prod_{\nu=1}^{n} (z - \zeta_\nu).$$

Proof: W.l.g., let $a_n = 1$ $\left(\text{otherwise we consider } \dfrac{g(z)}{a_n}\right)$.

For $n = 1$, we have

$$g(z) = a_0 + z = z - (- a_0).$$

To proceed from $n - 1$ to n for $n \geq 2$: By Theorem 333,

$$g(z) = 0$$

has a solution ζ_1. Therefore

$$g(z) = g(z) - g(\zeta_1) = \sum_{\nu=1}^{n} a_\nu(z^\nu - \zeta_1^\nu) = (z - \zeta_1) \sum_{\nu=1}^{n} a_\nu \sum_{\mu=0}^{\nu-1} z^\mu \zeta_1^{\nu-1-\mu}$$

$$= (z - \zeta_1)h(z)$$

for all z, where

$$h(z) = \sum_{\nu=0}^{n-1} b_\nu z^\nu, \quad b_{n-1} = 1.$$

The assertion follows from

$$h(z) = \prod_{\nu=2}^{n} (z - \zeta_\nu).$$

Theorem 335: *If $n > 0, a_n \neq 0$, and if the a_ν are real, then $g(z)$ is for real z representable as a product of factors, one of which is a_n, each of the others being of the form*

$$z - r, r \text{ real}$$

or

$$z^2 + tz + u, \ t \text{ and } u \text{ real}, \ t^2 - 4u < 0.$$

Preliminary Remark: The proof, of course, holds for complex z also. But I have already given notice that Theorem 335 will be of interest and of use to us only in the real domain.

Proof: W.l.g., let $a_n = 1$.

$n = 1$ is obvious. Let $n > 1$, and let the theorem be true with n' in place of n where $1 \leqq n' < n$, in particular for $n - 2$ if $n > 2$.

If

$$g(z) = 0$$

has only real solutions, then the assertion is obvious by Theorem 334. For, the ζ_ν appearing there satisfy

$$g(\zeta_\nu) = 0,$$

so that

$$z - \zeta_\nu = z - r, \; r \text{ real.}$$

Otherwise, there exists a ζ such that

$$g(\zeta) = 0,$$

$$\zeta = \alpha + \beta i, \; \alpha \text{ and } \beta \text{ real}, \; \beta \neq 0.$$

Then the complex conjugate number

$$\bar{\zeta} = \alpha - \beta i$$

is different from ζ, and

$$0 = \bar{0} = \overline{\sum_{\nu=0}^{n} a_\nu \zeta^\nu} = \sum_{\nu=0}^{n} a_\nu \overline{\zeta^\nu} = \sum_{\nu=0}^{n} a_\nu \bar{\zeta}^\nu,$$

so that

$$g(\bar{\zeta}) = 0.$$

Therefore in every factorization of the type given in Theorem 334, the factors $z - \zeta$ and $z - \bar{\zeta}$ appear; for if

$$g(z_0) = 0,$$

it follows that one

$$z_0 - \zeta_\nu = 0.$$

Hence we have

$$g(z) = (z - \zeta)(z - \bar{\zeta})G(z),$$

$$G(z) = \sum_{\nu=0}^{n-2} e_\nu z^\nu, \; e_{n-2} = 1.$$

Here we have

$$(z - \zeta)(z - \bar{\zeta}) = (z - \alpha - \beta i)(z - \alpha + \beta i) = (z - \alpha)^2 + \beta^2$$

$$= z^2 - 2\alpha z + \alpha^2 + \beta^2 = z^2 + tz + u,$$

where

$$t = -2\alpha, \quad u = \alpha^2 + \beta^2$$

are real, and where

$$t^2 - 4u = 4\alpha^2 - 4(\alpha^2 + \beta^2) = -4\beta^2 < 0.$$

Consequently,

$$g(z) = (z^2 + tz + u)\,G(z).$$

For real z, we have

$$z^2 + tz + u = (z - \alpha)^2 + \beta^2 > 0,$$

so that

$$G(z) = \frac{g(z)}{z^2 + tz + u}$$

is real, so that

$$0 = G(z) - \overline{G(z)} = \sum_{\nu=0}^{n-2} \left(e_\nu - \overline{e_\nu}\right)z^\nu.$$

By Theorem 334, we therefore have that all

$$e_\nu - \overline{e_\nu} = 0,$$

since the equation

$$\sum_{\nu=0}^{n-2} \left(e_\nu - \overline{e_\nu}\right)z^\nu = 0$$

would otherwise have at most $n - 2$ solutions (whereas it even has infinitely many real solutions).

Hence all e_ν are real.

For $n = 2$, $G(z)$ is the constant 1, and for $n > 2$ (since the theorem is assumed true for $n - 2$), $G(z)$ is factorable in the required way. Hence $g(z)$ is factorable in the required way.

Theorem 336: *Under the hypotheses of Theorem 335, let*

(1)
$$g(z) = (z - \varrho)G(z)$$

or

(2)
$$g(z) = (z^2 + \tau z + v)G(z)$$

for real z, in which $G(z)$ is a polynomial, and where ϱ is real, or τ, v are real and $\tau^2 - 4v < 0$, respectively.

Then in every representation of $g(z)$ as a product, in the sense of Theorem 335, the factor $z - \varrho$, or $z^2 + \tau z + v$ respectively, occurs.

Proof: The factorization (1) or (2) respectively must hold for all z. If we have (1), then

$$g(\varrho) = 0;$$

and hence, in every factorization in the sense of Theorem 335, we have that one

$$\varrho - r = 0,$$

i.e., that ϱ is an r.

If we have (2), then setting

$$-\frac{\tau}{2} + \frac{i}{2}\,\sqrt{4v - \tau^2} = \zeta,$$

we have

$$g(\zeta) = (\zeta^2 + \tau\zeta + v)\, G(\zeta) = \left(\left(\zeta + \frac{\tau}{2}\right)^2 + \frac{1}{4}\,(4v - \tau^2)\right) G(\zeta) = 0.$$

Since ζ is not real, we have for every factorization as in Theorem 335, that one

$$\zeta^2 + t\zeta + u = 0,$$

so that

$$(t - \tau)\,\zeta + u - v = 0,$$
$$t = \tau\,,\ u = v.$$

§ 2. Decomposition of Rational Functions Into Partial Fractions

Henceforth, we will again deal with real numbers only.

Definition 77: *If $\varphi(x)$ and $\psi(x)$ are polynomials, and if $\psi(x)$ is not identically zero* (and thus equals 0 for at most a finite number of x), *then*

$$f(x) = \frac{\varphi(x)}{\psi(x)}$$

is called a rational function.

Definition 78: *If $f(x)$ is a polynomial and not identically 0, then the degree of f is the highest exponent such that the coefficient of the corresponding power of x is not 0. We assign the degree -1 to the polynomial $f(x) = 0$.*

Notation (only for a short while) : $\{f\}$ denotes the degree of $f(x)$.

It is to be noted in Definition 78 that $\{f\}$ is, of course, uniquely determined by f. For if

$$\sum_{\nu=0}^{n} a_\nu x^\nu = \sum_{\nu=0}^{m} b_\nu x^\nu, \quad a_n \neq 0, \quad b_m \neq 0,$$

then

$$n = m$$

(and $a_\nu = b_\nu$ for $0 \leqq \nu \leqq n$).

Examples: $\{0\} = -1$, $\{3\} = 0$, $\{3 + x^2 + 0 \cdot x^3\} = 2$.

Theorem 337: *Let $f_1(x)$ and $f_2(x)$ be polynomials, and let*

$$\{f_2\} \geqq 0.$$

Then there exist polynomials $q(x)$, $r(x)$ such that

$$f_1(x) = q(x)f_2(x) + r(x), \quad \{r\} < \{f_2\}.$$

Proof: Let $f_2(x)$ be fixed, and let

$$\{f_2\} = n,$$

so that

$$n \geqq 0;$$

$$\{f_1\} = m.$$

If $m < n$, then the assertion, with

$$q(x) = 0, \ r(x) = f_1(x),$$

is obvious.

Suppose that $m \geq n$, and, w.l.g., that the assertion has been proved for all $g(x)$ with $\{g\} < m$ (in place of $f_1(x)$). Then

$$f_1(x) = Ax^m + g_1(x), \ A \neq 0, \ \{g_1\} < m,$$

$$f_2(x) = Bx^n + g_2(x), \ B \neq 0, \ \{g_2\} < n,$$

so that

$$f_1(x) - \frac{A}{B} x^{m-n} f_2(x) = Ax^m + g_1(x) - Ax^m - \frac{A}{B} x^{m-n} g_2(x) = g_3(x),$$

$$\{g_3\} < m,$$

so that

$$g_3(x) = q_1(x) f_2(x) + r(x),$$

$$q_1(x) \text{ a polynomial, } \{r\} < n,$$

and consequently

$$f_1(x) = \left(\frac{A}{B} x^{m-n} + q_1(x) \right) f_2(x) + r(x) = q(x) f_2(x) + r(x).$$

Example: $\qquad f_1(x) = x^3 - 1, \ f_2(x) = x + 1.$

$$f_1 - x^2 f_2 = x^3 - 1 - x^3 - x^2 = - x^2 - 1,$$

$$f_1 - x^2 f_2 + x f_2 = - x^2 - 1 + x^2 + x = x - 1,$$

$$f_1 - x^2 f_2 + x f_2 - f_2 = - 2,$$

$$f_1(x) = (x_1^2 - x + 1) f_2(x) - 2 = q(x) f_2(x) + r(x)$$

with

$$q(x) = x^2 - x + 1, \ r(x) = - 2.$$

Theorem 338: *Let $f_1(x)$ and $f_2(x)$ be polynomials, and let*

$$\{f_1\} \geqq 0, \ \{f_2\} \geqq 0.$$

Let no factor of first or second degree which occurs in a factorization of $f_1(x)$ in the sense of Theorem 335 occur in any such factorization of $f_2(x)$. Then there exists two polynomials $\Psi_1(x)$, $\Psi_2(x)$ with

$$\Psi_1(x) f_1(x) + \Psi_2(x) f_2(x) = 1.$$

Proof: I consider all polynomials $P(x)$ with $\{P\} \geqq 0$ such that for suitable polynomials $g_1(x)$, $g_2(x)$ we have

$$P(x) = g_1(x) f_1(x) + g_2(x) f_2(x).$$

Such a polynomial $P(x)$ exists, namely

$$f_1(x) = 1 \cdot f_1(x) + 0 \cdot f_2(x).$$

Among all these $P(x)$, we choose one of smallest possible degree. Then, by Theorem 337 (with $P(x)$ for $f_2(x)$), we have for a suitable polynomial $q(x)$ that

$$f_1(x) = q(x)P(x) + r(x), \quad \{r\} < \{P\},$$

$$r(x) = f_1(x) - q(x)P(x) = f_1(x) - q(x)(g_1(x)f_1(x) + g_2(x)f_2(x))$$

$$= G_1(x)f_1(x) + G_2(x)f_2(x),$$

where $G_1(x)$ and $G_2(x)$ are polynomials. Since

$$\{r\} < \{P\},$$

we have that

$$r(x) = 0,$$

$$f_1(x) = q(x)P(x).$$

For reasons of symmetry, we also have for a suitable polynomial $Q(x)$ that

$$f_2(x) = Q(x)P(x).$$

Hence we have

$$\{P\} = 0,\text{---}$$

for otherwise, every (and therefore one) factor of the first or second degree occurring in a factorization of $P(x)$ in the sense of Theorem 335 would occur in one such factorization of both $f_1(x)$ and $f_2(x)$.

Therefore we have

$$P(x) = c, \quad c \neq 0,$$

$$1 = \frac{g_1(x)}{c} f_1(x) + \frac{g_2(x)}{c} f_2(x) = \Psi_1(x)f_1(x) + \Psi_2(x)f_2(x).$$

Theorem 339: *Let $f_1(x)$ and $f_2(x)$ satisfy the hypotheses of Theorem 338. Then for every polynomial $\varphi(x)$, there exist polynomials $\varphi_1(x)$ and $\varphi_2(x)$ such that whenever*

$$f_1(x) \cdot f_2(x) \neq 0,$$

then

$$\frac{\varphi}{f_1 f_2} = \frac{\varphi_1}{f_1} + \frac{\varphi_2}{f_2}.$$

Proof: Using the polynomials Ψ_1 and Ψ_2 of Theorem 338, we have

$$\frac{\varphi}{f_1 f_2} = \varphi\left(\frac{\Psi_2}{f_1} + \frac{\Psi_1}{f_2}\right) = \frac{\varphi\Psi_2}{f_1} + \frac{\varphi\Psi_1}{f_2} = \frac{\varphi_1}{f_1} + \frac{\varphi_2}{f_2}.$$

Theorem 340: *Let $q \geqq 1$, and let $f_s(x)$ be a polynomial with $\{f_s\} \geqq 0$ for every integer s with $1 \leqq s \leqq q$. Let no factor of the first or second degree* *appear in a factorization of two $f_s(x)$ in the sense of Theorem 335. Let $\varphi(x)$ be a polynomial. Then there exist polynomials $\varphi_s(x)$, $1 \leq s \leq q$, with*

$$\frac{\varphi(x)}{\prod\limits_{s=1}^{q} f_s(x)} = \sum_{s=1}^{q} \frac{\varphi_s(x)}{f_s(x)}$$

for all x where no $f_s(x) = 0$.

Proof: $q = 1$ is obvious. To proceed from q to $q + 1$: By Theorem 339, we have for suitable polynomials $\chi(x)$, $\varphi_{q+1}(x)$ that

$$\frac{\varphi}{\prod\limits_{s=1}^{q+1} f_s} = \frac{\varphi}{\prod\limits_{s=1}^{q} f_s \cdot f_{q+1}} = \frac{\chi}{\prod\limits_{s=1}^{q} f_s} + \frac{\varphi_{q+1}}{f_{q+1}} \,,$$

and so, for suitable polynomials $\varphi_s(x)$, $1 \leq s \leq q$, that

$$\frac{\varphi}{\prod\limits_{s=1}^{q+1} f_s} = \sum_{s=1}^{q} \frac{\varphi_s}{f_s} + \frac{\varphi_{q+1}}{f_{q+1}} = \sum_{s=1}^{q+1} \frac{\varphi_s}{f_s} \,.$$

Theorem 341 (decomposition into partial fractions): *If $\varphi(x)$ and $\psi(x)$ are polynomials, $\{ \psi \} \geq 0$, then for those x with $\psi(x) \neq 0$, $\dfrac{\varphi(x)}{\psi(x)}$ can be represented as a finite sum of rational functions each of which is of one of the forms*

$$cx^\lambda, \ \lambda \geq 0 \ \text{integral,}$$

or

$$\frac{A}{(x - \alpha)^\lambda}, \ \lambda > 0 \ \text{integral,}$$

or

$$\frac{Bx + C}{((x - \beta)^2 + \gamma^2)^\lambda}, \ \lambda > 0 \ \text{integral,} \ \gamma > 0.$$

Proof: If $\{ \psi \} = 0$, then $\dfrac{\varphi(x)}{\psi(x)}$ is a polynomial, and there is nothing further to prove.

If $\{ \psi \} > 0$, let, w.l.g., 1 be the highest "coefficient" in $\psi(x)$ (i.e. the coefficient of $x^{\{\psi\}}$), since

$$\frac{\varphi(x)}{\psi(x)} = \frac{b\varphi(x)}{b\psi(x)} \ \text{for} \ b \neq 0 \,.$$

By Theorem 335, if equal factors $x - r$ or $x^2 + tx + u$, $t^2 - 4u < 0$, are combined, then $\psi(x)$ is a product of finitely many factors $f_s(x)$ each having the form $(x - \alpha)^\mu$, $\mu \geq 1$ and integral, or $((x - \beta)^2 + \gamma^2)^\mu$, $\gamma > 0$, $\mu \geq 1$ and integral. For simplicity, we have set

$$\alpha = r, \quad \beta = -\frac{t}{2}, \quad \gamma = \sqrt{u - \frac{t^2}{4}} \,.$$

Therefore, by Theorem 340, it remains to be shown that

$$\frac{g(x)}{(x-\alpha)^{\mu}} \quad \text{and} \quad \frac{g(x)}{((x-\beta)^2+\gamma^2)^{\mu}}, \quad \mu \geq 1 \text{ integral, } \gamma > 0,$$

may be decomposed in the required way for every polynomial $g(x)$.

1) Setting

$$x = \alpha + y,$$

then we have for $x \neq \alpha$ that

$$\frac{g(x)}{(x-\alpha)^{\mu}} = \frac{\displaystyle\sum_{\nu=0}^{k} c_{\nu} y^{\nu}}{y^{\mu}} = \sum_{\nu=0}^{k} c_{\nu} y^{\nu-\mu}$$

is the sum of a polynomial in y (and therefore in x) and possibly of a finite number of terms of the form

$$\frac{A}{y^{\lambda}} = \frac{A}{(x-\alpha)^{\lambda}}, \quad \lambda > 0 \text{ integral.}$$

2) If, as an abbreviation, we set

$$(x-\beta)^2 + \gamma^2 = \chi(x),$$

then we have by Theorem 337 that

$$g(x) = g_1(x)\chi(x) + g_2(x),$$

$$g_1(x) \text{ a polynomial,} \quad \{ g_2 \} \leq 1,$$

so that

$$\frac{g}{\chi^{\mu}} = \frac{g_2}{\chi^{\mu}} + \frac{g_1}{\chi^{\mu-1}}.$$

$\dfrac{g_2}{\chi^{\mu}}$ has the required form $\dfrac{Bx+C}{\chi^{\lambda}}$, $\lambda > 0$; $\dfrac{g_1}{\chi^{\mu-1}}$ is a polynomial for $\mu = 1$,

and the factorability of $\dfrac{g_1}{\chi^{\mu-1}}$ for $\mu > 1$ may be assumed.

Example to 2): $g(x) = x^7 + 1$, $\chi(x) = x^2+1$, $\mu = 2$.

$$g(x) = (x^5 - x^3+x)(x^2 + 1) + (-x + 1) = (x^5 - x^3 + x)\,\chi(x)+(-x+1),$$

$$\frac{g(x)}{\chi^2(x)} = \frac{-x+1}{(x^2+1)^2} + \frac{x^5-x^3+x}{x^2+1},$$

$$x^5 - x^3 + x = (x^3 - 2x)(x^2+1) + 3x = (x^3-2x)\chi(x) + 3x,$$

$$\frac{g(x)}{\chi^2(x)} = \frac{-x+1}{(x^2+1)^2} + \frac{3x}{x^2+1} + x^3 - 2x.$$

In practice, we do not apply the general method to decompose a rational function into partial fractions, but (since we already know the form of the result) we use the so-called method of undetermined coefficients.

Examples: 1) By the proof (not the statement) of Theorem 341, we surely have that

$$\frac{1}{x^3 - x} = \frac{1}{x(x+1)(x-1)} = \frac{a}{x} + \frac{b}{x+1} + \frac{c}{x-1} + G(x),$$

where a, b, and c, are constants, and $G(x)$ is a polynomial. Since

$$\lim_{x=\infty} \left(\frac{1}{x^3 - x} - \frac{a}{x} - \frac{b}{x+1} - \frac{c}{x-1} \right) = 0,$$

we have that

$$G(x) = 0,$$

$$1 = a(x^2 - 1) + b(x^2 - x) + c(x^2 + x),$$

$$0 = (a + b + c)x^2 + (c - b)x - (a + 1),$$

$$a + b + c = c - b = a + 1 = 0,$$

$$a = -1, \quad b = c = \tfrac{1}{2},$$

$$\frac{1}{x^3 - x} = -\frac{1}{x} + \frac{\tfrac{1}{2}}{x+1} + \frac{\tfrac{1}{2}}{x-1}.$$

2) In general, for

$$\psi(x) = \prod_{\nu=1}^{n} (x - \alpha_\nu),$$

where the α_ν are distinct, and for every polynomial $\varphi(x)$, we have by the proof of Theorem 341 that

(1)
$$\frac{\varphi(x)}{\psi(x)} = \sum_{\nu=1}^{n} \frac{A_\nu}{x - \alpha_\nu} + G(x),$$

where $G(x)$ is a polynomial. To determine the A_ν do not use the method of undetermined coefficients. Instead, we may prove the general formula

$$A_\nu = \frac{\varphi(\alpha_\nu)}{\psi'(\alpha_\nu)}.$$

(Then

$$G(x) = \frac{\varphi(x)}{\psi(x)} - \sum_{\nu=1}^{n} \frac{A_\nu}{x - \alpha_\nu}$$

is automatically a polynomial.) For, we have

$$\psi'(\alpha_\nu) = \lim_{x=\alpha_\nu} \frac{\psi(x)}{x-\alpha_\nu} = \prod_{\substack{\mu=1 \\ \mu\neq\nu}}^{n} (\alpha_\nu - \alpha_\mu)$$

(which means 1 in case $n=1$), so that

$$\psi'(\alpha_\nu) \neq 0.$$

By 1), we have for $0 < |x - \alpha_\nu| < p$ with a suitable $p > 0$, that

$$\varphi(x) = A_\nu \frac{\psi(x)}{x-\alpha_\nu} + \psi(x) \sum_{\substack{\mu=1 \\ \mu\neq\nu}}^{n} \frac{A_\mu}{x - \alpha_\mu} + \psi(x)G(x)$$

(the sum on the right means 0 in case $n=1$). Letting $x \to \alpha_\nu$, we obtain

$$\varphi(\alpha_\nu) = A_\nu \psi'(\alpha_\nu).$$

For example, for $\varphi(x) = 1$, $\psi(x) = x^3 - x$, we find, corresponding to the result of example 1) and setting $\alpha_1 = 0$, $\alpha_2 = -1$, $\alpha_3 = 1$, that

$$\psi'(x) = 3x^2 - 1,$$

$$A_1 = \frac{1}{-1} = -1, \; A_2 = A_3 = \frac{1}{3-1} = \frac{1}{2}.$$

3) An example where we use the method of undetermined coefficients. By the proof of Theorem 341, we have

$$\frac{x+2}{x^4+x^3} = \frac{x+2}{x^3(x+1)} = \frac{a}{x^3} + \frac{b}{x^2} + \frac{c}{x} + \frac{d}{x+1} + G(x),$$

where $G(x)$ is a polynomial.

$$\lim_{x=\infty} \left(\frac{x+2}{x^4+x^3} - \frac{a}{x^3} - \frac{b}{x^2} - \frac{c}{x} - \frac{d}{x+1} \right) = 0,$$

$$G(x) = 0,$$

$$x + 2 = a(x+1) + bx(x+1) + cx^2(x+1) + dx^3,$$

$$0 = (c+d)x^3 + (b+c)x^2 + (a+b-1)x + (a-2),$$

$$c + d = b + c = a + b - 1 = a - 2 = 0,$$

$$a = 2, \; b = -1, \; c = 1, \; d = -1,$$

$$\frac{x+2}{x^4+x^3} = \frac{2}{x^3} - \frac{1}{x^2} + \frac{1}{x} - \frac{1}{x+1}.$$

PART TWO

INTEGRAL
CALCULUS

CHAPTER 21

DEFINITION OF THE INTEGRAL

The integral calculus is the inverse of the differential calculus in the following sense.

Definition 79: *Let $a < b$, and let $f(x)$ be defined for $a < x < b$. If there exists a $g(x)$ defined for $a < x < b$ such that the equation*

$$g'(x) = f(x)$$

holds for $a < x < b$, then $g(x)$ is said to be an integral of $f(x)$.

The integral? No; **an** integral. For if c is any number, then $g(x) + c$ is also what is required, since

$$(g(x) + c)' = g'(x) = f(x).$$

And no other function will do, as we see by applying Theorem 162 to every interval $[\alpha, \beta]$ with $a < \alpha < \beta < b$.

Hence the problem of finding all $g(x)$ is equivalent to that of finding one of them. However, there need not exist any. For, as we already know, not every function defined for $a < x < b$ is a derivative. For example, in case

$$a < \alpha < \beta < b, \quad f(\alpha) = -1, \quad f(\beta) = 1,$$

then, by Theorem 164, $f(x)$ must assume the value 0 between α and β.

Definition 80: *If $a < b$, then x is said to be interior to the interval $[a, b]$ if $a < x < b$. The totality of such x is called an open interval.*

Example: If

$$f(x) = 4x^3,$$

then we have in the interior of every $[a, b]$ that

$$\frac{dx^4}{dx} = f(x) ;$$

and hence the most general function having derivative $4x^3$ thereon is $x^4 + c$.

Notation: *If $g(x)$ is a particular solution of*

$$g'(x) = f(x) \ \text{for} \ a < x < b$$

then we write

$$\int f(x)\,dx = g(x) + c\,.$$

The left-hand side to be read "integral $f(x)$ dee eks." $f(x)$ *is called the integrand.*

Thus, for example,

$$\int 4x^3\,dx = x^4 + c\,.$$

Why the funny dx following $g(x)$? We may not omit it, since we must know with respect to what variable we are to differentiate the right-hand side. For example,

$$\int zx^3\,dx = z\,\frac{x^4}{4} + c\,,$$

but

$$\int zx^3\,dz = \frac{z^2}{2}\,x^3 + c\,.$$

For $\displaystyle\int \frac{1}{\psi(x)}\,dx$ we also write $\displaystyle\int \frac{dx}{\psi(x)}$, for $\displaystyle\int \frac{\varphi(x)}{\psi(x)}\,dx$ also $\displaystyle\int \frac{\varphi(x)dx}{\psi(x)}$ or $\displaystyle\int \varphi(x)\,\frac{dx}{\psi(x)}$, for $\int 1\,dx$ also $\int dx$. (In other words, in this notation we manipulate the meaningless dx as though it were a number.)

We did not require in Definition 79 that $f(x)$ be continuous. But even if we assume this, we do not know for the moment whether such a $g(x)$ exists. I begin by proving in the simplest possible way that this is always the case. This will be very difficult, one of the most difficult proofs in the book. But all of the concepts to be introduced will be used again later on. Indeed, the entire chain of proof will come up once more later on, but in connection with much more general investigations in which Theorem 154 on uniform continuity will also be used. It will be new even to most of the advanced readers that Theorem 344 can be proved without the use of Theorem 154, a fact which I have learned from a paper by Poli.

Theorem 342: *To any interval $[a, b]$ and any function $f(x)$ bounded on this interval we may assign a number $\mathrm{L}(a, b)$ such that*

1) *if λ is the g.l.b., l the l.u.b. of $f(x)$ on $[a, b]$, then*

(1) $$\lambda(b - a) \leqq \mathrm{L}(a, b) \leqq l(b - a),$$

2)

(2) $$\mathrm{L}(a, b) = \mathrm{L}(a, c) + \mathrm{L}(c, b) \ \text{for} \ a < c < b.$$

Proof: 1) Let n be any integer > 0, and let a_ν be defined for every integer ν with $0 \leq \nu \leq n$ in such a way that

$$a_{\nu-1} < a_\nu \text{ for } 1 \leq \nu \leq n,$$

$$a_0 = a, \ a_n = b;$$

let

$$e_\nu = a_\nu - a_{\nu-1} \text{ for } 1 \leq \nu \leq n,$$

so that

$$l_\nu \text{ be the l.u.b. of } f(x) \text{ in } [a_{\nu-1}, a_\nu],$$

$$\lambda \leq l_\nu \leq l.$$

Then for every such "partition," we have

$$\lambda(b - a) = \lambda \sum_{\nu=1}^n e_\nu \leq \sum_{\nu=1}^n e_\nu l_\nu \leq l \sum_{\nu=1}^n e_\nu = l(b - a).$$

$\sum_{\nu=1}^n e_\nu l_\nu$ is therefore bounded from below and therefore has a greatest lower bound (for all partitions). We call this number $L(a, b)$. Then (1) holds.

2) For every $\delta > 0$, we choose a partition of $[a, c]$ such that

$$\sum e_\nu l_\nu < L(a, c) + \delta,$$

and a partition of $[c, b]$ such that

$$\sum e_\nu l_\nu < L(c, b) + \delta.$$

Then we have a partition of $[a, b]$ such that

$$L(a, b) \leq \sum e_\nu l_\nu < L(a, c) + L(c, b) + 2\delta.$$

Hence (since this holds for every $\delta > 0$), we have

(3) $$L(a, b) \leq L(a, c) + L(c, b).$$

On the other hand, let us choose for every $\delta > 0$ a partition of $[a, b]$ such that

$$\sum_{\nu=1}^n e_\nu l_\nu < L(a, b) + \delta.$$

We may assume that c is some a_ν of this partition. For otherwise, we add c to the a_ν of this partition. If c was between $\alpha = a_\mu$, $\beta = a_{\mu+1}$ and if l, l', and l'' are the least upper bounds of $f(x)$ on $[a, \beta]$, $[a, c]$, and $[c, \beta]$ respectively, then

$$l \geq l', \quad l \geq l'',$$

$$(\beta - \alpha)l = (c - \alpha)l + (\beta - c)l \geq (c - \alpha)l' + (\beta - c)l'',$$

so that $\sum e_\nu l_\nu$ does not increase.

Hence we have a partition of $[a, c]$ and one of $[c, b]$. Therefore,

$$L(a,\ c) + L(c,\ b) \leqq \sum_{\nu=1}^{n} e_\nu\, l_\nu < L\,(a,\ b) + \delta.$$

Therefore (since this true for every $\delta > 0$),

(4) $$L(a,\ c) + L(c,\ b) \leqq L(a,\ b).$$

(3) and (4) together imply (2).

Theorem 343: *If $f(x)$ is bounded on $[a, b]$, then there exists a $g(x)$ defined for $a < x < b$ such that, for all numbers ξ with $a < \xi < b$ at which $f(x)$ is continuous, we have*

$$g'(\xi) = f(\xi).$$

And, in fact,

$$g(x) = L(a,\ x)$$

is the required function.

Preliminary Remark: If $f(x)$ is discontinuous at every x between a and b, then the existence of a $g(x)$ with the required property is trivial, since then $g(x) = 0$ will do. If, for example, $f(x)$ is continuous for only one x between a and b, say at $x = \xi$, then we may choose $g(x) = f(\xi)x$. But this is not trivial if $f(x)$ is continuous everywhere in $a < x < b$. To establish the existence of a suitable $g(x)$ is substantially the purpose of this chapter.

Proof: Let

$$g(x) = L(a, x).$$

If $a < \xi < b$, and if $f(x)$ is continuous at ξ, then for every $\delta > 0$ we choose an ε with

$$0 < \varepsilon \leqq \text{Min}\ (b - \xi,\ \xi - a),$$

$$|\,f(x) - f(\xi)\,| < \delta \text{ for } |\,x - \xi\,| < \varepsilon.$$

For $0 < h < \varepsilon$ (or $-\varepsilon < h < 0$) we have by Theorem 342, 2) that

$$g(\xi + h) - g(\xi) = L(a, \xi + h) - L(a, \xi)$$

$$= L(\xi, \xi + h) \qquad (\text{or} -L(\xi + h, \xi)).$$

Hence by Theorem 342, 1) applied to $[\xi, \xi + h]$ (or to $[\xi + h, \xi]$), with $\lambda \geqq f(\xi) - \delta, l \leqq f(\xi) + \delta$, we have

$$h(f(\xi) - \delta) \leqq g(\xi + h) - g(\xi) \leqq h(f(\xi) + \delta) \text{ for } 0 < h < \varepsilon,$$

$$h(f(\xi) + \delta) \leqq g(\xi + h) - g(\xi) \leqq h(f(\xi) - \delta) \text{ for } -\varepsilon < h < 0.$$

Hence for $0 < |\,h\,| < \varepsilon$, we have

$$\left|\frac{g(\xi + h) - g(\xi)}{h} - f(\xi)\right| \leqq \delta.$$

Therefore we have

$$g'(\xi) = f(\xi).$$

Theorem 344: *If $a < b$, and if $f(x)$ is continuous for $a < x < b$, then there exists a $g(x)$ for $a < x < b$ such that*

$$g'(x) = f(x);$$

i.e.

$$\int f(x)\,dx$$

exists for $a < x < b$.

Proof: We set

$$c = \frac{a + b}{2},$$

$$g(x) = \begin{cases} -L(x, c) & \text{for } a < x < c, \\ 0 & \text{for } x = c, \\ L(c, x) & \text{for } c < x < b. \end{cases}$$

Let

$$a < \xi < b,$$

and set

$$\eta = \frac{a + \xi}{2} \quad (< c).$$

For $\eta < x < b$, we have by Theorem 342, 2) that

$$g(x) = L(\eta, x) - L(\eta, c).$$

By Theorem 343, applied to the interval $[\,\eta, \dfrac{\xi + b}{2}\,]$, the derivative of $L(\eta, x)$ exists for $x = \xi$ and equals $f(\xi)$. Hence,

$$g'(\xi) = f(\xi).$$

After this effort, we shall proceed to "integrate" a number of familiar continuous functions, and we will be successful in the sense that the integrals will also be among the functions familiar to us.

Theorem 345: *If $n \neq -1$, then*

$$\int x^n\,dx = \frac{x^{n+1}}{n + 1} + c \quad \text{for } a \geqq 0$$

(i.e. in every open interval $a < x < b$ with $a \geqq 0$).

Proof: For $x > 0$, we have by Theorem 109 that

(1) $\qquad \left(\dfrac{x^{n+1}}{n + 1}\right)' = \dfrac{1}{n + 1}\,(x^{n+1})' = \dfrac{1}{n + 1}\,(n + 1)x^n = x^n.$

Theorem 346: *If n is an integer $\neq 1$, then*

$$\int x^n \, dx = \frac{x^{n+1}}{n+1} + c \text{ for } a \geqq 0 \text{ and for } b \leqq 0.$$

Proof: By Theorem 119, (1) holds for $x \neq 0$.

Theorem 347: *If n is an integer $\geqq 0$, then for all x we have*

$$\int x^n \, dx = \frac{x^{n+1}}{n+1} + c.$$

Proof: By Theorem 103, (1) holds for all x.

Theorem 348: $\quad \displaystyle\int \frac{dx}{x} = \begin{cases} \log x + c \text{ for } a \geqq 0, \\ \log (-x) + c \text{ for } b \leqq 0. \end{cases}$

Preliminary Remarks: 1) With this, the gap $(n = -1)$ in Theorems 345 and 346 is filled. However, the existence of the integral has already been obtained in Theorem 344.

2) The result for both cases may be summarized as follows:

$$\int \frac{dx}{x} = \log |x| + c = \tfrac{1}{2} \log (x^2) + c.$$

Proof: Theorems 104 and 105.

Theorem 349: $\quad \displaystyle\int \sum_{\nu=0}^{n} a_\nu x^\nu \, dx = \sum_{\nu=0}^{n} a_\nu \frac{x^{\nu+1}}{\nu+1} + c.$

Preliminary Remark: Observe that the integral of a polynomial is a polynomial. We already know that the derivative of a polynomial is a polynomial.

Proof: The derivative of the right-hand side is the integrand.

Theorem 350: $\qquad\qquad \displaystyle\int e^x \, dx = e^x + c.$

Proof: $\qquad\qquad\qquad (e^x)' = e^x.$

Theorem 351: $\displaystyle\int \frac{dx}{x - \gamma} = \log |x - \gamma| + c \text{ for } a \geqq \gamma \text{ and for } b \leqq \gamma.$

Proof: For $x > \gamma$, we have

$$\big(\log (x - \gamma)\big)' = \frac{1}{x - \gamma} (x - \gamma)' = \frac{1}{x - \gamma};$$

for $x < \gamma$, we have

$$\big(\log (\gamma - x)\big)' = \frac{1}{\gamma - x} (\gamma - x)' = \frac{1}{x - \gamma}.$$

Therefore we have

$$g'(\xi) = f(\xi).$$

Theorem 344: *If $a < b$, and if $f(x)$ is continuous for $a < x < b$, then there exists a $g(x)$ for $a < x < b$ such that*

$$g'(x) = f(x);$$

i.e.

$$\int f(x)\,dx$$

exists for $a < x < b$.

Proof: We set

$$c = \frac{a+b}{2},$$

$$g(x) = \begin{cases} -L(x,\,c) & \text{for } a < x < c, \\ 0 & \text{for } x = c, \\ L(c,\,x) & \text{for } c < x < b. \end{cases}$$

Let

$$a < \xi < b,$$

and set

$$\eta = \frac{a+\xi}{2} \quad (< c).$$

For $\eta < x < b$, we have by Theorem 342, 2) that

$$g(x) = L(\eta,\,x) - L(\eta,\,c).$$

By Theorem 343, applied to the interval $[\,\eta,\,\dfrac{\xi+b}{2}\,]$, the derivative of $L(\eta,\,x)$ exists for $x = \xi$ and equals $f(\xi)$. Hence,

$$g'(\xi) = f(\xi).$$

After this effort, we shall proceed to "integrate" a number of familiar continuous functions, and we will be successful in the sense that the integrals will also be among the functions familiar to us.

Theorem 345: *If $n \neq -1$, then*

$$\int x^n\,dx = \frac{x^{n+1}}{n+1} + c \quad \text{for } a \geq 0$$

(i.e. in every open interval $a < x < b$ with $a \geq 0$).

Proof: For $x > 0$, we have by Theorem 109 that

$$(1) \qquad \left(\frac{x^{n+1}}{n+1}\right)' = \frac{1}{n+1}\,(x^{n+1})' = \frac{1}{n+1}\,(n+1)x^n = x^n.$$

Theorem 346: *If n is an integer $\neq 1$, then*

$$\int x^n \, dx = \frac{x^{n+1}}{n+1} + c \text{ for } a \geq 0 \text{ and for } b \leq 0.$$

Proof: By Theorem 119, (1) holds for $x \neq 0$.

Theorem 347: *If n is an integer ≥ 0, then for all x we have*

$$\int x^n \, dx = \frac{x^{n+1}}{n+1} + c.$$

Proof: By Theorem 103, (1) holds for all x.

Theorem 348: $\quad \int \frac{dx}{x} = \begin{cases} \log x + c & \text{for } a \geq 0, \\ \log(-x) + c & \text{for } b \leq 0. \end{cases}$

Preliminary Remarks: 1) With this, the gap $(n = -1)$ in Theorems 345 and 346 is filled. However, the existence of the integral has already been obtained in Theorem 344.

2) The result for both cases may be summarized as follows:

$$\int \frac{dx}{x} = \log|x| + c = \tfrac{1}{2}\log(x^2) + c.$$

Proof: Theorems 104 and 105.

Theorem 349: $\quad \int \sum_{\nu=0}^{n} a_\nu x^\nu \, dx = \sum_{\nu=0}^{n} a_\nu \frac{x^{\nu+1}}{\nu+1} + c.$

Preliminary Remark: Observe that the integral of a polynomial is a polynomial. We already know that the derivative of a polynomial is a polynomial.

Proof: The derivative of the right-hand side is the integrand.

Theorem 350: $\quad \int e^x \, dx = e^x + c.$

Proof: $\quad (e^x)' = e^x.$

Theorem 351: $\int \frac{dx}{x-\gamma} = \log|x-\gamma| + c$ *for* $a \geq \gamma$ *and for* $b \leq \gamma$.

Proof: For $x > \gamma$, we have

$$(\log(x-\gamma))' = \frac{1}{x-\gamma}(x-\gamma)' = \frac{1}{x-\gamma};$$

for $x < \gamma$, we have

$$(\log(\gamma-x))' = \frac{1}{\gamma-x}(\gamma-x)' = \frac{1}{x-\gamma}.$$

CHAPTER 22

BASIC FORMULAS OF THE INTEGRAL CALCULUS

Abbreviation: i.r.h.s.i.m. is an abbreviation for "if the right-hand side is meaningful."

Theorem 352: $\int (f(x) + g(x))\, dx = \int f(x)\, dx + \int g(x)\, dx$,
i.r.h.s.i.m. (i.e. if $f(x)$ and $g(x)$ are integrable for $a < x < b$).

Preliminary Remark: In such formulas, where an integral appears as a summand on the right-hand side, the additive constant may be omitted.

Proof: (Right-hand side)$' = \left(\int f(x)\, dx\right)' + \left(\int g(x)\, dx\right)'$
$$= f(x) + g(x) = \text{Integrand on the left.}$$

Example: $\int (x + e^x)\, dx = \dfrac{x^2}{2} + e^x + c$.

Theorem 353: $\int \sum_{n=1}^{m} f_n(x)\, dx = \sum_{n=1}^{m} \int f_n(x)\, dx$,
i.r.h.s.i.m.

Proof: (Right-hand side)$' =$ Integrand on the left.

Theorem 354: $\int \gamma f(x)\, dx = \gamma \int f(x)\, dx + c$,
i.r.h.s.i.m.

Proof: $\left(\gamma \int f(x)\, dx\right)' = \gamma \left(\int f(x)\, dx\right)' = \gamma f(x)$.

Theorem 355: $\int (f(x) - g(x))\, dx = \int f(x)\, dx - \int g(x)\, dx$,
i.r.h.s.i.m.

Proof: (Right-hand side)$' =$ Integrand on the left.

Examples: 1) If neither of the numbers -1 or 1 belongs to the open interval $a < x < b$, we have

$$\frac{1}{x^2 - 1} = \frac{1}{2(x-1)} - \frac{1}{2(x+1)} ,$$

so that

$$\int \frac{dx}{x^2 - 1} = \int \frac{dx}{2(x-1)} - \int \frac{dx}{2(x+1)} = \frac{1}{2} \log |x-1| - \frac{1}{2} \log |x+1| + c$$

$$= \frac{1}{2} \log \left| \frac{x-1}{x+1} \right| + c .$$

2) Let n be a positive integer. For $a \geq 1$ and for $b \leq 1$, we have

$$\int \frac{1 - x^n}{1 - x} dx = \int \sum_{\nu=1}^{n} x^{\nu-1} dx = \sum_{\nu=1}^{n} \frac{x^\nu}{\nu} + c .$$

Theorem 356 (integration by parts): *Let*

$$g'(x), \ h'(x), \ \int h(x) g'(x) dx$$

exist for $a < x < b$. Then

$$\int g(x) h'(x) dx$$

exists there, and

$$\int g(x) h'(x) dx = g(x) h(x) - \int h(x) g'(x) dx .$$

Preliminary Remark: Thus $\int f(x) dx$ exists if we can split $f(x)$ into $g(x) k(x)$, where $g(x)$ is differentiable and $k(x)$ and $g'(x) \int k(x) dx$ are integrable. In the formula

$$\int f(x) dx = g(x) \int k(x) dx - \int \left(g'(x) \int k(x) dx \right) dx ,$$

the last integral is, in certain cases, more easily calculated than the first.

Proof: $\left(gh - \int hg' dx \right)' = (gh)' - \left(\int hg' \, dx \right)' = gh' + hg' - hg' = gh' .$

Examples: 1) $\qquad g(x) = x, \qquad h(x) = e^x ,$
$\qquad\qquad\qquad\qquad g'(x) = 1, \qquad h'(x) = e^x ,$

$$\int x e^x dx = x e^x - \int e^x dx = x e^x - e^x + c .$$

2) $\qquad\qquad\qquad\qquad g(x) = x^2, \qquad h(x) = e^x ,$
$\qquad\qquad\qquad\qquad g'(x) = 2x, \qquad h'(x) = e^x ,$

$$\int x^2 e^x dx = x^2 e^x - \int 2x e^x dx = x^2 e^x - 2 \int x e^x dx$$

$$= x^2 e^x - 2(x e^x - e^x) + c = (x^2 - 2x + 2) e^x + c .$$

3) For $a \geqq 0$, we have

$$\int \log x \, dx = \int \log x \cdot 1 \, dx = \log x \cdot x - \int \frac{1}{x} \cdot x \, dx$$

$$= x \log x - \int dx = x \log x - x + c .$$

Theorem 357: *Let $a < b$. For $a < x < b$, let*

$$\int f(x) \, dx$$

exist. Let

$$x = g(z)$$

be continuous in the z-interval $[\alpha, \beta]$, let $g'(z)$ always be > 0 or always < 0, for $\alpha < z < \beta$, and let

$$g(\alpha) = a, \quad g(\beta) = b, \quad \text{or} \quad g(\alpha) = b, \quad g(\beta) = a ,$$

respectively. Then

$$\int f\big(g(z)\big) \, g'(z) \, dz$$

exists for $\alpha < z < \beta$, and

(1) $$\int f(x) \, dx = \int f\big(g(z)\big) \, g'(z) \, dz .$$

Preliminary Remark: On the right, we have a function of z. However, z is but an abbreviation for the inverse function $z = G(x)$ of the function $x = g(z)$ which, by Theorems 312 and 313, exists and is differentiable for $\alpha < z < \beta$. (This last fact will first be applied in the proof of Theorem 358.)

Proof: Setting

$$\int f(x) \, dx = \varphi(z) + c ,$$

we have for $\alpha < z < \beta$ that

$$\frac{d\varphi(z)}{dz} = \frac{d\varphi(z)}{dx} \frac{dx}{dz} = f(x) g'(z) = f\big(g(z)\big) g'(z) .$$

Example: $$f(x) = x^2,$$

$$b > a \geqq 0, \quad \alpha = \sqrt[4]{a}, \quad \beta = \sqrt[4]{b} ,$$

$$x = g(z) = z^4,$$

$$z = \sqrt[4]{x},$$

$$\int f(x) \, dx = \int x^2 \, dx = \frac{x^3}{3} + c,$$

$$\int f\big(g(z)\big) g'(z) \, dz = \int z^8 \cdot 4 z^3 \, dz = 4 \int z^{11} dz = \frac{z^{12}}{3 .} + c = \frac{x^3}{3} + c .$$

Theorem 357 is of no help to us as an existence proof of $\int f(x)\,dx$, if one is needed. For that purpose, the following theorem may be useful.

Theorem 358: *Formula (1) of Theorem 357 holds if we replace the hypothesis that the left-hand side exists by the hypothesis that the right-hand side exists.*

Proof: By Theorem 357, applied to

$$\int f\big(g(z)\big)\, g'(z)\, dz, \quad z = G(x),$$

we have, since (Theorem 313)

$$G'(x) = \frac{dz}{dx} = \frac{1}{\dfrac{dx}{dz}} = \frac{1}{g'(z)} = \frac{1}{g'(G(x))},$$

that

$$\int f\big(g(z)\big) g'(z)\, dz = \int f\big(g(G(x))\big)\, g'(G(x))\, G'(x)\, dx = \int f(x)\, dx.$$

Examples (we need not hesitate to calculate, using Theorem 357, from left to right, since we already know that the integrals of the given continuous functions of x exist; otherwise, we would have to calculate from right to left and apply Theorem 358):

1) For $\mu > 0$, setting

$$x = \mu z = g(z),$$

we have that

$$\int \frac{dx}{\mu^2 + x^2} = \int \frac{1}{\mu^2 + x^2}\, dx = \int \frac{1}{\mu^2 + \mu^2 z^2}\, \mu\, dz = \frac{1}{\mu} \int \frac{dz}{1 + z^2}$$

$$= \frac{1}{\mu}\, \text{arc tg } z + c = \frac{1}{\mu}\, \text{arc tg }\frac{x}{\mu} + c.$$

The following check is unnecessary, but it doesn't cost us anything:

$$\left(\frac{1}{\mu}\, \text{arc tg }\frac{x}{\mu}\right)' = \frac{1}{\mu}\, \frac{1}{1 + \dfrac{x^2}{\mu^2}}\, \frac{1}{\mu} = \frac{1}{\mu^2 + x^2}.$$

2) For $a \geqq 0$, if we set

$$x = \sqrt{z},$$

then we have

$$\int \sin(x^2)\, x\, dx = \int \sin z\, \sqrt{z}\, \frac{dz}{2\sqrt{z}} = \tfrac{1}{2} \int \sin z\, dz = -\tfrac{1}{2} \cos z + c$$

$$= -\tfrac{1}{2} \cos x^2 + c.$$

3) For $a \geqq 0$, if we set

$$\sqrt{x^2 + 1} = z, \quad x = \sqrt{z^2 - 1},$$

then we have

$$\int \frac{x\,dx}{\sqrt{x^2 + 1}} = \int \frac{\sqrt{z^2 - 1}}{z} \left(\sqrt{z^2 - 1}\right)' dz = \int \frac{\sqrt{z^2 - 1}}{z} \frac{z}{\sqrt{z^2 - 1}}\,dz = \int dz$$

$$= z + c = \sqrt{x^2 + 1} + c.$$

Check: $$\left(\sqrt{x^2 + 1}\right)' = \frac{x}{\sqrt{x^2 + 1}}.$$

This check pays us a dividend, for it holds also for $a < 0$.

Integration by parts (Theorem 356) and the method of substitution (Theorems 357 and 358) are the most important tools used to integrate given functions by explicit formulas — if we are lucky. To be sure, we will see later that this is by no means the principal task of the integral calculus—if only for the simple reason that this is possible, even for continuous functions, only in rare cases. It is with these particular cases that the next two chapters deal.

CHAPTER 23

INTEGRATION OF RATIONAL FUNCTIONS

Let $f(x)$ be a rational function, i.e., according to Definition 77, let

$$f(x) = \frac{\varphi(x)}{\psi(x)},$$

where $\varphi(x)$ and $\psi(x)$ are polynomials, $\{\psi\} \geqq 0$, and x is any number with $\psi(x) \neq 0$. For such x, we have

$$f'(x) = \frac{\psi(x)\varphi'(x) - \varphi(x)\psi'(x)}{\psi^2(x)},$$

which thus is also a rational function.

In every open interval in which $\psi(x) \neq 0$, we know that $\int f(x)\,dx$ exists (since $f(x)$ is continuous) but is not necessarily a rational function, as the example

$$\int \frac{dx}{x} = \log|x| + c$$

immediately shows.

Pardon me! I wanted to lead the reader on. In the formula

$$\int \frac{dx}{x} = \log|x| + c \quad \text{for } -11 < x < -10,$$

why is the right-hand side not, after all, a rational function? Actually, it is not, but this must be proved. If we had $0 \leqq a < b$ or $a < b \leqq 0$ and, for $a < x < b$,

$$\log|x| = \frac{\varphi(x)}{\psi(x)},$$

where $\varphi(x)$ and $\psi(x)$ are polynomials, then we should have there that

$$\frac{1}{x} = \frac{\psi(x)\varphi'(x) - \varphi(x)\psi'(x)}{\psi^2(x)},$$

$$\psi^2(x) = x\big(\psi(x)\varphi'(x) - \varphi(x)\psi'(x)\big).$$

Since both sides are polynomials, this equation would hold true for all x. $\psi(x) = 0$ would then have the solution $x = 0$, so that (since $\{\varphi\} \geq 0$) we would have by Theorem 334 (or even without it) that

$$\psi(x) = x^m \chi(x), \; m > 0, \; \chi(x) \quad \text{a polynomial,} \; \chi(0) \neq 0,$$

$$\varphi(x) = x^k \omega(x), \; k \geq 0, \; \omega(x) \quad \text{a polynomial,} \; \omega(0) \neq 0,$$

so that, for $x \neq 0$,

$$x^{2m}\chi^2(x) = x\left(x^m\chi(x)\left(kx^{k-1}\omega(x) + x^k\omega'(x)\right) - x^k\omega(x)\left(mx^{m-1}\chi(x) + x^m\chi'(x)\right)\right)$$

$$= x^{m+k}\left((k-m)\chi(x)\omega(x) + x\left(\chi(x)\omega'(x) - \omega(x)\chi'(x)\right)\right),$$

so that $m \geq k$, and for all x,

$$x^{m-k}\chi^2(x) = (k-m)\chi(x)\omega(x) + x\left(\chi(x)\omega'(x) - \omega(x)\chi'(x)\right).$$

If $m = k$, $x = 0$ would yield the contradiction

$$\chi^2(0) = 0,$$

and if $m > k$, the contradiction

$$0 = (k-m)\chi(0)\omega(0).$$

It is all the more surprising and gratifying that it will be possible to express the integral of every rational function in terms of functions with which we are familiar.

Once again I interrupt. Is

$$\int \frac{dx}{1 + x^2} = \text{arc tg } x + c$$

perhaps a rational function in some interval? No, for if we had

$$\frac{1}{1 + x^2} = \frac{\psi(x)\,\varphi'(x) - \varphi(x)\psi'(x)}{\psi^2(x)} \quad \text{for } a < x < b$$

($\varphi(x)$ and $\psi(x)$ polynomials), then we would have for all x that

$$\psi^2(x) = (x^2 + 1)\left(\psi(x)\varphi'(x) - \varphi(x)\psi'(x)\right).$$

By Theorem 336, we would have (since $\{\varphi\} \geq 0$) that

$$\psi(x) = (x^2+1)^m \chi(x), \; m > 0, \; \chi(x) \text{ a polynomial, but} \neq (x^2 + 1) \cdot \text{a polynomial,}$$

$$\varphi(x) = (x^2+1)^k \omega(x), \; k \geq 0, \; \omega(x) \text{ a polynomial, but} \neq (x^2 + 1) \cdot \text{a polynomial,}$$

so that

$$(x^2+1)^{2m}\chi^2(x) = (x^2+1)\Big((x^2+1)^m\chi(x)(2kx(x^2+1)^{k-1}\omega(x)+(x^2+1)^k\omega'(x))$$

$$-(x^2+1)^k\omega(x)(2mx(x^2+1)^{m-1}\chi(x)+(x^2+1)^m\chi'(x))\Big)$$

$$= (x^2+1)\Big(2(k-m)(x^2+1)^{m+k-1}x\chi(x)\omega(x)+(x^2+1)^{m+k}(\chi(x)\omega'(x)-\omega(x)\chi'(x))\Big)$$

$$= (x^2+1)^{m+k}\Big(2(k-m)x\chi(x)\omega(x)+(x^2+1)(\chi(x)\omega'(x)-\omega(x)\chi'(x))\Big),$$

$$(x^2+1)^{m-k}\chi^2(x) = 2(k-m)x\chi(x)\omega(x)+(x^2+1)\cdot\text{a polynomial}.$$

If $m \leq k$, we would have

$$\chi^2(x) = (x^2+1)\cdot\text{a polynomial},$$

$$\chi(x) = (x^2+1)\cdot\text{a polynomial}.$$

If $m > k$, we would have

$$x\chi(x)\omega(x) = (x^2+1)\cdot\text{a polynomial},$$

$$\chi(x) \quad\text{or}\quad \omega(x) = (x^2+1)\cdot\text{a polynomial}.$$

————————

Before we give the general proof that the integral of every rational function may be evaluated in "closed form," I must get out of the way three very important special cases which require long calculations, but to which the general case will later on be easily reduced. The reader need not memorize the final formulas of these three special cases, but need remember only the fact that the special cases can be settled, the tricks used to do this, and the fact that nothing "worse" than log x and arc tg x comes up.

First Example: $\qquad \int \dfrac{dx}{\alpha - 2\beta x + x^2}.$

We have

$$\alpha - 2\beta x + x^2 = (\alpha - \beta^2) + (x - \beta)^2.$$

If we set

$$\alpha - \beta^2 = \mu,$$

then we are dealing with

$$\int \dfrac{dx}{\mu + (x - \beta)^2}.$$

If we set

$$x = z + \beta,$$

then we are dealing with

$$\int \frac{dz}{\mu + z^2}.$$

We distinguish three cases.

1) If $\mu = 0$, then

$$\int \frac{dz}{\mu + z^2} = \int \frac{dz}{z^2} = -\frac{1}{z} + c = -\frac{1}{x - \beta} + c.$$

2) If $\mu > 0$, and if we set

$$\gamma = \sqrt{\mu},$$

then by the first example to Theorem 358 with γ replacing μ, we have

$$\int \frac{dz}{\mu + z^2} = \int \frac{dz}{\gamma^2 + z^2} = \frac{1}{\gamma} \operatorname{arc\,tg} \frac{z}{\gamma} + c = \frac{1}{\sqrt{\alpha - \beta^2}} \operatorname{arc\,tg} \frac{x - \beta}{\sqrt{\alpha - \beta^2}} + c.$$

3) If $\mu < 0$, and if we set

$$\gamma = \sqrt{-\mu},$$

then

$$\int \frac{dz}{\mu + z^2} = \int \frac{dz}{-\gamma^2 + z^2},$$

so that if we set

$$z = \gamma y,$$

this is

$$= \int \frac{\gamma dy}{-\gamma^2 + \gamma^2 y^2} = \frac{1}{\gamma} \int \frac{dy}{y^2 - 1},$$

which, by the first example to Theorem 355, is

$$= \frac{1}{2\gamma} \log \left| \frac{y - 1}{y + 1} \right| + c = \frac{1}{2\sqrt{\beta^2 - \alpha}} \log \left| \frac{x - \beta - \sqrt{\beta^2 - \alpha}}{x - \beta + \sqrt{\beta^2 - \alpha}} \right| + c.$$

Second Example: $\int \dfrac{dx}{((x - \beta)^2 + \gamma^2)^n}$, n an integer $> 0, \gamma > 0$.

We have calculated this above for $n = 1$. If we set

$$x = \gamma y + \beta,$$

then we obtain

$$\int \frac{dx}{((x - \beta)^2 + \gamma^2)^n} = \int \frac{\gamma \, dy}{(\gamma^2 y^2 + \gamma^2)^n} = \gamma^{1-2n} \int \frac{dy}{(y^2 + 1)^n}.$$

Thus we need only deal with

$$\int \frac{dy}{(y^2 + 1)^n} = I_n.$$

We have

$$I_1 = \text{arc tg } y + c.$$

Let $n > 1$, and suppose that I_{n-1} is expressible in terms of "familiar" functions among which nothing "worse" than arc tg appears. Then we have

$$I_n = \int \frac{(y^2 + 1) - y^2}{(y^2 + 1)^n} \, dy = \int \frac{y^2 + 1}{(y^2 + 1)^n} \, dy - \int \frac{y^2}{(y^2 + 1)^n} \, dy$$

$$= \int \frac{dy}{(y^2 + 1)^{n-1}} - \frac{1}{2} \int \frac{2y}{(y^2 + 1)^n} \, y \, dy$$

$$= I_{n-1} - \frac{1}{2} \left(- \frac{1}{n-1} \frac{1}{(y^2 + 1)^{n-1}} \, y + \frac{1}{n-1} \int \frac{dy}{(y^2 + 1)^{n-1}} \right)$$

$$= I_{n-1} + \frac{y}{(2n - 2)(y^2 + 1)^{n-1}} - \frac{1}{2n - 2} I_{n-1}$$

$$= \frac{2n - 3}{2n - 2} I_{n-1} + \frac{y}{(2n - 2)(y^2 + 1)^{n-1}},$$

so that I_n also can be expressed in the above way.

Third Example: $\int \dfrac{x \, dx}{((x - \beta)^2 + \gamma^2)^n}$, n an integer $> 0, \gamma > 0$.

We have

$$\int \frac{x - \beta}{((x - \beta)^2 + \gamma^2)^n} \, dx = \begin{cases} -\dfrac{1}{2(n-1)} \dfrac{1}{((x - \beta)^2 + \gamma^2)^{n-1}} + c & \text{for } n > 1, \\[2mm] \dfrac{1}{2} \log \left((x - \beta)^2 + \gamma^2 \right) + c & \text{for } n = 1, \end{cases}$$

$$\int \frac{x \, dx}{((x - \beta)^2 + \gamma^2)^n} = \int \frac{x - \beta}{((x - \beta)^2 + \gamma^2)^n} \, dx + \beta \int \frac{dx}{((x - \beta)^2 + \gamma^2)^n},$$

which is settled by the above formula and the second example.

Corollary: If $\gamma > 0$ and n is an integer > 0, then

$$\int \frac{Bx + C}{((x - \beta)^2 + \gamma^2)^n} \, dx = B \int \frac{x \, dx}{((x - \beta)^2 + \gamma^2)^n} + C \int \frac{dx}{((x - \beta)^2 + \gamma^2)^n},$$

and so is settled by the third and second examples.

Theorem 359: *The integral of every rational function may be expressed in closed form.*

Moreover, nothing worse than log and arc tg will occur.

Proof: By Theorem 341, it suffices to prove the assertion for

1) $$cx^\lambda, \quad \lambda \geq 0 \text{ an integer,}$$

2) $$\frac{A}{(x-\alpha)^\lambda}, \quad \lambda > 0 \text{ an integer,}$$

3) $$\frac{Bx + C}{((x-\beta)^2 + \gamma^2)^\lambda}, \quad \lambda > 0 \text{ an integer, } \gamma > 0.$$

As regards 1): $$\int x^\lambda dx = \frac{x^{\lambda+1}}{\lambda + 1} + c.$$

As regards 2): $$\int \frac{dx}{(x-\alpha)^\lambda} = \begin{cases} -\dfrac{1}{\lambda - 1}\dfrac{1}{(x-\alpha)^{\lambda-1}} + c & \text{for } \lambda > 1, \\ \log|x - \alpha| + c & \text{for } \lambda = 1. \end{cases}$$

As regards 3): corollary to the third example above.

Examples: 1) (cf. the first example at the end of Chap. 20):

$$\int \frac{dx}{x^3 - x} = \int \left(-\frac{1}{x} + \frac{1}{2}\frac{1}{x+1} + \frac{1}{2}\frac{1}{x-1} \right) dx$$

$$= -\log|x| + \tfrac{1}{2}\log|x+1| + \tfrac{1}{2}\log|x-1| + c$$

$$= \tfrac{1}{2}\log\frac{|(x+1)(x-1)|}{x^2} + c$$

in every open interval which contains none of the numbers 0, 1, and — 1.

2) (cf. the third example at the end of Chap. 20):

$$\int \frac{x+2}{x^4 + x^3} dx = \int \left(\frac{2}{x^3} - \frac{1}{x^2} + \frac{1}{x} - \frac{1}{x+1} \right) dx$$

$$= -\frac{1}{x^2} + \frac{1}{x} + \log\left|\frac{x}{x+1}\right| + c$$

in every open interval which does not include 0 and — 1.

CHAPTER 24

INTEGRATION OF SOME
NON-RATIONAL FUNCTIONS

1) Let

$$R(x,\ y) = \frac{\sum a_{\mu\nu}\, x^{\mu} y^{\nu}}{\sum b_{\mu\nu}\, x^{\mu} y^{\nu}}\,,$$

where a finite number of terms appear in the numerator and denominator and where the μ, ν are integers ≥ 0. Let the denominator be not identically 0. We call this function a rational function of x and y. It is defined where the denominator is $\neq 0$. We may also say that the numerator and denominator are polynomials

$$\sum_{\nu=0}^{k} A_{\nu}(x)\, y^{\nu}$$

in y whose coefficients are polynomials in x.

Now let $F(x)$ be a polynomial of the first or second degree and consider an open x-interval (if there is one) where

$$F(x) > 0$$

and where, if we set

$$y = \sqrt{F(x)},$$

$R(x, y)$ is defined and thus depends continuously on x.

We shall then be able to calculate

$$\int R(x,\ y)\, dx$$

explicitly, in terms of functions known to us.

We shall quickly settle the case

$$\{F\} = 1.$$

In this case, we have

$$F(x) = \alpha + \beta x,\ \ \beta \neq 0.$$

The substitution

$$x = \frac{z^2 - \alpha}{\beta}, \quad z > 0$$

yields

$$y = \sqrt{F(x)} = z,$$

$$\int R(x, y)\, dx = \int R\left(\frac{z^2 - \alpha}{\beta}, z\right) \frac{2z}{\beta}\, dz,$$

where the integrand is a rational function of z, so that the case is settled by Chap. 23.

In the case

$$\{F\} = 2,$$

we have

$$F(x) = A + Bx + Cx^2, \quad C \neq 0.$$

Here, we shall reduce

$$\int R(x, y)\, dx$$

to the three types

(1) $\int R\left(x, \sqrt{x^2 + 1}\right) dx, \quad \int R\left(x, \sqrt{x^2 - 1}\right) dx, \quad \int R\left(x, \sqrt{1 - x^2}\right) dx,$

and these integrals will in turn be reduced to integrals of rational functions by means of a new variable.

If $C > 0$, then we have

$$y = \sqrt{C}\, \sqrt{x^2 + B_1 x + A_1} = \sqrt{C}\, \sqrt{(x + \beta)^2 + \alpha}\,.$$

If $\alpha = 0$, then, in our interval, y is equal to $\sqrt{C}(x + \beta)$ or $-\sqrt{C}(x + \beta)$, so that $R(x, y)$ is a rational function of x, and we are done. Therefore we may assume that $\alpha \neq 0$, so that

$$y = \sqrt{C}\, \sqrt{(x + \beta)^2 \pm \gamma^2}\,, \quad \gamma > 0.$$

If $C < 0$, then we have

$$y = \sqrt{-C}\, \sqrt{-x^2 - B_1 x - A_1} = \sqrt{-C}\, \sqrt{-(x + \beta)^2 - \alpha}\,;$$

α must be negative, so that

$$y = \sqrt{-C}\, \sqrt{-(x + \beta)^2 + \gamma^2}\,, \quad \gamma > 0.$$

In all cases, the substitution

$$x = \gamma z - \beta$$

yields

$$y = \sqrt{C}\, \gamma \sqrt{z^2 + 1}, \quad \text{or} \quad \sqrt{C}\, \gamma \sqrt{z^2 - 1}, \quad \text{or} \quad \sqrt{-C}\, \gamma \sqrt{1 - z^2},$$

$$\int R(x, y)\, dx = \int R_1(z, Y)\, dz,$$

where

$$Y = \sqrt{z^2 + 1}, \quad \text{or} \quad \sqrt{z^2 - 1}, \quad \text{or} \quad \sqrt{1 - z^2},$$

and $R_1(z, Y)$ is a rational function of z and Y.

With this, we have completed the reduction to the three types (1).

First Type: $\qquad \int R\left(x, \sqrt{x^2 + 1}\right) dx.$

For every x,

(2) $\qquad\qquad x = \frac{1}{2}\left(u - \frac{1}{u}\right), \quad u > 0$

has exactly one solution u. For, we must necessarily have

$$u^2 - 2xu - 1 = 0,$$

$$(u - x)^2 - (x^2 + 1) = 0,$$

$$u = x \pm \sqrt{x^2 + 1},$$

and, since $u > 0$, we must have

$$u = x + \sqrt{x^2 + 1}.$$

For every x, we have

$$u = x + \sqrt{x^2 + 1} > 0,$$

and (2) is satisfied, since

$$\frac{1}{u} = \frac{1}{x + \sqrt{x^2 + 1}} = \frac{x - \sqrt{x^2 + 1}}{x^2 - \left(\sqrt{x^2 + 1}\right)^2} = -x + \sqrt{x^2 + 1},$$

$$u - \frac{1}{u} = 2x.$$

Now if u in (2) is regarded as an independent variable, we have

$$\frac{dx}{du} = \frac{1}{2}\left(1 + \frac{1}{u^2}\right) > 0,$$

$$\sqrt{x^2 + 1} = u - x = \frac{1}{2}\left(u + \frac{1}{u}\right),$$

so that

$$\int R\left(x, \sqrt{x^2 + 1}\right) dx = \int R\left(\frac{1}{2}\left(u - \frac{1}{u}\right), \frac{1}{2}\left(u + \frac{1}{u}\right)\right)\frac{1}{2}\left(1 + \frac{1}{u^2}\right) du$$

$$= \int R_1(u)\, du,$$

where $R_1(u)$ is a rational function.

Example: $\displaystyle\int\frac{dx}{\sqrt{x^2+1}}=\int\frac{\frac{1}{2}\left(1+\frac{1}{u^2}\right)}{\frac{1}{2}\left(u+\frac{1}{u}\right)}\,du=\int\frac{du}{u}=\log u+c$

$$=\log\left(x+\sqrt{x^2+1}\right)+c\,.$$

Second Type: $\displaystyle\int R\!\left(x,\ \sqrt{x^2-1}\right)dx\,.$

Here, we must have $x>1$ or $x<-1$ in the interior of our given interval. W.l.g., let the first be the case. For otherwise, we set $x=-z$ and consider

$$R\!\left(-z,\ \sqrt{(-z)^2-1}\right)(-1)=R_1\!\left(z,\ \sqrt{z^2-1}\right),$$

where $R_1(z,v)$ is a rational function of z and v.

For every $x>1$,

(3) $$x=\frac{1}{2}\left(u+\frac{1}{u}\right),\ \ u>1$$

has exactly one solution u. For we must have

$$u^2-2xu+1=0\,,$$

$$(u-x)^2-(x^2-1)=0\,,$$

$$u=x\pm\sqrt{x^2-1}\,,$$

and since $u>1$, we must have

$$u=x+\sqrt{x^2-1}\,.$$

$\Bigg($For,

$$x-\sqrt{x^2-1}=\frac{1}{x+\sqrt{x^2-1}}<1\,.\Bigg)$$

For every $x>1$, we have

$$u=x+\sqrt{x^2-1}>1,$$

and (3) is satisfied, since

$$\frac{1}{u}=x-\sqrt{x^2-1}\,,$$

$$u+\frac{1}{u}=2x\,.$$

Conversely, we have for every $u>1$ that

$$x=\frac{1}{2}\left(u+\frac{1}{u}\right)=\frac{1}{2}\frac{u^2+1}{u}=\frac{1}{2}\frac{(u-1)^2}{u}+1>1\,.$$

Now, if u in (3) is regarded as an independent variable, we have

$$\frac{dx}{du} = \frac{1}{2}\left(1 - \frac{1}{u^2}\right) > 0,$$

$$\sqrt{x^2 - 1} = u - x = \frac{1}{2}\left(u - \frac{1}{u}\right),$$

so that

$$\int R\left(x, \sqrt{x^2 - 1}\right) dx = \int R\left(\frac{1}{2}\left(u + \frac{1}{u}\right), \frac{1}{2}\left(u - \frac{1}{u}\right)\right) \frac{1}{2}\left(1 - \frac{1}{u^2}\right) du$$

$$= \int R_1(u) \, du,$$

where $R_1(u)$ is a rational function.

Example: $\displaystyle \int \sqrt{x^2 - 1} \, dx = \int \frac{1}{2}\left(u - \frac{1}{u}\right) \frac{1}{2}\left(1 - \frac{1}{u^2}\right) du$

$$= \frac{1}{4}\int\left(u - \frac{1}{u} - \frac{1}{u} + \frac{1}{u^3}\right) du = \frac{1}{4}\left(\frac{u^2}{2} - 2\log u - \frac{1}{2u^2}\right) + c$$

$$= \frac{1}{8}\left(u + \frac{1}{u}\right)\left(u - \frac{1}{u}\right) - \frac{1}{2}\log u + c$$

$$= \frac{1}{8}\, 2x \cdot 2\sqrt{x^2 - 1} - \frac{1}{2}\log\left(x + \sqrt{x^2 - 1}\right) + c$$

$$= \frac{1}{2}\, x\sqrt{x^2 - 1} - \frac{1}{2}\log\left(x + \sqrt{x^2 - 1}\right) + c.$$

Third Type: $\displaystyle \int R\left(x, \sqrt{1 - x^2}\right) dx.$

(The substitution $x = \dfrac{1}{z}$ formally carries us back into the second type, but the neighborhood of $x = 0$ is lost.)

Here, we must have

$$|x| < 1$$

For every x with $|x| < 1$,

$$(4) \qquad x = \frac{2u}{u^2 + 1}, \quad |u| < 1$$

has exactly one solution u. For if $x = 0$, then we must have

$$u = 0.$$

And for $0 < |x| < 1$, we must have

$$u^2 - \frac{2}{x}\,u + 1 = 0 \,,$$

$$\left(u - \frac{1}{x}\right)^2 - \left(\frac{1}{x^2} - 1\right) = 0 \,,$$

$$u = \frac{1 \pm \sqrt{1 - x^2}}{x} \,.$$

Here, we must have the lower sign $\Big($ for otherwise we would have

$$|u| > \frac{1}{|x|} > 1 \Big) \,;$$

if

$$u = \frac{1 - \sqrt{1 - x^2}}{x} \,,$$

then we do have

$$|u| < 1 \,,$$

$\Big($ since

$$|u| = \left|\frac{x}{1 + \sqrt{1 - x^2}}\right| < |x| < 1 \Big)$$

and (4) is satisfied, since

$$u \neq 0,$$

$$\frac{1}{u} = \frac{1 + \sqrt{1 - x^2}}{x} \,,$$

$$\frac{u^2 + 1}{u} = u + \frac{1}{u} = \frac{2}{x} \,.$$

Conversely, if

$$|u| < 1, \quad x = \frac{2u}{u^2 + 1} \,,$$

then if $u = 0$ we have

$$|x| = 0 < 1 \,,$$

and if $u \neq 0$ we have

$$x \neq 0 \,,$$

$$\left|\frac{1}{x}\right| = \frac{u^2 + 1}{2|u|} = \frac{(|u| - 1)^2}{2|u|} + 1 > 1,$$

$$|x| < 1.$$

Now if u in (4) is regarded as an independent variable, we have

$$\frac{dx}{du} = \frac{(u^2+1)2 - 2u \cdot 2u}{(u^2+1)^2} = \frac{2(1-u^2)}{(u^2+1)^2} > 0,$$

$$\sqrt{1-x^2} = 1 - xu = 1 - \frac{2u^2}{u^2+1} = \frac{1-u^2}{1+u^2},$$

so that

$$\int R\left(x, \sqrt{1-x^2}\right) dx = \int R\left(\frac{2u}{1+u^2}, \frac{1-u^2}{1+u^2}\right) \frac{2(1-u^2)}{(1+u^2)^2} du = \int R_1(u) du,$$

where $R_1(u)$ is a rational function of u.

Example: I purposely choose an old one.

$$\int \frac{dx}{\sqrt{1-x^2}} = \int \frac{1}{\dfrac{1-u^2}{1+u^2}} \frac{2(1-u^2)}{(1+u^2)^2} du = 2 \int \frac{du}{1+u^2} = 2 \text{ arc tg } u + c.$$

Since we know that

$$(\text{arc sin } x)' = \frac{1}{\sqrt{1-x^2}} \quad (\text{for } |x| < 1),$$

we must naturally have for suitable c that

$$2 \text{ arc tg } u = \text{arc sin } x + c \text{ for } |x| < 1.$$

Since $u = 0$ for $x = 0$, only $c = 0$ is possible. Indeed (but this check is unnecessary), this formula (for $c = 0$) is true for $x = 0$, and for $0 < |x| < 1$ we have

$$2 \text{ arc tg } \frac{1 - \sqrt{1-x^2}}{x} = \text{arc sin } x,$$

since

$$|u| < 1,$$

$$\left| 2 \text{ arc tg } u \right| < 2 \frac{\pi}{4} = \frac{\pi}{2},$$

$$\sin (2 \text{ arc tg } u) = 2 \sin (\text{arc tg } u) \cos (\text{arc tg } u)$$

$$= 2 \text{ tg } (\text{arc tg } u) \cos^2 (\text{arc tg } u)$$

$$= 2 \frac{\text{tg } (\text{arc tg } u)}{1 + \text{tg}^2 (\text{arc tg } u)} = \frac{2u}{1+u^2} = x.$$

To conclude 1) I advise the reader to try special tricks on a problem before having recourse to the general method, which of course always works.

2) Let $R(x, y, z)$ be a rational function of x, y, and z, i.e. a rational function of y and z whose coefficients in the numerator and denominator are polynomials in x. We will investigate

$$\int R\left(x, \ \sqrt{A + Bx}, \ \sqrt{\alpha + \beta x}\right) dx$$

in an open interval where the expressions under the radical signs are > 0, and where R is meaningful. W.l.g., let $B \neq 0$, since otherwise, for $\beta \neq 0$, we are back to the old type

$$\int R_1\left(x, \ \sqrt{\alpha + \beta x}\right) dx$$

and for $\beta = 0$, we even have a rational integrand.

$$x = \frac{u^2}{B} - \frac{A}{B}, \ u > 0$$

yields

$$\int R\left(x, \ \sqrt{A + Bx}, \ \sqrt{\alpha + \beta x}\right) dx$$

$$= \int R\left(\frac{u^2}{B} - \frac{A}{B}, \ u, \ \sqrt{\alpha - \frac{\beta A}{B} + \frac{\beta}{B} u^2}\right) \frac{2u}{B} du = \int R_1\left(u, \ \sqrt{A_1 + C_1 u^2}\right) du,$$

which we already have.

Example:

$$\int \frac{\sqrt{-4 + x}}{\sqrt{x}} dx.$$

$$x = u^2, \ u > 0, \ u = 2v$$

yields

$$\int \frac{\sqrt{-4 + x}}{\sqrt{x}} dx = \int \frac{\sqrt{-4 + u^2}}{u} 2u \, du = 2 \int \sqrt{-4 + u^2} \, du$$

$$= 2 \int \sqrt{-4 + 4v^2} \, 2dv = 8 \int \sqrt{v^2 - 1} \, dv$$

etc., by the example to the second type of 1).

3) Let $R(y)$ be a rational function. The substitution

$$x = \log u$$

yields

$$\int R(e^x) \, dx = \int R(u) \frac{du}{u} = \int R_1(u) \, du.$$

Example:
$$\int \frac{dx}{e^x + e^{-x}} = \int \frac{1}{u + \dfrac{1}{u}} \frac{du}{u} = \int \frac{du}{1 + u^2}$$

$$= \text{arc tg } u + c = \text{arc tg } e^x + c.$$

4) Let $R(y, z)$ be a rational function of y and z. Let our interval be contained in $[-\pi, \pi]$ and let $R(\sin x, \cos x)$ be meaningful in it. The substitution

$$x = 2 \text{ arc tg } u$$

yields

$$u = \text{tg } \frac{x}{2},$$

$$\sin x = 2 \sin \frac{x}{2} \cos \frac{x}{2} = \frac{2 \text{ tg } \dfrac{x}{2}}{1 + \text{tg}^2 \dfrac{x}{2}} = \frac{2u}{1 + u^2},$$

$$\cos x = 2 \cos^2 \frac{x}{2} - 1 = \frac{2}{1 + \text{tg}^2 \dfrac{x}{2}} - 1 = \frac{1 - u^2}{1 + u^2},$$

$$\frac{dx}{du} = \frac{2}{1 + u^2},$$

$$\int R(\sin x, \cos x)\, dx = \int R\left(\frac{2u}{1 + u^2}, \frac{1 - u^2}{1 + u^2}\right) \frac{2}{1 + u^2}\, du = \int R_1(u)\, du.$$

Example:
$$\int \frac{dx}{\sin x} = \int \frac{1}{\dfrac{2u}{1 + u^2}} \frac{2}{1 + u^2}\, du = \int \frac{du}{u}$$

$$= \log |u| + c = \log \left| \text{tg } \frac{x}{2} \right| + c.$$

5) If $a \geqq 0$, then

$$\int x^n \log x\, dx$$

may be calculated for every n. For $n = -1$, the integral is

$$= \tfrac{1}{2} \log^2 x + c;$$

and for $n \neq -1$, an integration by parts yields

$$\int x^n \log x \, dx = \frac{x^{n+1}}{n+1} \log x - \int \frac{x^{n+1}}{n+1} \frac{dx}{x}$$

$$= \frac{x^{n+1}}{n+1} \log x - \frac{1}{n+1} \int x^n \, dx$$

$$= \frac{x^{n+1}}{n+1} \log x - \frac{x^{n+1}}{(n+1)^2} + c.$$

6) If $a \geqq 0$ or $b \leqq 0$, then

$$\int \frac{\sin x}{x} \, dx = \int \sum_{n=0}^{\infty} \frac{(-1)^n x^{2n}}{(2n+1)!} \, dx = \sum_{n=0}^{\infty} \frac{(-1)^n x^{2n+1}}{(2n+1)(2n+1)!} + c.$$

7) By Theorem 247, we have for $|x| < 1$ that

$$\frac{1}{\sqrt{1-x^4}} = (1-x^4)^{-\frac{1}{2}} = \sum_{n=0}^{\infty} \binom{-\frac{1}{2}}{n} (-1)^n x^{4n},$$

so that

$$\int \frac{dx}{\sqrt{1-x^4}} = \sum_{n=0}^{\infty} \binom{-\frac{1}{2}}{n} (-1)^n \frac{x^{4n+1}}{4n+1} + c.$$

Moreover, we have for $n > 0$ that

$$\binom{-\frac{1}{2}}{n} (-1)^n = \frac{\prod_{\nu=0}^{n-1} (-\frac{1}{2} - \nu)}{n!} (-1)^n = \frac{\prod_{\nu=0}^{n-1} \frac{1+2\nu}{2}}{n!}$$

$$= \frac{(2n)!}{n! \, 2^n \prod_{\nu=1}^{n} 2\nu} = \frac{(2n)!}{4^n (n!)^2}$$

and, evidently, we also have for $n = 0$ that

$$\binom{-\frac{1}{2}}{n} (-1)^n = \frac{(2n)!}{4^n (n!)^2}.$$

Therefore we have for $|x| < 1$ that

$$\int \frac{dx}{\sqrt{1-x^4}} = \sum_{n=0}^{\infty} \frac{(2n)!}{4^n (n!)^2 (4n+1)} x^{4n+1} + c.$$

CHAPTER 25

THE CONCEPT OF DEFINITE INTEGRAL

The real task of the integral calculus is to set up the theory of the definite integral. What we have hitherto called an integral (it will still occur occasionally) will from now on be called an indefinite integral, in constrast to the definite integral.

What is a definite integral? We ask the reader to be patient while we first dispose of some preliminaries.

Definition 81: *If l is the l.u.b. and λ the g.l.b. of a bounded set, then $s = l - \lambda$ is called its oscillation.*

Hence we always have $s \geqq 0$, and $s = 0$ only when the set contains exactly one number.

Theorem 360: *s is the least upper bound of the numbers $z_1 - z_2$, where z_1 and z_2 belong to the set.*

Preliminary Remark: Therefore, s is the l.u.b. of all $|z_1 - z_2|$.

Proof: 1) For every z_1 and every z_2 of the set, we have

$$z_1 \leqq l, \quad z_2 \geqq \lambda,$$

so that

$$z_1 - z_2 \leqq l - \lambda = s.$$

2) For $\delta > 0$ there exists a z_1 and a z_2 in the set such that

$$z_1 > l - \frac{\delta}{2}, \quad z_2 < \lambda + \frac{\delta}{2},$$

so that

$$z_1 - z_2 > l - \lambda - \delta = s - \delta.$$

Notations: Let $a < b$, let $f(x)$ be defined on $[a, b]$, let n be an integer > 0, let a_ν be defined for integral ν with $0 \leqq \nu \leqq n$,

$$a_0 = a, \quad a_n = b,$$

$$e_\nu = a_\nu - a_{\nu-1} > 0 \quad \text{for } 1 \leqq \nu \leqq n,$$

so that

$$\sum_{\nu=1}^{n} e_\nu = b - a.$$

If $f(x)$ is bounded on $[a, b]$, so that

$$|f(x)| < c \quad \text{for} \quad a \leq x \leq b,$$

then for $1 \leq \nu \leq n$, let

$$\left.\begin{array}{l} l_\nu \text{ be the l.u.b.} \\ \lambda_\nu \text{ be the g.l.b.} \\ s_\nu \text{ be the oscillation} \end{array}\right\} \text{ of } f(x) \text{ on } [a_{\nu-1}, a_\nu],$$

so that

$$s_\nu = l_\nu - \lambda_\nu,$$

$$-c \leq \lambda_\nu \leq l_\nu \leq c,$$

$$0 \leq s_\nu \leq 2c.$$

Then we call

$$\sum_{\nu=1}^{n} e_\nu s_\nu,$$

or more briefly, $\sum es$, the Riemann sum corresponding to the partition. The quantities

$$\sum_{\nu=1}^{n} e_\nu l_\nu \quad \text{and} \quad \sum_{\nu=1}^{n} e_\nu \lambda_\nu,$$

or more briefly, $\sum el$ and $\sum e\lambda$, will also occur. For every partition we have

$$-c(b-a) = -c \sum e \leq \sum e\lambda \leq \sum el \leq c \sum e = c(b-a),$$

$$0 \leq \sum es \leq 2c \sum e = 2c(b-a).$$

Definition 82: *Let $f(x)$ be bounded on $[a, b]$. Then $f(x)$ is said to satisfy the Riemann condition on $[a, b]$ if for every $\delta > 0$ there exists an $\varepsilon > 0$ such that for every partition with all $e_\nu < \varepsilon$, we have for the Riemann sum that*

$$\sum es < \delta.$$

Definition 83: *Let $a < b$. $f(x)$ is said to be integrable from a to b if $f(x)$ is defined on $[a, b]$ and if there is a number I such that for every $\delta > 0$ there exists an $\varepsilon > 0$ with the following property. For every partition for which all $e_\nu < \varepsilon$, and for every choice of ξ_ν in $[a_{\nu-1}, a_\nu]$, we have*

$$\left| \sum_{\nu=1}^{n} e_\nu f(\xi_\nu) - I \right| < \delta.$$

For example, we must have

$$\lim_{n=\infty} \sum_{\nu=1}^{n} \frac{b-a}{n} \cdot f\left(a + \frac{\nu(b-a)}{n}\right) = I.$$

Theorem 361: *There is at most one I in the sense of Definition 83.*

Proof: If I_1 and $I_2 > I_1$ had the required properties, then if we took

$$\delta = \frac{I_2 - I_1}{2},$$

we would have for suitable $\varepsilon > 0$ and for every partition with $e_\nu < \varepsilon$ and for every choice of ξ_ν that

$$\sum_{\nu=1}^{n} e_\nu f(\xi_\nu) < I_1 + \delta = I_2 - \delta < \sum_{\nu=1}^{n} e_\nu f(\xi_\nu).$$

Definition 84: *If for a, b, f(x), there exists an I in the sense of Definition 83, then I is said to be the (definite) integral of the function f(x) from a to b.*

Notation:
$$I = \int_a^b f(x)\, dx.$$

To be read "Integral a to b $f(x)$ dee eks."

The connection with the original concept $\int f(x)\, dx$ will appear later.

There will be sufficient reason for using similar symbols for both concepts.

For $\int_a^b \frac{1}{\psi(x)}\, dx$ we also write $\int_a^b \frac{dx}{\psi(x)}$, for $\int_a^b \frac{\varphi(x)}{\psi(x)}\, dx$ also $\int_a^b \frac{\varphi(x)\, dx}{\psi(x)}$ or

$\int_a^b \varphi(x) \frac{dx}{\psi(x)}$, for $\int_a^b 1\, dx$ also $\int_a^b dx$. (Similarly for all later extensions of the

concept of definite integral.)

Examples: 1) $\qquad f(x) = 1$ on $[a, b]$.

Then we always have

$$\sum_{\nu=1}^{n} e_\nu f(\xi_\nu) = \sum_{\nu=1}^{n} e_\nu = b - a.$$

The number

$$I = b - a$$

is as required, and we write

$$\int_a^b dx = \int_a^b 1\, dx = b - a.$$

2) $\qquad f(x) = x$ on $[a, b]$.

Let all $e_\nu < \varepsilon$, where ε for the time being is some arbitrary positive number.

We have

$$\sum_{\nu=1}^{n} e_\nu f(\xi_\nu) = \sum_{\nu=1}^{n} (a_\nu - a_{\nu-1}) \frac{a_\nu + a_{\nu-1}}{2} + \sum_{\nu=1}^{n} (a_\nu - a_{\nu-1})\left(\xi_\nu - \frac{a_\nu + a_{\nu-1}}{2}\right)$$

$$= \frac{1}{2}\sum_{\nu=1}^{n}(-a_{\nu-1}^2 + a_\nu^2) + \sum_{\nu=1}^{n} e_\nu\left(\xi_\nu - \frac{a_\nu + a_{\nu-1}}{2}\right)$$

$$= \frac{b^2 - a^2}{2} + \sum_{\nu=1}^{n} e_\nu\left(\xi_\nu - \frac{a_\nu + a_{\nu-1}}{2}\right),$$

$$-\frac{e_\nu}{2} = a_{\nu-1} - \frac{a_\nu + a_{\nu-1}}{2} \leqq \xi_\nu - \frac{a_\nu + a_{\nu-1}}{2} \leqq a_\nu - \frac{a_\nu + a_{\nu-1}}{2} = \frac{e_\nu}{2},$$

$$\left|\sum_{\nu=1}^{n} e_\nu f(\xi_\nu) - \frac{b^2 - a^2}{2}\right| \leqq \frac{1}{2}\sum_{\nu=1}^{n} e_\nu^2 \leqq \frac{\varepsilon}{2}\sum_{\nu=1}^{n} e_\nu = \frac{\varepsilon}{2}(b - a).$$

Therefore if

$$\varepsilon = \frac{\delta}{b - a},$$

and if we set

$$\frac{b^2 - a^2}{2} = I,$$

then we have

$$\left|\sum_{\nu=1}^{n} e_\nu f(\xi_\nu) - I\right| \leqq \frac{\delta}{2} < \delta.$$

Hence

$$\int_a^b x\,dx = \frac{b^2 - a^2}{2}.$$

Theorem 362: If $\int_a^b f(x)dx$ exists, then $f(x)$ is bounded on $[a, b]$.

Proof: We choose a partition such that for every choice of the ξ_ν, we have

$$\left|\sum_{\nu=1}^{n} e_\nu f(\xi_\nu) - I\right| < 2,$$

so that

$$\left|\sum_{\nu=1}^{n} e_\nu f(\xi_\nu)\right| < |I| + 2.$$

If the assertion were false, then $f(x)$ would be unbounded on at least one of the intervals $[a_{\nu-1}, a_\nu]$, say for $\nu = \mu$. For all other intervals (i.e. for $\nu \neq \mu$), I choose $\xi_\nu = a_{\nu-1}$; then all ξ_ν other than ξ_μ are fixed, and ξ_μ may be chosen so that

$$\left|\sum_{\nu=1}^{n} e_\nu f(\xi_\nu)\right| \geqq |I| + 2.$$

Theorem 363: *The converse of Theorem 362 is not true.*
Proof: Let $a = 0$, $b = 1$.

$$f(x) = \left\{ \begin{array}{l} 0 \quad \text{for rational } x \\ 1 \quad \text{for irrational } x \end{array} \right\} \quad \text{on } [a, b].$$

For every partition there is a rational as well as an irrational ξ_ν in every interval $[a_{\nu-1}, a_\nu]$. Therefore the ξ_ν may be chosen in such a way that

$$\sum_{\nu=1}^{n} e_\nu f(\xi_\nu) = 0 ,$$

as well as

$$\sum_{\nu=1}^{n} e_\nu f(\xi_\nu) = 1 .$$

Hence no I can exist.

Theorem 364: *If $\int_a^b f(x)\,dx$ exists, then $f(x)$ satisfies the Riemann condition.*
Proof: By Theorem 362, $f(x)$ is bounded on $[a, b]$. Let $\delta > 0$ be given. For every fixed partition with all $e_\nu < \varepsilon$ and for ξ_ν' and ξ_ν'' on $[a_{\nu-1}, a_\nu]$, we have for suitable $\varepsilon > 0$ that

$$\left| \sum_{\nu=1}^{n} e_\nu f(\xi_\nu') - I \right| < \frac{\delta}{3} , \quad \left| \sum_{\nu=1}^{n} e_\nu f(\xi_\nu'') - I \right| < \frac{\delta}{3} ,$$

so that

$$\left| \sum_{\nu=1}^{n} e_\nu \left(f(\xi_\nu') - f(\xi_\nu'') \right) \right| < \frac{2\delta}{3} .$$

By Theorem 360, ξ_ν' and ξ_ν'' for $1 \leqq \nu \leqq n$ can be chosen so that

$$f(\xi_\nu') - f(\xi_\nu'') > s_\nu - \frac{\delta}{3ne_\nu} ,$$

so that

$$e_\nu s_\nu < e_\nu \left(f(\xi_\nu') - f(\xi_\nu'') \right) + \frac{\delta}{3n} ,$$

$$\sum_{\nu=1}^{n} e_\nu s_\nu < \sum_{\nu=1}^{n} e_\nu \left(f(\xi_\nu') - f(\xi_\nu'') \right) + \frac{\delta}{3} < \frac{2\delta}{3} + \frac{\delta}{3} = \delta .$$

We shall prove the converse of Theorem 364 (Theorem 368), but for this we must do some preliminary spade work.

Theorem 365: *Let*

$$|f(x)| < c \quad on \quad [a, b];$$

let Σ_1 and Σ_2 be the sums $\Sigma\, e\, l$ corresponding to two partitions of which the second contains all of the points of division of the first, and contains at most q more. Let all e_ν of the first partition be $< \varepsilon$. Then we have

$$\Sigma_1 \geqq \Sigma_2 \geqq \Sigma_1 - 2qc\varepsilon.$$

Proof: W.l.g., let $q = 1$. If a new point of division is introduced, so that one term el is replaced by $e'l' + e''l''$, then

$$el - (e'l' + e''l'') = e'(l - l') + e''(l - l'') \begin{cases} \geqq 0, \\ \leqq e' \cdot 2c + e'' \cdot 2c \leqq 2c\varepsilon. \end{cases}$$

Theorem 366: Let $f(x)$ be bounded on $[a, b]$, and let L be the greatest lower bound of Σel for all partitions. Then for every $\delta > 0$ there exists an $\varepsilon > 0$ such that, if all $e < \varepsilon$,

$$\Sigma el < L + \delta.$$

Proof: Choose c so that

$$|f(x)| < c \text{ on } [a, b]$$

Choose a partition such that

$$\Sigma_1 < L + \frac{\delta}{2};$$

let it consist of q sub-intervals. We set

$$\varepsilon = \frac{\delta}{4qc}$$

and consider any partition with all $e_\nu < \varepsilon$. Let Σ be the corresponding $\Sigma\, el$. Let Σ_2 correspond to the partition which contains all points of division of both Σ_1 and Σ. Since to the points of Σ at most $q - 1$ others have to be added, we have by Theorem 365 that

$$L + \frac{\delta}{2} > \Sigma_1 \geqq \Sigma_2 \geqq \Sigma - 2cq\varepsilon = \Sigma - \frac{\delta}{2},$$

$$\Sigma < L + \delta.$$

Theorem 367: Let $f(x)$ be bounded on $[a, b]$, and let Λ be the least upper bound of $\Sigma e\lambda$ for all partitions. Then for every $\delta > 0$ there exists an $\varepsilon > 0$ such that, if all $e < \varepsilon$,

$$\Sigma e\lambda > \Lambda - \delta.$$

Proof: Theorem 366 with $-f(x)$ in place of $f(x)$.

Theorem 368: Let $a < b$. Suppose that $f(x)$ satisfies the Riemann condition, or only the weaker condition that $f(x)$ is defined and bounded on $[a, b]$ and that for every $\delta > 0$ there exists a partition with

$$\Sigma e\, s < \delta.$$

Then $\int_a^b f(x)\, dx$ exists.

Preliminary Remark: By Theorems 368 and 364, it follows that this weaker condition implies the Riemann condition, i.e. that it is not really a weaker condition.

Proof: For every $\delta > 0$ there exists a partition with

$$\delta > \Sigma es = \Sigma el - \Sigma e\lambda \geqq L - \Lambda .$$

Therefore we have

$$\Lambda \geqq L .$$

By Theorems 366 and 367, there exists for every $\delta > 0$ an $\varepsilon > 0$ such that for every partition with all $e_\nu < \varepsilon$, we have

$$\Sigma el < L + \delta$$

as well as

$$\Sigma e\lambda > \Lambda - \delta \geqq L - \delta .$$

If in addition each ξ_ν lies on the corresponding interval $[a_{\nu-1}, a_\nu]$, then we have

$$L - \delta < \Sigma e\lambda \leqq \Sigma ef(\xi) \leqq \Sigma el < L + \delta ,$$

$$| \Sigma ef(\xi) - L | < \delta .$$

However, this shows the existence of

$$\int_a^b f(x) \, dx = L .$$

Theorem 369: *Every function continuous on $[a, b]$ is integrable from a to b.*

Proof: Let the function be $f(x)$. Let $\delta > 0$ be given. By Theorem 154, there exists an $\varepsilon > 0$ such that

$$| f(\alpha) - f(\beta) | < \frac{\delta}{2(b-a)} \text{ for } a \leqq \alpha \leqq b, \, a \leqq \beta \leqq b, | \alpha - \beta | < \varepsilon .$$

Therefore if every $e_\nu < \varepsilon$, then every

$$s_\nu \leqq \frac{\delta}{2(b-a)} ,$$

$$\Sigma es \leqq \frac{\delta}{2(b-a)} \Sigma e = \frac{\delta}{2} < \delta .$$

With this, we have verified the Riemann condition (which, by Theorem 368, is even stronger than necessary).

Definition 85: *If $f(x)$ is defined on $[a, b]$, then it is said to be monotonic there if for $a \leqq \alpha < \beta \leqq b$ we always have*

$$f(\alpha) \leqq f(\beta)$$

or always

$$f(\alpha) \geqq f(\beta) .$$

In the first case, $f(x)$ is said to be monotonically non-decreasing (rising), *in the last case, monotonically non-increasing* (falling).

(Definitions 71 and 72 excluded an equality sign between $f(\alpha)$ and $f(\beta)$.)

Theorem 370: *Every function monotonic on $[a, b]$ is integrable from a to b.*

Proof: Let the function be $f(x)$. In the first case of Definition 85, we have

$$l_\nu = f(a_\nu), \quad \lambda_\nu = f(a_{\nu-1}), \quad s_\nu = f(a_\nu) - f(a_{\nu-1}) \, ;$$

$e_\nu < \varepsilon$ yields

$$\Sigma es \leq \varepsilon \, \Sigma s = \varepsilon \big(f(b) - f(a) \big) \, .$$

In the second case, we have

$$l_\nu = f(a_{\nu-1}), \quad \lambda_\nu = f(a_\nu), \quad s_\nu = f(a_{\nu-1}) - f(a_\nu) \, ,$$

and $e_\nu < \varepsilon$ yields

$$\Sigma es \leq \varepsilon \, \Sigma s = \varepsilon \big(f(a) - f(b) \big) \, .$$

Therefore for every $\delta > 0$, if we set

$$\varepsilon = \frac{\delta}{|f(b) - f(a)| + 1} \, ,$$

then for $e_\nu < \varepsilon$ we have

$$\Sigma es < \delta \, .$$

Theorem 371: *Every function bounded on $[a, b]$ which does not have infinitely many points of discontinuity in the interior of this interval is integrable from a to b.*

Proof: Let the function be $f(x)$, and let

$$|f(x)| < c \text{ on } [a, b].$$

We denote the interior points of discontinuity and the numbers a and b by

$$\eta_k, \quad 0 \leq k \leq m, \quad k \text{ an integer,}$$

in such a way that

$$\eta_{k-1} < \eta_k \text{ for } 1 \leq k \leq m,$$

$$\eta_0 = a, \quad \eta_m = b.$$

Let $\delta > 0$. We set

$$\underset{1 \leq k \leq m}{\text{Min}} \; (\eta_k - \eta_{k-1}) = \zeta,$$

$$\gamma = \text{Min} \left(\frac{\delta}{8mc}, \frac{\zeta}{3} \right).$$

Then we have

$$\eta_{k-1} + \gamma < \eta_k - \gamma \quad \text{for } 1 \le k \le m .$$

$f(x)$ if continuous on each of the intervals $[\eta_{k-1} + \gamma, \eta_k - \gamma]$. Hence there is a partition of each such that, summing over all these intervals, we have

$$\Sigma\, es < \frac{\delta}{2} .$$

For the intervals $[\eta_0, \eta_0 + \gamma]$, $[\eta_k - \gamma, \eta_k + \gamma]$ with $0 < k < m$, and $[\eta_m - \gamma, \eta_m]$, we have without having to partition any of them further that

$$s \le 2c ,$$

so that, summing over these intervals, we have

$$\Sigma\, es \le 2c\, \Sigma\, e = 2c \cdot 2m\gamma \le \frac{\delta}{2} .$$

Hence we have produced a partition of $[a, b]$ such that

$$\Sigma\, es < \frac{\delta}{2} + \frac{\delta}{2} = \delta .$$

Definition 86:
$$\int_a^b f(x)\, dx = -\int_b^a f(x)\, dx ,$$

i. r. h. s. i. m.

Example:
$$\int_4^3 x\, dx = -\int_3^4 x\, dx = -\frac{4^2 - 3^2}{2} = -\frac{7}{2} .$$

Definition 87: *If $f(a)$ is defined, then*

$$\int_a^a f(x)\, dx = 0.$$

Example:
$$\int_0^0 \frac{x-1}{x-1}\, dx = 0 .$$

CHAPTER 26

THEOREMS ON THE DEFINITE INTEGRAL

Theorem 372: $\qquad \int\limits_{a}^{b} f(x)\, dx + \int\limits_{b}^{a} f(x)\, dx = 0\,,$

if one of the two integrals is meaningful.

Proof: Definitions 86 and 87.

Theorem 373: *If* $a \leqq \alpha \leqq \beta \leqq b$ *or* $a \geqq \alpha \geqq \beta \geqq b$, *then* $\int\limits_{\alpha}^{\beta} f(x)\, dx$ *exists provided that* $\int\limits_{a}^{b} f(x)\, dx$ *exists.*

Proof: The case $\alpha = \beta$ is obvious; therefore let $\alpha \neq \beta$, so that w.l.g., $a \leqq \alpha < \beta \leqq b$.

By Theorem 362, $f(x)$ is bounded on $[a, b]$ and so on $[\alpha, \beta]$. For $\delta > 0$, we choose a partition of $[a, b]$ with

$$\Sigma\, es < \delta\,.$$

W.l.g., let α and β be points of division; for by Theorem 365 (applied to $f(x)$ and $-f(x)$), $\Sigma\, es$ does not increase if we add one or two points of division to a partition (since $\Sigma\, el$ and $-\Sigma\, e\lambda$ do not increase).

In this way, if we discard the interval from a to α and the one from β to b, we have a partition of $[\alpha, \beta]$ with

$$\Sigma\, es < \delta\,.$$

Theorem 374: *If* $a < b < c$ *and if* $\int\limits_{a}^{b} f(x)\, dx$ *and* $\int\limits_{b}^{c} f(x)\, dx$ *exist, then* $\int\limits_{a}^{c} f(x)\, dx$ *exists and*

$$\int\limits_{a}^{c} f(x)\, dx = \int\limits_{a}^{b} f(x)\, dx + \int\limits_{b}^{c} f(x)\, dx\,.$$

Proof: 1) By Theorem 362, $f(x)$ is bounded on $[a, b]$ and on $[b, c]$ and so on $[a, c]$. For $\delta > 0$ we choose a partition of $[a, b]$ with

$$\Sigma\, es < \frac{\delta}{2}$$

and one of $[b, c]$ with

$$\Sigma es < \frac{\delta}{2}.$$

Then we have a partition of $[a, c]$ with

$$\Sigma es < \delta.$$

Therefore, $\int_a^c f(x)\, dx$ exists.

2) We divide each of the intervals $[a, b]$ and $[b, c]$ into n equal parts and we always let ξ_ν be the smaller of the two end points of the corresponding sub-interval. Then we have

$$\underset{[a, b]}{\Sigma} ef(\xi) + \underset{[b, c]}{\Sigma} ef(\xi) = \underset{[a, c]}{\Sigma} ef(\xi),$$

and letting $n \to \infty$, we have

$$\int_a^b f(x)\, dx + \int_b^c f(x)\, dx = \int_a^c f(x)\, dx.$$

Theorem 375: $\int_a^b f(x)\, dx + \int_b^c f(x)\, dx + \int_c^a f(x)\, dx = 0$,

if two of the integrals are meaningful.

Proof: The assertion is true for $a < b < c$ by Theorems 373 and 374; it is obvious for $a = b \leqq c$ and for $a \leqq b = c$. Hence it is true for $a \leqq b \leqq c$. Multiplication by -1 gives the theorem for $c \leqq b \leqq a$. Now the assertion does not change if we permute a, b, and c "cyclically" on the left-hand side, i.e. only the order of the terms is changed if a, b, c is replaced by b, c, a or by c, a, b, so that the first, second, and third term is sent into the second, third, and first term, or into the third, first, and second term. Therefore, the assertion is true for $b \leqq c \leqq a$, $c \leqq a \leqq b$, $b \leqq a \leqq c$, and $a \leqq c \leqq b$, and hence always.

Theorem 376: $\int_a^b \left(f(x) + g(x) \right) dx = \int_a^b f(x)\, dx + \int_a^b g(x)\, dx$,

i. r. h. s. i.m.

Proof: W.l.g., let $a < b$ (since $a = b$ is obvious and $a > b$ follows by multiplication of the equation by -1).

$$\sum_{\nu=1}^n e_\nu \left(f(\xi_\nu) + g(\xi_\nu) \right) = \sum_{\nu=1}^n e_\nu f(\xi_\nu) + \sum_{\nu=1}^n e_\nu g(\xi_\nu).$$

For every $\delta > 0$, we have for suitable $\varepsilon > 0$ and for $e_\nu < \varepsilon$ that

$$\left| \sum_{\nu=1}^n e_\nu f(\xi_\nu) - \int_a^b f(x)\, dx \right| < \frac{\delta}{2}$$

as well as

$$\left| \sum_{\nu=1}^n e_\nu g(\xi_\nu) - \int_a^b g(x)\, dx \right| < \frac{\delta}{2},$$

so that

$$\left| \sum_{\nu=1}^{n} e_{\nu} \left(f(\xi_{\nu}) + g(\xi_{\nu}) \right) - \left(\int_{a}^{b} f(x)\, dx + \int_{a}^{b} g(x)\, dx \right) \right| < \delta \,.$$

Example: $\displaystyle \int_{3}^{4} (1+x)\, dx = \int_{3}^{4} dx + \int_{3}^{4} x\, dx = (4-3) + \frac{4^{2}-3^{2}}{2} = \frac{9}{2} \,.$

Theorem 377: $\displaystyle \int_{a}^{b} \sum_{k=1}^{m} f_{k}(x)\, dx = \sum_{k=1}^{m} \int_{a}^{b} f_{k}(x)\, dx,$

i. r. h. s. i. m.

Briefly,

$$\int \Sigma = \Sigma \int \,.$$

Proof: $m=1$: Obvious. To proceed from m to $m+1$: By Theorem 376, we have

$$\sum_{k=1}^{m+1} \int_{a}^{b} f_{k}(x)\, dx = \sum_{k=1}^{m} \int_{a}^{b} f_{k}(x)\, dx + \int_{a}^{b} f_{m+1}(x)\, dx$$

$$= \int_{a}^{b} \sum_{k=1}^{m} f_{k}(x)\, dx + \int_{a}^{b} f_{m+1}(x)\, dx = \int_{a}^{b} \left(\sum_{k=1}^{m} f_{k}(x) + f_{m+1}(x) \right) dx$$

$$= \int_{a}^{b} \sum_{k=1}^{m+1} f_{k}(x)\, dx \,.$$

Theorem 378: $\displaystyle \int_{a}^{b} C f(x)\, dx = C \int_{a}^{b} f(x)\, dx \,,$

i. r. h. s. i. m.

Proof: W.l.g., let $a < b$.

$$\sum_{\nu=1}^{n} e_{\nu} C f(\xi_{\nu}) = C \sum_{\nu=1}^{n} e_{\nu} f(\xi_{\nu}) \,.$$

For every $\delta > 0$, we have for suitable $\varepsilon > 0$ and for $e_{\nu} < \varepsilon$ that

$$\left| \sum_{\nu=1}^{n} e_{\nu} f(\xi_{\nu}) - \int_{a}^{b} f(x)\, dx \right| < \frac{\delta}{|C| + 1} \,,$$

so that

$$\left| \sum_{\nu=1}^{n} e_{\nu} C f(\xi_{\nu}) - C \int_{a}^{b} f(x)\, dx \right| \leqq |C| \frac{\delta}{|C| + 1} < \delta \,.$$

Theorem 379: $\displaystyle \int_{a}^{b} \left(f(x) - g(x) \right) dx = \int_{a}^{b} f(x)\, dx - \int_{a}^{b} g(x)\, dx \,,$

i. r. h. s. i. m.

Proof: $$f - g = f + (-1)g,$$

Theorems 378 and 376.

Theorem 380: *If* $\int_a^b f(x)\,dx$ *and* $\int_a^b g(x)\,dx$ *exist, then* $\int_a^b f(x)\,g(x)\,dx$

exists.

Proof: W.l.g., let $a < b$. By Theorem 362, $f(x)$ and $g(x)$ and hence $f(x)g(x)$ are bounded on $[a, b]$. We have for x_1 and x_2 on $[a, b]$ that

(1) $\quad f(x_1)\,g(x_1) - f(x_2)\,g(x_2) = f(x_1)\big(g(x_1) - g(x_2)\big) + g(x_2)\big(f(x_1) - f(x_2)\big).$

Choose c such that

$$|f(x)| < c, \quad |g(x)| < c \text{ on } [a, b],$$

and let s', s'', and s be the oscillations of $f(x)$, $g(x)$, and $f(x)g(x)$ respectively on a sub-interval. Then by (1), if x_1 and x_2 are in the same sub-interval, we have

$$f(x_1)\,g(x_1) - f(x_2)\,g(x_2) \leqq |f(x_1)|\,|g(x_1) - g(x_2)| + |g(x_2)|\,|f(x_1) - f(x_2)|$$

$$\leqq c s'' + c s',$$

so that, by Theorem 360,

$$s \leqq c s'' + c s',$$

$$\Sigma e s \leqq c \Sigma e s'' + c \Sigma e s',$$

which is $< \delta$ for any $\delta > 0$, for a suitable partition.

Theorem 381: *If m is an integer > 0 and if* $\int_a^b f_k(x)\,dx$ *exists for every*

integral k with $1 \leqq k \leqq m$, then $\int_a^b \prod_{k=1}^m f_k(x)\,dx$ *exists.*

Proof: $m = 1$: Obvious. To proceed from m to $m + 1$:

$$\prod_{k=1}^{m+1} f_k(x) = \prod_{k=1}^m f_k(x) \cdot f_{m+1}(x),$$

and Theorem 380.

Theorem 382: *If* $\int_a^b f(x)\,dx$ *exists and if*

$$|f(x)| > p > 0$$

for $a \leqq x \leqq b$ (or $b \leqq x \leqq a$), then $\int_a^b \dfrac{dx}{f(x)}$ *exists.*

Proof: W.l.g., let $a < b$; let s' be the oscillation of $f(x)$ in a sub-interval and s that of $\dfrac{1}{f(x)}$. For x_1 and x_2 in the sub-interval, we have

$$\left| \frac{1}{f(x_1)} - \frac{1}{f(x_2)} \right| = \left| \frac{f(x_2) - f(x_1)}{f(x_1)\, f(x_2)} \right| \leq \frac{1}{p^2} \left| f(x_1) - f(x_2) \right| \leq \frac{s'}{p^2},$$

so that

$$s \leq \frac{s'}{p^2},$$

$$\Sigma es \leq \frac{1}{p^2}\, \Sigma es',$$

which is $< \delta$ for every $\delta > 0$, for a suitable partition.

Theorem 383: *If* $\int_a^b f(x)\, dx$ *and* $\int_a^b g(x)\, dx$ *exist, and if*

$$|g(x)| > p > 0$$

for $a \leq x \leq b$ *(or* $b \leq x \leq a$*), then* $\int_a^b \dfrac{f(x)}{g(x)}\, dx$ *exists.*

Proof:
$$\frac{f}{g} = f\, \frac{1}{g},$$

Theorems 382 and 380.

Theorem 384: *If* $\int_a^b f(x)\, dx$ *exists and if* l *(or* λ*) is the l.u.b. (or g.l.b.) of* $f(x)$ *for* $a \leq x \leq b$ *(or* $b \leq x \leq a$*), then*

$$\lambda(b - a) \leq \int_a^b f(x)\, dx \leq l(b - a)$$

(or

$$l(b - a) \leq \int_a^b f(x)\, dx \leq \lambda(b - a),$$

respectively).

Proof: 1) $a = b$ is obvious.

2) If $a < b$ then

$$\lambda(b - a) = \sum_{\nu=1}^{n} e_\nu \lambda \leq \sum_{\nu=1}^{n} e_\nu f(\xi_\nu) \leq \sum_{\nu=1}^{n} e_\nu l = l(b - a),$$

so that

$$\lambda(b - a) \leq \int_a^b f(x)\, dx \leq l(b - a).$$

3) If $a > b$, then by 2), we have

$$\lambda(a - b) \leq \int_b^a f(x)\, dx \leq l(a - b),$$

and our assertion follows upon multiplication by -1.

Theorem 385: *Let* $\int_a^b f(x)\,dx$ *exist and let*

$$|f(x)| \leqq c \text{ for } a \leqq x \leqq b \ (or \ b \leqq x \leqq a).$$

Then we have

$$\left| \int_a^b f(x)\,dx \right| \leqq c \, |b - a|.$$

Proof: 1) $a = b$ is obvious.

2) For $a < b$, since

$$-c \leqq \lambda \leqq l \leqq c,$$

we have by Theorem 384 that

$$-c(b - a) \leqq \int_a^b f(x)\,dx \leqq c(b - a).$$

3) For $a > b$, the assertion follows from 2) since

$$\int_a^b f(x)\,dx = -\int_b^a f(x)\,dx.$$

Theorem 386: *Let* $a < b$, *let* $\int_a^b f(x)\,dx$ *exist, and let*

$$f(x) \geqq 0 \text{ on } [a, b].$$

Then we have

$$\int_a^b f(x)\,dx \geqq 0.$$

Preliminary Remark: If we assume the stronger hypothesis

$$f(x) > 0 \text{ on } [a, b],$$

then we still get only

$$\int_a^b f(x)\,dx \geqq 0$$

from the following proof. This is why Theorem 388 will be so gratifying.

Proof: $\lambda \geqq 0$ and Theorem 384.

Theorem 387: *If* $a < b$ *and if* $\int_a^b f(x)\,dx$ *exists, then* $f(x)$ *is continuous at some* ξ *with* $a < \xi < b$.

Preliminary Remark: From this it follows that $f(x)$ is continuous at infinitely many ξ with $a < \xi < b$.

Proof: If $a < \beta$ and if $\int_\alpha^\beta f(x)\,dx$ exists, then for every $\eta > 0$ there exists a closed interval in the interior of $[a, \beta]$ such that

$$s < \eta.$$

For, we choose a partition with

$$\sum_{\nu=1}^{n} e_\nu \, s_\nu < \eta(\beta - \alpha).$$

Then we have

$$\eta(\beta - \alpha) > \underset{1 \leq \nu \leq n}{\text{Min}} \, s_\nu \cdot \sum_{\nu=1}^{n} e_\nu = (\beta - \alpha) \underset{1 \leq \nu \leq n}{\text{Min}} \, s_\nu,$$

so that one

$$s_\nu < \eta.$$

We obtain the required interval by "cutting off both ends."

In the interior of $[a, b]$, we choose a $[a^{(1)}, b^{(1)}]$ with

$$s < 1,$$

in the interior of $[a^{(1)}, b^{(1)}]$ a $[a^{(2)}, b^{(2)}]$ with

$$s < \tfrac{1}{2},$$

etc. I.e. (as is obvious by proceeding from m to $m + 1$), we choose two sequences of numbers

$$a^{(m)}, \; b^{(m)}, \; m \geq 1 \text{ an integer}$$

with

$$a < a^{(1)}, \; b^{(1)} < b,$$

$$a^{(m)} < a^{(m+1)}, \; b^{(m+1)} < b^{(m)},$$

$$a^{(m)} < b^{(m)},$$

so that on $[a^{(m)}, b^{(m)}]$ we have

(1)
$$s < \frac{1}{m}.$$

The $a^{(m)}$ are bounded from above (they are $< b$); hence

$$\lim_{m = \infty} a^{(m)} = \xi$$

exists. We have

$$a < \xi < b,$$

and, in fact,

$$a^{(m)} < \xi < b^{(m)} \text{ for every } m.$$

Let δ be given and let $m > \dfrac{1}{\delta}$. For a suitable $\varepsilon > 0$ which is dependent on m, and hence on δ, we have

$$a^{(m)} < \xi - \varepsilon, \; \xi + \varepsilon < b^{(m)}.$$

Hence by (1), we have for $|x - \xi| \leq \varepsilon$ that

$$|f(x) - f(\xi)| < \frac{1}{m} < \delta.$$

Therefore $f(x)$ is continuous at ξ.

Theorem 388: *Let $a < b$, let $\int_a^b f(x)\,dx$ exist, and let*

$$f(x) > 0 \ \text{on} \ [a, b].$$

Then we have

$$\int_a^b f(x)\,dx > 0.$$

Proof: By Theorem 387, let ξ be a value in the interior of the interval at which $f(x)$ is continuous. We set

$$f(\xi) = p \ (> 0).$$

Hence there exist α, β with

$$a < \alpha < \xi < \beta < b,$$

$$f(x) > \frac{p}{2} \ \text{on} \ [\alpha, \beta].$$

Therefore we have by Theorems 384 and 386 that

$$\int_a^b = \int_a^\alpha + \int_\alpha^b = \int_a^\alpha + \int_\alpha^\beta + \int_\beta^b \geqq 0 + \frac{p}{2}\,(\beta - \alpha) + 0 > 0.$$

Theorem 389: *If $a < b$, if $\int_a^b f(x)\,dx$ and $\int_a^b g(x)\,dx$ exist, and if*

$$f(x) \leqq g(x) \quad \text{on} \ [a, b],$$

then

$$\int_a^b f(x)\,dx \leqq \int_a^b g(x)\,dx.$$

Proof:
$$g(x) - f(x) \geqq 0,$$

so that, by Theorems 379 and 386,

$$\int_a^b g(x)\,dx - \int_a^b f(x)\,dx = \int_a^b (g(x) - f(x))\,dx \geqq 0.$$

Theorem 390: *Let $a < b$, let $f(x)$ be bounded from above on $[a, b]$, and let l be the l.u.b. of $f(x)$ on $[a, b]$. Let $\int_a^b g(x)\,dx$ and $\int_a^b f(x)g(x)\,dx$ exist, and let*

$$g(x) \geqq 0 \quad \text{on} \ [a, b].$$

Then we have

$$\int_a^b f(x)\,g(x)\,dx \leqq l \int_a^b g(x)\,dx.$$

Preliminary Remark: If $f(x)$ is bounded from below (instead of from above), and if λ is its g.l.b., then by applying this result to $-f(x)$ we obtain

$$\int_a^b (-f(x))\, g(x)\, dx \leq (-\lambda) \int_a^b g(x)\, dx\,,$$

$$\int_a^b f(x)\, g(x)\, dx \geq \lambda \int_a^b g(x)\, dx\,.$$

Proof:
$$(l - f(x))\, g(x) \geq 0.$$

$$(l - f(x))\, g(x) = l g(x) - f(x) g(x)$$

is integrable from a to b. Therefore by Theorem 386, we have

$$l \int_a^b g(x)\, dx - \int_a^b f(x)\, g(x)\, dx = \int_a^b (l - f(x))\, g(x)\, dx \geq 0\,.$$

Theorem 391 (first mean-value theorem of the integral calculus): *Let $a < b$, let $f(x)$ be continuous on $[a, b]$, let $\int_a^b g(x)\, dx$ exist, and let*

$$g(x) \geq 0 \ \ on \ \ [a, b].$$

Then there exists a ξ on $[a, b]$ such that

$$\int_a^b f(x)\, g(x)\, dx = f(\xi) \int_a^b g(x)\, dx\,.$$

Proof: Let λ be the least, l the largest value of $f(x)$ on $[a, b]$. $\int_a^b f(x)\, g(x)\, dx$ exists by Theorems 369 and 380. Therefore we have by Theorem 390 and its preliminary remark that

(1)
$$\lambda \int_a^b g(x)\, dx \leq \int_a^b f(x)\, g(x)\, dx \leq l \int_a^b g(x)\, dx\,.$$

$$f(z) \int_a^b g(x)\, dx$$

is continuous on the z-interval $[a, b]$ and attains thereon its least value $\lambda \int_a^b g(x)\, dx$, and its greatest value $l \int_a^b g(x)\, dx$. Therefore, by (1) and Theorem 152, there exists a ξ on $[a, b]$ such that

$$\int_a^b f(x)\, g(x)\, dx = f(\xi) \int_a^b g(x)\, dx\,.$$

Theorem 392: *If $a < b$ and if $f(x)$ is continuous on $[a, b]$, then there exists a ξ on $[a, b]$ such that*

$$\int_a^b f(x)\, dx = f(\xi)\, (b - a).$$

Proof: Theorem 391 with $g(x) = 1$.

Theorem 393: *Let $a < b$ and let $\int_a^b f(x)\, dx$ exist, so that*

$$\int_a^x f(y)\, dy = F(x)$$

exists on $[a, b]$. Then $F(x)$ is continuous on $[a, b]$.

Proof: If ξ and $\xi + h$ belong to $[a, b]$, then we have by Theorem 375 that

$$F(\xi + h) - F(\xi) = \int_a^{\xi+h} f(x)\, dx - \int_a^{\xi} f(x)\, dx = \int_{\xi}^{\xi+h} f(x)\, dx\,.$$

Choose c such that

$$\left| f(x) \right| < c \text{ on } [a, b].$$

Then we have by Theorem 385 that

$$\left| F(\xi + h) - F(\xi) \right| = \left| \int_{\xi}^{\xi+h} f(x)\, dx \right| \leq c\, | h |\,;$$

and therefore for every $\delta > 0$ we have for $| h | < \varepsilon = \dfrac{\delta}{c}$ that

$$\left| F(\xi + h) - F(\xi) \right| < \delta.$$

Theorem 394: *Let $a < b$ and let $\int_a^b f(x)\, dx$ exist, so that*

$$\int_x^b f(y)\, dy = G(x)$$

exists on $[a, b]$. Then $G(x)$ is continuous on $[a, b]$.

Proof:
$$F(x) + G(x) = \int_a^b f(y)\, dy\,,$$

$$G(x) = -F(x) + \text{ a constant,}$$

and Theorem 393.

Theorem 395: *Let $a < b$, let $\int_a^b f(x)\, dx$ exist, and let $f(x)$ be continuous at some ξ with $a < \xi < b$. Then*

$$F(x) = \int_a^x f(y)\, dy$$

is differentiable at ξ, and

$$F'(\xi) = f(\xi)\,.$$

Proof: We have for $0 < |h| \leq \mathrm{Min}\,(b - \xi,\ \xi - a)$ that

$$\mathrm{F}(\xi + h) - \mathrm{F}(\xi) = \int_{\xi}^{\xi+h} f(x)\,dx\,,$$

$$h\,f(\xi) = \int_{\xi}^{\xi+h} f(\xi)\,dx\,,$$

$$\mathrm{F}(\xi + h) - \mathrm{F}(\xi) - h\,f(\xi) = \int_{\xi}^{\xi+h} \big(f(x) - f(\xi)\big)\,dx\,.$$

If $\delta > 0$ is given, then for a suitable positive $\varepsilon \leq \mathrm{Min}\,(b - \xi,\ \xi - a)$ we have

$$\big|f(x) - f(\xi)\big| < \delta \ \text{ for } \ |x - \xi| < \varepsilon\,;$$

and hence, by Theorem 385, we have for $0 < |h| < \varepsilon$ that

$$\big|\mathrm{F}(\xi + h) - \mathrm{F}(\xi) - h\,f(\xi)\big| \leq |h|\,\delta\,,$$

$$\left|\frac{\mathrm{F}(\xi + h) - \mathrm{F}(\xi)}{h} - f(\xi)\right| \leq \delta\,.$$

Therefore,

$$\mathrm{F}'(\xi) = f(\xi)\,.$$

Theorem 396: *Let $a < b$, let $\int_{a}^{b} f(x)\,dx$ exist, and let $f(x)$ be continuous at some ξ with $a < \xi < b$. Then we have that*

$$\mathrm{G}(x) = \int_{x}^{b} f(y)\,dy$$

is differentiable at ξ and that

$$\mathrm{G}'(\xi) = -f(\xi)\,.$$

Proof: $\qquad\qquad \mathrm{G}(x) = -\,\mathrm{F}(x) + \text{a constant,}$

and Theorem 395.

Theorem 397: *Let $a < b$ and let $f(x)$ and $g(x)$ be continuous on $[a,b]$. Let $g(x)$ be an indefinite integral of $f(x)$ for $a < x < b$ (i.e. $g'(x) = f(x)$). Then we have*

$$\int_{a}^{b} f(x)\,dx = g(b) - g(a)\,.$$

Proof: If we set

$$\mathrm{F}(x) = \int_{a}^{x} f(y)\,dy \ \text{ on } \ [a, b],$$

then we have by Theorem 395 that

$$\mathrm{F}'(x) = f(x) = g'(x) \ \text{ for } \ a < x < b\,.$$

Therefore, we have by Theorems 393 and 162 that

$$\int_a^b f(y)\,dy - g(b) = F(b) - g(b) = F(a) - g(a) = -g(a).$$

Theorem 398: *Let $a > b$ and let $f(x)$ and $g(x)$ be continuous on $[b, a]$. Let $g(x)$ be an indefinite integral of $f(x)$ for $b < x < a$. Then we have*

$$\int_a^b f(x)\,dx = g(b) - g(a).$$

Proof: By Theorem 397, we have

$$\int_b^a f(x)\,dx = g(a) - g(b).$$

This is to be multiplied by -1.

Examples: In practical calculations, we set

$$g(b) - g(a) = \{g(x)\}_a^b.$$

1) For $a \neq b$ we have by Theorems 397 and 398, and for $a = b$ we have trivially,

$$\int_a^b x^3\,dx = \left\{\frac{x^4}{4}\right\}_a^b = \frac{b^4}{4} - \frac{a^4}{4}\,;$$

for we have

$$\left(\frac{x^4}{4}\right)' = x^3.$$

More generally, Theorems 397 and 398 allow us to calculate a definite integral of a continuous function provided we know a continuous function on the closed interval which is the indefinite integral in the open interval.

2) $$\int_1^b \frac{dx}{x} = \{\log x\}_1^b = \log b \text{ for } b > 0.$$

Theorem 399: *Let $a < b$, let $\int_a^b f(x)\,dx$ exist, and let $g(x)$ be continuous on $[a, b]$ with*

$$g'(x) = f(x) \text{ for } a < x < b.$$

Then we have

$$\int_a^b f(x)\,dx = g(b) - g(a).$$

Preliminary Remark: Theorem 399 contains Theorem 397 as a special case, but it is hardly any more difficult to prove.

Proof: For every partition of $[a, b]$, we have by Theorem 159 that

$$g(b) - g(a) = \sum_{\nu=1}^{n} \left(g(a_\nu) - g(a_{\nu-1}) \right) = \sum_{\nu=1}^{n} e_\nu\, g'(\xi_\nu)$$

$$= \sum_{\nu=1}^{n} e_\nu\, f(\xi_\nu), \quad a_{\nu-1} < \xi_\nu < a_\nu.$$

For $\delta > 0$, we choose a partition such that for an arbitrary choice of ξ_ν on $[a_{\nu-1}, a_\nu]$, and in particular for the above choice, we have

$$\left| \sum_{\nu=1}^{n} e_\nu\, f(\xi_\nu) - \int_a^b f(x)\, dx \right| < \delta.$$

Then we have

$$\left| g(b) - g(a) - \int_a^b f(x)\, dx \right| < \delta.$$

The left-hand side is independent of δ and so is equal to 0.

Theorem 400: *If $a < b$ and if $\int_a^b f(x)\, dx$ exists, then $\int_a^b |f(x)|\, dx$ exists, and*

$$\left| \int_a^b f(x)\, dx \right| \leq \int_a^b |f(x)|\, dx.$$

Proof: 1) By Theorem 362, $f(x)$ and hence $|f(x)|$ is bounded on $[a, b]$. Let S be the oscillation of $f(x)$ in a sub-interval, s the oscillation of $|f(x)|$. Since

$$\left| f(x_1) \right| - \left| f(x_2) \right| \leq \left| f(x_1) - f(x_2) \right|,$$

we have

$$s \leq S,$$

so that for every $\delta > 0$ and for a suitable partition, we have

$$\Sigma\, es \leq \Sigma\, eS < \delta.$$

2) Since

$$-|f(x)| \leq f(x) \leq |f(x)|,$$

we have by Theorem 389 and by 1) that

$$-\int_a^b |f(x)|\, dx \leq \int_a^b f(x)\, dx \leq \int_a^b |f(x)|\, dx.$$

We now come to the most important and the only deep theorem of this chapter, the so-called second mean-value theorem (Theorem 405), which requires a few preliminaries. Theorem 401, which follows, and which is often very useful, does not involve integrals but expresses a property of finite sums.

Theorem 401: *Let*

$$n \geq 1 \ \textit{be an integer,}$$

$$\varepsilon_\nu \geq \varepsilon_{\nu+1} \ \textit{for} \ 1 \leq \nu \leq n-1, \ \nu \ \textit{an integer}$$

(so that nothing is required for $n = 1$),

$$\varepsilon_n \geq 0,$$

$$\alpha_\nu \ \textit{arbitrary for} \ 1 \leq \nu \leq n, \ \nu \ \textit{an integer} \ ,$$

$$\left. \begin{array}{l} S_q = \sum\limits_{\nu=1}^{q} \alpha_\nu \\[2mm] A \leq S_q \leq B \end{array} \right\} \ \textit{for} \ 1 \leq q \leq n, \ q \ \textit{an integer} \ ,$$

where A and B are independent of q (e.g. $A = \underset{1 \leq q \leq n}{\text{Min}} S_q$, $B = \underset{1 \leq q \leq n}{\text{Max}} S_q$).
Then we have

$$A\varepsilon_1 \leq \sum_{\nu=1}^{n} \varepsilon_\nu \alpha_\nu \leq B\varepsilon_1 .$$

Proof: $n = 1$ is obvious. If $n > 1$ then

$$\sum_{\nu=1}^{n} \varepsilon_\nu \alpha_\nu = \varepsilon_1 S_1 + \sum_{\nu=2}^{n} \varepsilon_\nu (S_\nu - S_{\nu-1}) = \sum_{\nu=1}^{n-1} S_\nu (\varepsilon_\nu - \varepsilon_{\nu+1}) + S_n \varepsilon_n$$

$$\left\{ \begin{array}{l} \leq B \left(\sum\limits_{\nu=1}^{n-1} (\varepsilon_\nu - \varepsilon_{\nu+1}) + \varepsilon_n \right) = B\varepsilon_1 , \\[4mm] \geq A \left(\sum\limits_{\nu=1}^{n-1} (\varepsilon_\nu - \varepsilon_{\nu+1}) + \varepsilon_n \right) = A\varepsilon_1 . \end{array} \right.$$

Theorem 402: *Let* $a < b$, *let* $\int_a^b f(x)\, dx$ *exist, and let* $\psi(x)$ *be monotonically non-increasing on* $[a, b]$. *Furthermore let*

$$\psi(a) = 1, \quad \psi(b) \geq 0.$$

Then there exists a ξ *on* $[a, b]$ *such that*

$$\int_a^b f(x)\, \psi(x)\, dx = \int_a^\xi f(x)\, dx.$$

Proof: For an arbitrary partition of $[a, b]$, let $e_\nu, l_\nu, \lambda_\nu, s_\nu$ be defined as usual with respect to $f(x)$. Let $\xi_1 = a$ and choose the remaining ξ_ν arbitrarily on $[a_{\nu-1}, a_\nu]$. Then by Theorem 384, we have for integral q with $1 \leqq q \leqq n$ that

$$\sum_{\nu=1}^{q} e_\nu \lambda_\nu \leqq \sum_{\nu=1}^{q} \int_{a_{\nu-1}}^{a_\nu} f(x)\, ax = \int_{a}^{a_q} f(x)\, dx \leqq \sum_{\nu=1}^{q} e_\nu l_\nu.$$

Furthermore, we have

$$\sum_{\nu=1}^{q} e_\nu \lambda_\nu \leqq \sum_{\nu=1}^{q} e_\nu f(\xi_\nu) \leqq \sum_{\nu=1}^{q} e_\nu l_\nu,$$

so that

$$\left| \int_{a}^{a_q} f(x)\, dx - \sum_{\nu=1}^{q} e_\nu f(\xi_\nu) \right| \leqq \sum_{\nu=1}^{q} e_\nu s_\nu \leqq \sum_{\nu=1}^{n} e_\nu s_\nu.$$

$\int_{a}^{y} f(x)\, dx$ is by Theorem 393 continuous on the y-interval $[a, b]$. Let its least value there be C, its largest value D. Then we have for $1 \leqq q \leqq n$ that

$$C - \sum_{\nu=1}^{n} e_\nu s_\nu \leqq \int_{a}^{a_q} f(x)\, dx - \sum_{\nu=1}^{n} e_\nu s_\nu \leqq \sum_{\nu=1}^{q} e_\nu f(\xi_\nu)$$

$$\leqq \int_{a}^{a_q} f(x)\, dx + \sum_{\nu=1}^{n} e_\nu s_\nu \leqq D + \sum_{\nu=1}^{n} e_\nu s_\nu.$$

In Theorem 401 we take

$$\varepsilon_\nu = \psi(\xi_\nu) \text{ for } 1 \leqq \nu \leqq n$$

(so that all of the hypotheses on the ε_ν are satisfied),

$$\alpha_\nu = e_\nu f(\xi_\nu),$$

$$A = C - \sum_{\nu=1}^{n} e_\nu s_\nu,$$

$$B = D + \sum_{\nu=1}^{n} e_\nu s_\nu.$$

By this theorem, we have (since $\varepsilon_1 = 1$)

$$C - \sum_{\nu=1}^{n} e_\nu s_\nu \leqq \sum_{\nu=1}^{n} e_\nu f(\xi_\nu)\, \psi(\xi_\nu) \leqq D + \sum_{\nu=1}^{n} e_\nu s_\nu.$$

$\int_{a}^{b} f(x)\, \psi(x)\, dx$ exists by Theorems 370 and 380. For sufficiently small

Max e_ν, the three members of this last formula are arbitrarily close to
$1 \leq \nu \leq n$

$$C, \quad \int_a^b f(x)\, \psi(x)\, dx, \quad D.$$

Therefore

$$C \leq \int_a^b f(x)\, \psi(x)\, dx \leq D.$$

Since $\int_a^\nu f(x)\, dx$ is continuous on $[a, b]$, there exists a ξ on $[a, b]$ such that

$$\int_a^b f(x)\, \psi(x)\, dx = \int_a^\xi f(x)\, dx.$$

Theorem 403: *If in the hypotheses of Theorem 402, we dispense with the hypothesis*

$$\psi(a) = 1,$$

then there exists a ξ on $[a, b]$ such that

$$\int_a^b f(x)\, \psi(x)\, dx = \psi(a) \int_a^\xi f(x)\, dx.$$

Proof:
1) If

$$\psi(a) \geq 0.$$

$$\psi(a) = 0,$$

then

$$\psi(x) = 0 \text{ on } [a, b],$$

$$\int_a^b f(x)\, \psi(x)\, dx = 0,$$

and every ξ on $[a, b]$ is of the required kind.
2) If

$$\psi(a) > 0,$$

then Theorem 402 is applicable to $\dfrac{\psi(x)}{\psi(a)}$ in place of $\psi(x)$ and yields for a suitable ξ on $[a, b]$ that

$$\int_a^b f(x)\, \frac{\psi(x)}{\psi(a)}\, dx = \int_a^\xi f(x)\, dx.$$

Theorem 404: *Let $a < b$, let $\int_a^b f(x)\, dx$ exist, and let $\psi(x)$ be monotonically non-increasing and ≥ 0 on $[a, b]$. Let*

$$\psi(a) \le c_1 ,$$

$$\left| \int_a^y f(x)\, dx \right| \le c_2 \quad on \ [a, b].$$

Then we have

$$\left| \int_a^b f(x)\, \psi(x)\, dx \right| \le c_1 c_2 .$$

Preliminary Remark: This theorem is not needed for the proof of Theorem 405, but it is important for many applications.

Proof: Theorem 403.

Examples: 1) For $0 < a < b$ we have

$$\left| \int_a^b \frac{\sin x}{x}\, dx \right| \le \frac{2}{a} ;$$

for, Theorem 404 can be applied with

$$f(x) = \sin x, \quad \psi(x) = \frac{1}{x}, \quad c_1 = \frac{1}{a}, \quad c_2 = 2,$$

since

$$\left| \int_a^y \sin x\, dx \right| = \left| \{-\cos x\}_a^y \right| = \left| -\cos y + \cos a \right| \le 2 .$$

2) For $0 < a < b$ we have, setting

$$f(x) = 2x \cos (x^2), \quad \psi(x) = \frac{1}{2x}, \quad c_1 = \frac{1}{2a}, \quad c_2 = 2,$$

that, since

$$\left| \int_a^y 2x \cos (x^2)\, dx \right| = \left| \{\sin (x^2)\}_a^y \right| = \left| \sin (y^2) - \sin (a^2) \right| \le 2 ,$$

$$\left| \int_a^b \cos (x^2)\, dx \right| = \left| \int_a^b f(x)\, \psi(x)\, dx \right| \le c_1 c_2 = \frac{1}{a} .$$

Theorem 405 (second mean-value theorem of the integral calculus): *Let* $a < b$, *let* $\int_a^b f(x)\, dx$ *exist, and let* $g(x)$ *be monotonic on* $[a, b]$. *Then there exists a* ξ *on* $[a, b]$ *such that*

$$\int_a^b f(x)\, g(x)\, dx = g(a) \int_a^\xi f(x)\, dx + g(b) \int_\xi^b f(x)\, dx .$$

Proof: W.l.g., let $g(x)$ be monotonically non-increasing (otherwise consider $-g(x)$ instead of $g(x)$), so that

$$\psi(x) \doteq g(x) - g(b)$$

is monotonically non-increasing and

$$\psi(b) = 0 \, .$$

Hence, by Theorem 403, there exists a ξ on $[a, b]$ such that

$$\int_a^b f(x) \, (g(x) - g(b)) \, dx = (g(a) - g(b)) \int_a^\xi f(x) \, dx \, ,$$

$$\int_a^b f(x) \, g(x) \, dx = g(b) \int_a^b f(x) \, dx + g(a) \int_a^\xi f(x) dx - g(b) \int_a^\xi f(x) \, dx$$

$$= g(a) \int_a^\xi f(x) \, dx + g(b) \int_\xi^b f(x) \, dx \, .$$

Theorem 406 (translation): *Let $a < b$ and let $\int_a^b f(x) \, dx$ exist. Then*

$$\int_a^b f(x) \, dx = \int_{a-c}^{b-c} f(y + c) \, dy \, .$$

Proof: For an arbitrary partition of $[a - c, \, b - c]$, we have that if ξ_ν is in the ν-th sub-interval, then

$$\sum_{\nu=1}^n e_\nu f(\xi_\nu + c) = \sum_{\nu=1}^n e_\nu f(\zeta_\nu) \, ,$$

where on the right we have the corresponding $(A_\nu = a_\nu + c)$ partition of $[a, b]$ and $\zeta_\nu = \xi_\nu + c$. The right-hand side of this equation is, for suitably small $\underset{1 \leq \nu \leq n}{\text{Max}} e_\nu$, arbitrarily close to the left-hand side of the equation in the theorem.

Theorem 407 (reflection): *Let $a < b$ and let $\int_a^b f(x) \, dx$ exist. Then*

$$\int_a^b f(x) \, dx = \int_{-b}^{-a} f(-y) \, dy \, .$$

Proof: For an arbitrary partition of $[-b, \, -a]$, we have that if ξ_ν is in the ν-th sub-interval then

$$\sum_{\nu=1}^n e_\nu f(-\xi_\nu) = \sum_{\nu=1}^n e_\nu f(\zeta_\nu) \, ,$$

where on the right we have the corresponding $(A_\nu = -a_\nu)$ partition of $[a, b]$ labeled in reverse order, and $\zeta_\nu = -\xi_\nu$. The right-hand side of this equation is, for suitably small $\text{Max}_{1 \leq \nu \leq n} e_\nu$, arbitrarily close to the left-hand side of the equality in the theorem.

Theorem 408 (elongation): *Let $a < b$, let $\int_a^b f(x)\,dx$ exist, and let $\mu > 0$. Then*

$$\int_a^b f(x)\,dx = \mu \int_{\frac{a}{\mu}}^{\frac{b}{\mu}} f(\mu y)\,dy .$$

Proof: For an arbitrary partition of $[\dfrac{a}{\mu}, \dfrac{b}{\mu}]$, we have that if ξ_ν is in the ν-th sub-interval then

(1) $$\sum_{\nu=1}^{n} e_\nu f(\mu \xi_\nu) = \frac{1}{\mu} \sum_{\nu=1}^{n} E_\nu f(\zeta_\nu) ,$$

where on the right we have the corresponding "elongated" ($A_\nu = \mu a_\nu$, $E_\nu = \mu e_\nu$) partition of $[a, b]$, and $\zeta_\nu = \mu \xi_\nu$. If

$$\text{Max}_{1 \leq \nu \leq n} e_\nu < \frac{\varepsilon}{\mu}$$

then

$$\text{Max}_{1 \leq \nu \leq n} E_\nu = \text{Max}_{1 \leq \nu \leq n} (\mu e_\nu) < \varepsilon .$$

The right-hand side of (1) is, for suitably small $\text{Max}_{1 \leq \nu \leq n} e_\nu$, arbitrarily close to $\dfrac{1}{\mu}$ times the left-hand side of the equality in the theorem.

Theorem 409: (Van der Corput—Landau): *There exists a universal constant p with the following property. Let $a < b, r > 0$, and*

$$f''(x) > r \quad on \quad [a, b].$$

Then we have

$$\left| \int_a^b \cos f(x)\,dx \right| < \frac{p}{\sqrt{r}} .$$

Preliminary Remark: This theorem, important in analytic number theory, is an application of Theorem 404. Incidentally, we prove this with

$$p = 6.$$

Proof: 1) Since $f''(x) > 0, f'(x)$ is continuous and monotonically increasing on $[a, b]$. The interval $[a, b]$ thus breaks into at most two intervals such that $f'(x) \geq 0$ on one and $f'(x) \leq 0$ on the other.

Consequently, it suffices to prove our assertion for every **such** interval with $p = 3$.

W.l.g., let

$$f'(x) \geqq 0.$$

For otherwise we consider

$$g(x) = f(-x) \quad \text{on} \quad [-b, -a];$$

and since

$$g'(x) = -f'(-x) \geqq 0,$$

$$g''(x) = f''(-x) > r,$$

we have by Theorem 407 that

$$\left| \int_a^b \cos f(x)\, dx \right| = \left| \int_{-b}^{-a} \cos f(-x)\, dx \right| = \left| \int_{-b}^{-a} \cos g(x)\, dx \right| < \frac{3}{\sqrt{r}}.$$

2) Hence for $[a, b]$, let

$$f'(x) \geqq 0, \quad f''(x) > r > 0.$$

I) If

$$b - a \leqq \frac{1}{\sqrt{r}},$$

then by Theorem 385 we have

$$\left| \int_{a,}^b \cos f(x)\, dx \right| \leqq b - a \leqq \frac{1}{\sqrt{r}} < \frac{3}{\sqrt{r}}.$$

II) If

$$b - a > \frac{1}{\sqrt{r}},$$

then we have by I) that

$$\left| \int_a^{a + \frac{1}{\sqrt{r}}} \cos f(x)\, dx \right| \leqq \frac{1}{\sqrt{r}},$$

so that it suffices to prove

$$\left| \int_{a + \frac{1}{\sqrt{r}}}^b \cos f(x)\, dx \right| < \frac{2}{\sqrt{r}}.$$

By Theorem 159, we have

$$f'\left(a + \frac{1}{\sqrt{r}}\right) = f'(a) + \frac{1}{\sqrt{r}} f''(\xi), \quad a < \xi < a + \frac{1}{\sqrt{r}},$$

so that

$$f'\left(a + \frac{1}{\sqrt{r}}\right) > 0 + \frac{1}{\sqrt{r}} r = \sqrt{r}.$$

Since

$$\psi(x) = \frac{1}{f'(x)}$$

is monotonically decreasing and > 0 on $[a + \dfrac{1}{\sqrt{r}}, b]$, we have by Theorem 404 (with the continuous

$$\frac{d \sin f(x)}{dx} = f'(x) \cos f(x)$$

in place of $f(x)$,

$$c_1 = \frac{1}{f'\left(a + \dfrac{1}{\sqrt{r}}\right)}, \quad c_2 = 2)$$

that

$$\left| \int_{a+\frac{1}{\sqrt{r}}}^{b} \cos f(x)\, dx \right| = \left| \int_{a+\frac{1}{\sqrt{r}}}^{b} \frac{d \sin f(x)}{dx} \psi(x)\, dx \right| \leqq c_1 c_2 < \frac{2}{\sqrt{r}};$$

in fact, we have for y in $[a + \dfrac{1}{\sqrt{r}}, b]$ that

$$\left| \int_{a+\frac{1}{\sqrt{r}}}^{y} \frac{d \sin f(x)}{dx}\, dx \right| = \left| \{\sin f(x)\}_{a+\frac{1}{\sqrt{r}}}^{y} \right| \leqq 2 = c_2.$$

Theorem 410 (analogue to integration by parts): *Let $a < b$, and let $\int_a^b f(x)\, dx$ and $\int_a^b g(x)\, dx$ exist. Let A and B be arbitrary, and let*

$$\left. \begin{aligned} F(x) &= \int_a^x f(y)\, dy + A \\ G(x) &= \int_a^x g(y)\, dy + B \end{aligned} \right\} \quad \text{on } [a, b].$$

Then we have

$$\int_a^b F(x)\, g(x)\, dx = \{F(x)\, G(x)\}_a^b - \int_a^b f(x)\, G(x)\, dx.$$

Preliminary Remark: If in addition, $f(x)$ and $g(x)$ are continuous on $[a, b]$, then the assertion follows from Theorems 393, 395, and 397, since we then have for $a < x < b$ that

$$(F(x)\, G(x))' = F(x)\, g(x) + f(x)\, G(x),$$

so that

$$\int_a^b \left(F(x)\, g(x) + f(x)\, G(x)\right) dx = \left\{F(x)\, G(x)\right\}_a^b.$$

Proof: Choose c such that

$$\left|\, F(x)\,\right| \leqq c, \quad \left|\, G(x)\,\right| \leqq c \quad \text{on } [a, b].$$

For every partition we have

$$\left\{F(x)\, G(x)\right\}_a^b = \sum_{\nu=1}^n \left(F(a_\nu)\, G(a_\nu) - F(a_{\nu-1})\, G(a_{\nu-1})\right)$$

$$= \sum_{\nu=1}^n G(a_\nu)\, \left(F(a_\nu) - F(a_{\nu-1})\right) + \sum_{\nu=1}^n F(a_{\nu-1})\left(G(a_\nu) - G(a_{\nu-1})\right)$$

$$= \sum_{\nu=1}^n G(a_\nu)\, \int_{a_{\nu-1}}^{a_\nu} f(x)\, dx + \sum_{\nu=1}^n F(a_{\nu-1}) \int_{a_{\nu-1}}^{a_\nu} g(x)\, dx.$$

Let s_ν be the oscillation of $f(x)$ and S_ν the oscillation of $g(x)$ on $[a_{\nu-1},\ a_\nu]$. Then we have thereon that

$$f(a_\nu) - s_\nu \leqq f(x) \leqq f(a_\nu) + s_\nu,$$

$$g(a_{\nu-1}) - S_\nu \leqq g(x) \leqq g(a_{\nu-1}) + S_\nu;$$

and hence we have

$$e_\nu f(a_\nu) - e_\nu s_\nu \leqq \int_{a_{\nu-1}}^{a_\nu} f(x)\, dx \leqq e_\nu f(a_\nu) + e_\nu s_\nu,$$

$$e_\nu g(a_{\nu-1}) - e_\nu S_\nu \leqq \int_{a_{\nu-1}}^{a_\nu} g(x)\, dx \leqq e_\nu g(a_{\nu-1}) + e_\nu S_\nu,$$

$$\left|\, \int_{a_{\nu-1}}^{a_\nu} f(x)\, dx - e_\nu f(a_\nu)\, \right| \leqq e_\nu s_\nu,$$

$$\left|\, \int_{a_{\nu-1}}^{a_\nu} g(x)\, dx - e_\nu g(a_{\nu-1})\, \right| \leqq e_\nu S_\nu,$$

$$\left|\, G(a_\nu) \int_{a_{\nu-1}}^{a_\nu} f(x)\, dx - e_\nu f(a_\nu)\, G(a_\nu)\, \right| \leqq c\, e_\nu s_\nu,$$

$$\left|\, F(a_{\nu-1}) \int_{a_{\nu-1}}^{a_\nu} g(x)\, dx - e_\nu F(a_{\nu-1}) g(a_{\nu-1})\, \right| \leqq c\, e_\nu S_\nu,$$

$$\left|\, \left\{F(x)\, G(x)\right\}_a^b - \sum_{\nu=1}^n e_\nu f(a_\nu)\, G(a_\nu) - \sum_{\nu=1}^n e_\nu F(a_{\nu-1})\, g(a_{\nu-1})\, \right|$$

$$\leqq c \left(\sum_{\nu=1}^n e_\nu s_\nu + \sum_{\nu=1}^n e_\nu S_\nu \right).$$

Now by Theorem 380, $\int_a^b f(x)\, G(x)\, dx$ and $\int_a^b F(x)\, g(x)\, dx$ exist. Hence

for a suitable partition, the right-hand side is arbitrarily close to 0, the left-hand side arbitrarily close to

$$\left| \{F(x)\, G(x)\}_a^b - \int_a^b f(x)\, G(x)\, dx - \int_a^b F(x)\, g(x)\, dx \right|.$$

Therefore this number is 0.

As a conclusion to this chapter I give two more proofs of Weierstrass' Theorem (Theorem 155). We had reduced everything by trivial transformations to the proof of the following statement (old first case):

Let $f(x)$ be continuous on $[0, 1]$ and let

$$|f(x)| \leq 1$$

thereon. Then for every $\delta > 0$ there exists a polynomial $P(x)$ such that

(1) $|f(x) - P(x)| < \delta$ on $[\frac{1}{3}, \frac{2}{3}]$.

1) Our previous proof of this is Simon's revision of the following earlier proof of mine. Applying the theory of the definite integral makes the matter more transparent.

Let n be an integer ≥ 1. I set

$$I_\varepsilon = \int_\varepsilon^1 (1 - u^2)^n\, du \text{ for } 0 \leq \varepsilon < 1$$

and first prove that

$$\lim_{n=\infty} \frac{I_\varepsilon}{I_0} = 0 \text{ for } 0 < \varepsilon < 1.$$

In fact, we have

$$\int_\varepsilon^1 (1 - u^2)^n\, du \leq (1 - \varepsilon)(1 - \varepsilon^2)^n < (1 - \varepsilon^2)^n,$$

and furthermore

$$\int_0^1 (1 - u^2)^n\, du \geq \int_0^1 (1 - u)^n\, du = \int_{-1}^0 (1 + v)^n\, dv = \int_0^1 w^n\, dw = \frac{1}{n+1},$$

so that

$$0 \leq \frac{I_\varepsilon}{I_0} < (n + 1)(1 - \varepsilon^2)^n \to 0.$$

I now consider the polynomial (sic!)

$$P(x) = \frac{\int_0^1 f(z)(1-(z-x)^2)^n \, dz}{2I_0} = \frac{Q(x)}{2I_0},$$

and will prove the inequality (1) for a suitable n, i.e.

$$\left| Q(x) - 2f(x)\, I_0 \right| < 2\delta I_0 \quad \text{on } [\tfrac{1}{3}, \tfrac{2}{3}].$$

By Theorem 154, we choose for a given $\delta > 0$ an ε with $0 < \varepsilon < \tfrac{1}{3}$ such that

(2) $\quad \left| f(z) - f(x) \right| < \dfrac{\delta}{2}$ for $0 \leq z \leq 1$, $0 \leq x \leq 1$, $\left| z - x \right| \leq \varepsilon$.

Now let

$$\tfrac{1}{3} \leq x \leq \tfrac{2}{3},$$

so that

$$0 < x - \varepsilon < x < x + \varepsilon < 1.$$

We set

$$Q_1(x) = \int_0^{x-\varepsilon} f(z)\,(1-(z-x)^2)^n \, dz,$$

$$Q_2(x) = \int_{x-\varepsilon}^{x+\varepsilon} f(z)\,(1-(z-x)^2)^n \, dz,$$

$$Q_3(x) = \int_{x+\varepsilon}^1 f(z)\,(1-(z-x)^2)^n \, dz.$$

Then we have

$$Q(x) = Q_1(x) + Q_2(x) + Q_3(x).$$

Now by Theorem 400 we have

$$\left| Q_1(x) \right| \leq \int_0^{x-\varepsilon} (1-(z-x)^2)^n \, dz = \int_{-x}^{-\varepsilon} (1-v^2)^n \, dv = \int_\varepsilon^x (1-u^2)^n \, du < I_\varepsilon,$$

$$\left| Q_3(x) \right| \leq \int_{x+\varepsilon}^1 (1-(z-x)^2)^n \, dz = \int_\varepsilon^{1-x} (1-u^2)^n \, du < I_\varepsilon;$$

and furthermore we have

$$Q_2(x) - 2f(x)\, I_0 = \int_{-\varepsilon}^\varepsilon f(x+u)(1-u^2)^n \, du - 2f(x) \int_0^1 (1-u^2)^n \, du$$

$$= \int_{-\varepsilon}^\varepsilon f(x+u)(1-u^2)^n \, du - 2f(x) \int_0^\varepsilon (1-u^2)^n \, du - 2f(x)\, I_\varepsilon$$

$$= \int_{-\varepsilon}^\varepsilon (f(x+u) - f(x))\,(1-u^2)^n \, du - 2f(x)\, I_\varepsilon,$$

so that, by Theorem 400,

$$\left| Q_2(x) - 2f(x)\,I_0 \right| \leq \frac{\delta}{2} \int_{-\varepsilon}^{\varepsilon}(1-u^2)^n\,du + 2I_\varepsilon = \delta \int_0^\varepsilon (1-u^2)^n + 2I_\varepsilon$$

$$< \delta I_0 + 2I_\varepsilon.$$

Therefore we have

$$\left| Q(x) - 2f(x)\,I_0 \right| = \left| (Q_2(x) - 2f(x)\,I_0) + Q_1(x) + Q_3(x) \right|$$

$$< \delta I_0 + 2I_\varepsilon + I_\varepsilon + I_\varepsilon = \delta I_0 + 4I_\varepsilon.$$

Finally, we have for suitable n that

$$4I_\varepsilon < \delta I_0.$$

2) The following proof of S. Bernstein's, in which integrals do not occur, yields a $P(x)$ valid for the entire interval $[0,1]$ and is distinguished for its brevity.

As an abbreviation, let $\varphi_\nu = \varphi_\nu(x;\,n)$ for integral ν, n with $0 \leq \nu \leq n$ be the function $\binom{n}{\nu} x^\nu (1-x)^{n-\nu}$. Then by Theorem 180, we have for $n > 1$ that

$$\sum_{\nu=0}^{n} \varphi_\nu = 1,$$

$$\sum_{\nu=0}^{n} \nu\varphi_\nu = nx \sum_{\mu=0}^{n-1} \binom{n-1}{\mu} x^\mu (1-x)^{n-1-\mu} = nx,$$

$$\sum_{\nu=0}^{n} \nu(\nu-1)\varphi_\nu = n(n-1)x^2 \sum_{\mu=0}^{n-2} \binom{n-2}{\mu} x^\mu (1-x)^{n-2-\mu} = n(n-1)\,x^2,$$

$$\sum_{\nu=0}^{n} (\nu - nx)^2\,\varphi_\nu = \sum_{\nu=0}^{n} (n^2x^2 - (2nx-1)\,\nu + \nu(\nu-1))\,\varphi_\nu$$

$$= n^2x^2 - (2nx-1)\,nx + n(n-1)\,x^2 = nx(1-x).$$

Let $\delta > 0$ be given. Choose an $\varepsilon > 0$ such that (2) holds, and choose an n greater than both 1 and $\dfrac{2}{\delta\varepsilon^2}$. Then we have for $0 \leq x \leq 1$ that

$$\left| f(x) - \sum_{\nu=0}^{n} f\left(\frac{\nu}{n}\right) \varphi_\nu \right| = \left| \sum_{\nu=0}^{n} \left(f(x) - f\left(\frac{\nu}{n}\right)\right) \varphi_\nu \right|$$

$$\leq \frac{\delta}{2} \sum_{\substack{\nu=0 \\ |\nu-nx|\leq \varepsilon n}}^{n} \varphi_\nu + 2 \sum_{\substack{\nu=0 \\ |\nu-nx|> \varepsilon n}}^{n} \varphi_\nu \leq \frac{\delta}{2} \sum_{\nu=0}^{n} \varphi_\nu + \frac{2}{\varepsilon^2 n^2} \sum_{\nu=0}^{n} (\nu - nx)^2\,\varphi_\nu$$

$$= \frac{\delta}{2} + \frac{2x(1-x)}{\varepsilon^2 n} < \delta.$$

CHAPTER 27

INTEGRATION OF INFINITE SERIES

Introduction

Let $a < b$. When do we have

(1)
$$\int_a^b \sum_{n=1}^{\infty} f_n(x)\, dx = \sum_{n=1}^{\infty} \int_a^b f_n(x)\, dx \text{ ?}$$

In any case, two hypotheses must be made.

I)
$$F_n = \int_a^b f_n(x)\, dx$$

exists for every $n \geqq 1$.

II)
$$f(x) = \sum_{n=1}^{\infty} f_n(x)$$

exists on $[a, b]$ (i.e. this series converges).

In any case the following three questions are involved:

1) Does $\int_a^b f(x)\, dx$ exist, i.e. is the left-hand side of (1) meaningful?

2) Does $\sum_{n=1}^{\infty} F_n$ exist, i.e. is the right-hand side of (1) meaningful?

3) (If 1) and 2) are answered in the affirmative): Is the left-hand side of (1) equal to the right-hand side of (1)?

We shall now give an example where I) and II) hold, and where 1) and 2) are answered in the affirmative, but where 3) is answered in the negative.

In fact, we shall have

$$a = 0, \ b = 1,$$

$$f_n(x) \text{ continuous on } [0, 1],$$

$$f(x) \text{ continuous on } [0, 1].$$

We set

$$f_n(x) = x \left(n e^{-nx^2} - (n-1) e^{-(n-1)x^2} \right).$$

$f_n(x)$ is then continuous on $[0, 1]$. For integral $m \geq 1$ we have

$$\sum_{n=1}^{m} f_n(x) = x m e^{-mx^2}.$$

The right-hand side is 0 at $x = 0$, and therefore converges to 0 at this point as $m \to \infty$; for $0 < x \leq 1$ it also converges to 0 as $m \to \infty$. Therefore we have for $[0, 1]$ that

$$\sum_{n=1}^{\infty} f_n(x) = 0.$$

This

$$f(x) = 0$$

is continuous on $[0, 1]$. We have

$$\int_0^1 f(x)\, dx = \int_0^1 0\, dx = 0.$$

Furthermore,

$$F_n = \int_0^1 f_n(x)\, dx$$

exists. For integral $m \geq 1$ we have

$$\sum_{n=1}^{m} F_n = \sum_{n=1}^{m} \int_0^1 f_n(x)\, dx = \int_0^1 \sum_{n=1}^{m} f_n(x)\, dx = \int_0^1 x m e^{-mx^2} dx$$

$$= \left\{ -\tfrac{1}{2} e^{-mx^2} \right\}_0^1 = -\tfrac{1}{2} e^{-m} + \tfrac{1}{2};$$

and hence we have

$$\sum_{n=1}^{\infty} F_n = \tfrac{1}{2}.$$

Finally, we have

$$0 \neq \tfrac{1}{2}.$$

And yet we will save (1) by adding further hypotheses.

Theorem 411: *Let*

$$\sum_{n=1}^{\infty} f_n(x)$$

converge uniformly on $[a, b]$. *Let every* $f_n(x)$ *be integrable from a to b* (say, for example, continuous on $[a, b]$). *Set*

$$\sum_{n=1}^{\infty} f_n(x) = f(x)$$

and let $f(x)$ *be integrable from a to b. Then we have*

$$\int_a^b \sum_{n=1}^{\infty} f_n(x)\, dx = \sum_{n=1}^{\infty} \int_a^b f_n(x)\, dx.$$

Preliminary Remark: The existence of the left-hand side is one of our hypotheses, and our conclusion is that

$$\lim_{m=\infty} \sum_{n=1}^{m} \int_a^b f_n(x)\, dx = \int_a^b f(x)\, dx.$$

Proof: Let $\delta > 0$ be given. Then there exists a μ independent of x such that if we set

$$\sum_{n=1}^{m} f_n(x) = S_m(x),$$

and

$$f(x) - S_m(x) = r_m(x),$$

then we have

$$\left| r_m(x) \right| < \frac{\delta}{2(b-a)} \quad \text{for } m \geq \mu,\ x \text{ on } [a, b].$$

Since $f(x)$ and $S_m(x)$ are integrable from a to b, so is $r_m(x)$ also, and we find that for $m \geq \mu$ we have

$$\left| \int_a^b f(x)\,dx - \sum_{n=1}^{m} \int_a^b f_n(x)\, dx \right| = \left| \int_a^b f(x)\, dx - \int_a^b S_m(x)\, dx \right|$$

$$= \left| \int_a^b r_m(x)\, dx \right| \leq \frac{\delta}{2(b-a)}(b-a) = \frac{\delta}{2} < \delta.$$

Theorem 412: *Let*

$$\sum_{n=1}^{\infty} f_n(x)$$

converge uniformly on $[a, b]$. *Let every* $f_n(x)$ *be integrable from* a *to* b. *Then we have*

$$\int_a^b \sum_{n=1}^{\infty} f_n(x)\, dx = \sum_{n=1}^{\infty} \int_a^b f_n(x)\, dx.$$

Preliminary Remark: Hence in Theorem 411 the hypothesis that $f(x)$ be integrable may be removed. I proved Theorem 411 first because its proof was shorter. In any event, it now suffices to show that

$$f(x) = \sum_{n=1}^{\infty} f_n(x)$$

is integrable.

Proof: Let $\delta > 0$ be given and define $S_m(x)$ and $r_m(x)$ for $m \geqq 1$ as in the preceding proof. Choose m such that

$$(1) \qquad\qquad |r_m(x)| < \frac{\delta}{4(b-a)} \quad \text{on } [a, b].$$

Therefore $r_m(x)$ is bounded; so is $S_m(x)$, and hence $f(x)$ is also bounded.

Now let s, s', s'' be the oscillations of $f(x)$, $S_m(x)$, and $r_m(x)$, respectively, in some sub-interval. Then if α and β are in this sub-interval, we have

$$f(\alpha) - f(\beta) = \left(S_m(\alpha) - S_m(\beta)\right) + \left(r_m(\alpha) - r_m(\beta)\right) \leqq s' + s''.$$

Therefore we have

$$s \leqq s' + s''.$$

For every partition of $[a, b]$ (we cannot very well call the number of intervals n, since n is now employed as a summation index; anyway it does not figure in our abbreviated notation), we have therefore that

$$\Sigma es \leqq \Sigma es' + \Sigma es''.$$

By (1) we have that every

$$s'' \leqq \frac{\delta}{2(b-a)}.$$

Therefore we have

$$\Sigma es \leqq \Sigma es' + \frac{\delta}{2}.$$

Since $S_m(x)$ is integrable, we have for a suitable partition that

$$\Sigma e s' < \frac{\delta}{2},$$

so that

$$\Sigma e s < \delta.$$

Therefore $f(x)$ is integrable.

CHAPTER 28

THE IMPROPER INTEGRAL

We shall define (for example)

$$\int_0^1 \frac{dx}{\sqrt{x}} = 2.$$

Why?

Definition 88: *If for every* $\delta > 0$ *there exists a suitable* $\varepsilon > 0$ *such that*

$$\left| f(x) - \gamma \right| < \delta \quad \text{for} \quad \xi < x < \xi + \varepsilon,$$

then we say that

$$\lim_{\substack{x=\xi \\ \leftarrow}} f(x) = \gamma.$$

To be read "limit from the right."

Example:
$$\lim_{\substack{x=0 \\ \leftarrow}} \sqrt{x} = 0.$$

Definition 89: *If for every* $\delta > 0$ *there exists a suitable* $\varepsilon > 0$ *such that*

$$\left| f(x) - \gamma \right| < \delta \quad \text{for} \quad \xi - \varepsilon < x < \xi,$$

then we say that

$$\lim_{\substack{x=\xi \\ \rightarrow}} f(x) = \gamma.$$

To be read "limit from the left."

Example:
$$\lim_{\substack{x=0 \\ \rightarrow}} \sqrt{-x} = 0.$$

Theorem 413: *Let* $a < b$. *If*

$$\int_a^b f(x)\, dx$$

exists, then

$$\lim_{\substack{\alpha = a \\ \leftarrow}} \int_\alpha^b f(x)\,dx = \int_a^b f(x)\,dx$$

and

$$\lim_{\substack{\beta = b \\ \rightarrow}} \int_a^\beta f(x)\,dx = \int_a^b f(x)\,dx\,.$$

Proof: Theorems 394 and 393, respectively.

Theorem 414: *Let $a < b$. If*

(1)
$$\lim_{\substack{\alpha = a \\ \leftarrow}} \int_\alpha^b f(x)\,dx$$

and

(2)
$$\lim_{\substack{\beta = b \\ \rightarrow}} \int_a^\beta f(x)\,dx$$

exist, then these two numbers are equal.

Proof: From the existence of (1), it follows that

$$\int_{\frac{a+b}{2}}^b f(x)\,dx$$

exists; from the existence of (2), it follows that

$$\int_a^{\frac{a+b}{2}} f(x)\,dx$$

exists. Therefore

$$\int_a^b f(x)\,dx$$

exists, and Theorem 413 proves our assertion.

Definition 90: *Let $a < b$ and let*

(1)
$$\lim_{\substack{\alpha = a \\ \leftarrow}} \int_\alpha^b f(x)\,dx$$

or

(2)
$$\lim_{\substack{\beta = b \\ \rightarrow}} \int_a^\beta f(x)\,dx$$

exist. Then the number (1) or (2) is said to be the improper integral, or more briefly, the integral, of $f(x)$ from a to b. What has up to now been denoted by $\int_a^b$ will from now on be called a proper integral.

Notation:
$$\int_a^b f(x)\,dx.$$

The use of the old symbol is justified by Theorem 413; Theorem 414 also had to precede Definition 90. By Definition 90 and Theorem 413, every proper integral is also an improper one.

Examples: 1)
$$\int_0^1 \frac{dx}{\sqrt{x}} = 2\,;$$

for if $0 < \alpha < 1$, then the proper integral

$$\int_\alpha^1 \frac{dx}{\sqrt{x}} = \left\{ 2\sqrt{x} \right\}_\alpha^1 = 2 - 2\sqrt{\alpha}\,;$$

and thus we have

$$\lim_{\substack{\alpha = 0 \\ \leftarrow}} \int_\alpha^1 \frac{dx}{\sqrt{x}} = 2\,.$$

2)
$$\int_{-1}^0 \frac{dx}{\sqrt{-x}} = 2\,;$$

for if $-1 < \beta < 0$, then the proper integral

$$\int_{-1}^\beta \frac{dx}{\sqrt{-x}} = \left\{ -2\sqrt{-x} \right\}_{-1}^\beta = -2\sqrt{-\beta} + 2;$$

and thus we have

$$\lim_{\substack{\beta = 0 \\ \rightarrow}} \int_{-1}^\beta \frac{dx}{\sqrt{-x}} = 2\,.$$

Theorem 415: *Let $a < c < b$; let*

$$\int_a^b f(x)\,dx$$

exist. Then

$$\int_a^c f(x)\,dx\,, \quad \int_c^b f(x)\,dx\,,$$

exist, and we have

$$\int_a^b f(x)\,dx = \int_a^c f(x)\,dx + \int_c^b f(x)\,dx\,.$$

Proof: 1) If $\int_a^b$ is defined by (1), then for $a < \alpha < c$ we have

$$\int_\alpha^c = \int_\alpha^b - \int_c^b,$$

where the three integrals are proper; hence the improper integral $\int_a^c$ exists, and

$$\int_a^c = \int_a^b - \int_c^b.$$

2) If $\int_a^b$ is defined by (2), then for $c < \beta < b$ we have

$$\int_c^\beta = \int_a^\beta - \int_a^c,$$

where the three integrals are proper; hence the improper integral $\int_c^b$ exists, and

$$\int_c^b = \int_a^b - \int_a^c.$$

Theorem 416: *Let* $a < b$*; let*

$$\int_a^b f(x)\,dx$$

exist. Let

$$k \geqq 1 \text{ be an integer,}$$

$$c_{\nu-1} < c_\nu \text{ for } 1 \leqq \nu \leqq k, \ \nu \text{ an integer,}$$

$$c_0 = a, \ c_k = b;$$

then we have

$$\int_a^b f(x)\,dx = \sum_{\nu=1}^k \int_{c_{\nu-1}}^{c_\nu} f(x)\,dx.$$

Proof: $k = 1$ is obvious. $k + 1$ follows from k by Theorem 415, since

$$\int_a^b = \int_a^{c_k} + \int_{c_k}^b = \sum_{\nu=1}^k \int_{c_{\nu-1}}^{c_\nu} + \int_{c_k}^b = \sum_{\nu=1}^{k+1} \int_{c_{\nu-1}}^{c_\nu}$$

Theorem 417: *Let*

$$k \geqq 1 \text{ and } l \geqq 1 \text{ both be integers,}$$

$$\gamma_{\nu-1} < \gamma_\nu \text{ for } 1 \leqq \nu \leqq k; \quad \mu_{\nu-1} < \mu_\nu \text{ for } 1 \leqq \nu \leqq l; \ \nu \text{ an integer,}$$

$$\gamma_0 = \mu_0 = a, \quad \gamma_k = \mu_l = b,$$

$$\int_{\gamma_{\nu-1}}^{\gamma_\nu} f(x)\,dx \text{ exist for } 1 \leqq \nu \leqq k,$$

$$\int_{\mu_{\nu-1}}^{\mu_\nu} f(x)\,dx \text{ exist for } 1 \leqq \nu \leqq l.$$

Then we have

$$\sum_{\nu=1}^{k} \int_{\gamma_{\nu-1}}^{\gamma_\nu} f(x)\, dx = \sum_{\nu=1}^{l} \int_{\mu_{\nu-1}}^{\mu_\nu} f(x)\, dx .$$

Proof: We "superimpose" the two partitions of $[a, b]$, i.e. we consider the different γ, μ arranged in increasing order. Every $\displaystyle\int_{\gamma_{\nu-1}}^{\gamma_\nu}$ and every $\displaystyle\int_{\mu_{\nu-1}}^{\mu_\nu}$ is, by Theorem 416, the sum of a finite number of integrals over the new sub-intervals and, in all, both sides of the above equality are the sum of all of these integrals, and so are equal.

Definition 91: *If for a, b, $f(x)$, the γ_ν may be chosen in the sense of Theorem 417, then the sum*

$$\sum_{\nu=1}^{k} \int_{\gamma_{\nu-1}}^{\gamma_\nu} f(x)\, dx$$

(which, by Theorem 417, is independent of the choice of the γ_ν) *is said to be the improper integral of $f(x)$ from a to b.*

Notation: $\displaystyle\int_a^b f(x)\, dx .$

(For $k = 1$ this definition yields the earlier concept of Definition 90.)

The term integral in this chapter will mean the integral as defined in Definition 91, unless otherwise stated.

Example: $\displaystyle\int_{-1}^{1} \frac{dx}{\sqrt[3]{x}} = 0 ;$

for in the sense of Definition 90, we have

$$\int_{-1}^{0} \frac{dx}{\sqrt[3]{x}} = \lim_{\substack{\beta=0 \\ \rightarrow}} \int_{-1}^{\beta} \frac{dx}{\sqrt[3]{x}} = \lim_{\substack{\beta=0 \\ \rightarrow}} \left\{ \frac{3}{2} \left(\sqrt[3]{x} \right)^2 \right\}_{-1}^{\beta} = -\frac{3}{2},$$

$$\int_{0}^{1} \frac{dx}{\sqrt[3]{x}} = \lim_{\substack{\alpha=0 \\ \leftarrow}} \int_{\alpha}^{1} \frac{dx}{\sqrt[3]{x}} = \lim_{\substack{\alpha=0 \\ \leftarrow}} \left\{ \frac{3}{2} \left(\sqrt[3]{x} \right)^2 \right\}_{\alpha}^{1} = \frac{3}{2} .$$

Theorem 418: *Let $a < b$ and let $f(x)$ be properly integrable from a to β for all α, β with $a < \alpha < \beta < b$. Let $f(x)$ be bounded for $a < x < b$.*

Then

$$\int_a^b f(x)\,dx$$

exists.

Proof: We set

$$c = \frac{a+b}{2}.$$

It suffices to show the existence of

(1) $$\lim_{\substack{\alpha \to a \\ \leftarrow}} \int_\alpha^c f(x)\,dx \,, \ \lim_{\substack{\beta = b \\ \to}} \int_c^\beta f(x)\,dx\,.$$

W.l.g., let

$$f(a) = f(b) = 0$$

(even if $f(x)$ was previously undefined, or differently defined, at a or at b);
for this does not affect the assertion of the existence of the limits (1).

Then $f(x)$ is bounded on $[a, b]$:

$$\big| f(x) \big| \leqq M\,.$$

Let $\delta > 0$ be given. We choose α, β with

$$a < \alpha < \beta < b, \ \ 2(\alpha - a)M \leqq \frac{\delta}{4}, \ \ 2(b - \beta)\,M \leqq \frac{\delta}{4}\,.$$

Since $f(x)$ is properly integrable from α to β, there exists a partition of $[\alpha, \beta]$
with

$$\Sigma e\,s < \frac{\delta}{2}\,.$$

Then if we introduce the intervals $[a, \alpha]$ and $[\beta, b]$ as the first and last
intervals respectively, we obtain a partition of $[a, b]$ such that

$$\sum_{\nu=1}^n e_\nu s_\nu < (\alpha - a)\,2M + \frac{\delta}{2} + (b - \beta)\,2M \leqq \delta,$$

so that our $f(x)$ is properly integrable from a to b. Therefore the limits (1)
exist (by Theorem 413).

Theorem 419: *If $a < b$ and if $f(x)$ is bounded on $[a, b]$, then $\int_a^b f(x)\,dx$
does not necessarily exist.*

Proof: Let $a = 0$, $b = 1$,

$$f(x) = \begin{Bmatrix} 0 & \text{for rational} & x \\ 1 & \text{for irrational} & x \end{Bmatrix} \text{ on } [0, 1].$$

On no sub-interval $[\alpha, \beta]$ is $f(x)$ properly integrable, since we always have

$$\sum_{\nu=1}^{n} e_\nu s_\nu = \beta - \alpha.$$

Definition 92: $\quad \int_a^b f(x)\,dx = - \int_b^a f(x)\,dx,$

i. r. h. s. i. m.

This is in agreement with Definition 86.

Example: $\quad \int_1^0 \dfrac{dx}{\sqrt{x}} = - \int_0^1 \dfrac{dx}{\sqrt{x}} = -2.$

Definition 93: *If $f(a)$ is not defined, then*

$$\int_a^a f(x)\,dx = 0.$$

Theorem 420: $\quad \int_a^b f(x)\,dx + \int_b^a f(x)\,dx = 0,$

if one of the two integrals is meaningful.

(The same wording as in Theorem 372.)

Proof: $a = b$ is obvious by Definitions 87 and 93; $a \neq b$ is obvious by Definition 92.

Theorem 421: *If $a \leqq \alpha \leqq \beta \leqq b$ or $a \geqq \alpha \geqq \beta \geqq b$, then if $\int_a^b f(x)\,dx$ exists, so does $\int_\alpha^\beta f(x)\,dx$.*

(The same wording as in Theorem 373.)

Proof: W.l.g., let $a \leqq \alpha < \beta \leqq b$. W.l.g., let α be a γ-number (since otherwise, by Theorem 415, we may introduce it as a new one); the same for β. If $\alpha = \gamma_\varrho$, $\beta = \gamma_\sigma$, then the existence of

$$\int_\alpha^\beta = \sum_{\nu = \varrho + 1}^{\sigma} \int_{\gamma_{\nu-1}}^{\gamma_\nu}$$

follows from Definition 91.

Theorem 422: *If $a < b < c$ and if $\int_a^b f(x)\,dx$ and $\int_b^c f(x)\,dx$ exist, then $\int_a^c f(x)\,dx$ exists and*

$$\int_a^c f(x)\,dx = \int_a^b f(x)\,dx + \int_b^c f(x)\,dx.$$

(The same wording as in Theorem 374.)

Proof: There exist increasing numbers γ_ν, $0 \leqq \nu \leqq k + l$, with

$$\gamma_0 = a\,, \quad \gamma_k = b\,, \quad \gamma_{k+l} = c\,,$$

$$\int_a^b = \sum_{\nu=1}^{k} \int_{\gamma_{\nu-1}}^{\gamma_\nu}\,,$$

$$\int_b^c = \sum_{\nu=k+1}^{k+l} \int_{\gamma_{\nu-1}}^{\gamma_\nu}\,,$$

where all the integrals on the right are integrals in the sense of Definition 90. With this, we have subdivided the interval $[a, c]$ into $k + l$ sub-intervals in the sense of Definition 91, and our conclusion is obvious.

Theorem 423: $\int_a^b (f(x) + g(x))\, dx = \int_a^b f(x)\, dx + \int_a^b g(x)\, dx\,,$

i. r. h. s. i. m.

(The same wording as in Theorem 376.)

Proof: W.l.g., let $a < b$ and let $f(x)$ and $g(x)$ be properly integrable from α to β for all α, β with $a < \alpha < \beta < b$. By Theorem 376, we have

$$\int_\alpha^\beta (f(x) + g(x))\, dx = \int_\alpha^\beta f(x)\, dx + \int_\alpha^\beta g(x)\, dx\,.$$

$\lim\limits_{\substack{\beta=b \\ \rightarrow}}$ and then $\lim\limits_{\substack{\alpha=a \\ \leftarrow}}$ gives the conclusion.

Theorem 424: $\qquad \int_a^b C\, f(x)\, dx = C \int_a^b f(x)\, dx\,,$

i. r. h. s. i. m.

(The same wording as in Theorem 378.)

Proof: W.l.g., as in the above proof. Theorem 378 with α in place of a, β in place of b, $\lim\limits_{\substack{\beta=b \\ \rightarrow}}$, $\lim\limits_{\substack{\alpha=a \\ \leftarrow}}$.

Theorem 425: $\quad \int_a^b (f(x) - g(x))\, dx = \int_a^b f(x)\, dx - \int_a^b g(x)\, dx\,,$

i. r. h. s. i. m.

(The same wording as in Theorem 379.)

Proof: $\qquad\qquad\qquad f - g = f + (-1)\, g\,,$

Theorem 424 and Theorem 423.

———————

There is no analogue to Theorem 380 since this analogue admits of a **counter-example:** If

$$f(x) = g(x) = \frac{1}{\sqrt{x}}\,,$$

then the integrals $\int_0^1 f(x)\,dx$ and $\int_0^1 g(x)\,dx$ exist, as we know. But $\int_0^1 f(x)\,g(x)\,dx$ does not exist, since

$$\int_\alpha^1 \frac{dx}{x} = \{\log x\}_\alpha^1 = -\log \alpha \quad \text{for } 0 < \alpha < 1,$$

which has no $\lim_{\substack{\alpha=0 \\ \leftarrow}}$.

Theorem 426: *If $\int_a^b f(x)\,dx$ exists and if*

$$|f(x)| > p > 0 \quad \text{on } [a, b] \text{ except at the } \gamma\text{'s,}$$

then $\displaystyle\int_a^b \frac{dx}{f(x)}$ *exists.*

(Almost the same wording as in Theorem 382.)

Proof: W.l.g., let $k = 1$. The proper integral $\displaystyle\int_\alpha^\beta \frac{dx}{f(x)}$ exists for

$$a < a < \beta < b$$

by Theorem 382; $\dfrac{1}{f(x)}$ is bounded for $a < x < b$ and so, by Theorem 418, it is integrable from a to b.

Theorem 427: *Let $a < b$ and let $\int_a^b f(x)\,dx$ exist. Let $f(x)$ be bounded from above on $[a, b]$ except at the γ's, and let l be the l.u.b. of $f(x)$ on $[a, b]$; or let $f(x)$ be bounded from below on $[a, b]$ except at the γ's, and let λ be the g.l.b. of $f(x)$ on $[a, b]$. Then we have*

$$\int_a^b f(x)\,dx \leqq l(b - a) \quad \text{or} \quad \int_a^b f(x)\,dx \geqq \lambda(b - a),$$

respectively.

(Almost the same wording as in Theorem 384; we probably need not even write down the corresponding statement for $a \geqq b$.)

Proof: Let $[\gamma_{\nu-1}, \gamma_\nu]$ be a sub-interval in the sense of Definition 91. By Theorem 384, we have for $\gamma_{\nu-1} < \alpha < \beta < \gamma_\nu$ that

$$\int_\alpha^\beta \leqq l\,(\beta - \alpha) \quad \text{or} \quad \geqq \lambda\,(\beta - \alpha)$$

respectively, so that $\left(\lim_{\substack{\beta=\gamma_\nu \\ \longrightarrow}}, \text{ and then } \lim_{\substack{\alpha=\gamma_{\nu-1} \\ \longleftarrow}} \right)$

$$\int_{\gamma_{\nu-1}}^{\gamma_\nu} \leqq l(\gamma_\nu - \gamma_{\nu-1}) \quad \text{or} \quad \geqq \lambda(\gamma_\nu - \gamma_{\nu-1}),$$

respectively, and $\displaystyle\sum_{\nu=1}^k$ yields the conclusion.

Theorem 428: *Let $a < b$, let $\int_a^b f(x)\,dx$ exist, and let*

$$|f(x)| \leqq c \ \text{on} \ [a, b] \ \text{except at the γ's.}$$

Then we have

$$\left| \int_a^b f(x)\,dx \right| \leqq c\,(b - a)$$

(Almost the same wording as in Theorem 385.)
Proof: Theorem 427 with

$$l \leqq c, \quad \lambda \geqq - c.$$

Theorem 429: *Let $a < b$, let $\int_a^b f(x)\,dx$ exist, and let*

$$f(x) \geqq 0 \ \text{on} \ [a, b] \ \text{except at the γ's.}$$

Then we have

$$\int_a^b f(x)\,dx \geqq 0.$$

(Almost the same wording as in Theorem 386.)
Proof: Theorem 427 with $\lambda \geqq 0$.

Theorem 430: *Let $a < b$, let $\int_a^b f(x)\,dx$ exist, and let*

$$f(x) > 0 \ \text{on} \ [a, b] \ \text{except at the γ's.}$$

Then we have

$$\int_a^b f(x)\,dx > 0.$$

(Almost the same wording as in Theorem 388.)
Proof: Since $f(x)$ is properly integrable on some sub-interval $[\alpha, \beta]$ of $[a, b]$, we have by Theorems 421, 422, 429, and 388, that

$$\int_a^b = \int_a^\alpha + \int_\alpha^b = \int_a^\alpha + \int_\alpha^\beta + \int_\beta^b \geqq \int_\alpha^\beta > 0.$$

Theorem 431: *If $a < b$, if $\int_a^b g(x)\,dx$ and $\int_a^b g(x)\,dx$ exist* (w.l.g. with the same γ's, since we may superimpose them), *and if*

$$f(x) \leqq g(x) \ \text{on} \ [a, b] \ \text{except at the γ's,}$$

then

$$\int_a^b f(x)\,dx \leqq \int_a^b g(x)\,dx.$$

(Almost the same wording as in Theorem 389.)

Proof: $\qquad g(x) - f(x) \geqq 0$ except at the γ's,

so that, by Theorems 425 and 429,

$$\int_a^b g(x)\, dx - \int_a^b f(x)\, dx = \int_a^b \left(g(x) - f(x) \right) dx \geqq 0.$$

Theorem 432: *Let $a < b$, let $\int_a^b g(x)\, dx$ and $\int_a^b f(x)\, g(x)\, dx$ exist (w.l.g. with the same γ's), and let*

$$g(x) \geqq 0 \quad on \ \ [a, b] \ \ except \ at \ the \ \gamma's.$$

Let $f(x)$ be bounded from above on $[a, b]$ except at the γ's, and let l be the l.u.b. of $f(x)$ thereon. Then

$$\int_a^b f(x)\, g(x)\, dx \leqq l \int_a^b g(x)\, dx.$$

(Almost the same wording as in Theorem 390.)

Preliminary Remark: If we assume that $f(x)$ is bounded from below on $[a, b]$ (instead of from above) except at the γ's, and that its g.l.b. is λ, then by applying this theorem to $-f(x)$ we obtain

$$\int_a^b f(x)\, g(x)\, dx \geqq \lambda \int_a^b g(x)\, dx.$$

Proof: By Theorem 429, we have

$$\int_a^b \left(l\, g(x) - f(x)\, g(x) \right) dx \geqq 0.$$

Theorem 433: *Let $a < b$, let $f(x)$ be continuous on $[a, b]$, let $\int_a^b g(x)\, dx$ and $\int_a^b f(x)\, g(x)\, dx$ exist (w.l.g. with the same γ's) and let*

$$g(x) \geqq 0 \quad on \ \ [a, b] \ \ except \ at \ the \ \gamma's.$$

Then there exists a ξ on $[a, b]$ such that

$$\int_a^b f(x)\, g(x)\, dx = f(\xi) \int_a^b g(x)\, dx.$$

(Almost the same wording as in Theorem 391.)

Proof: Like that of Theorem 391, using Theorem 432 and its preliminary remark, with the difference here that the existence of $\int_a^b f(x)\, g(x)\, dx$ is already known.

Theorem 434: *Let $a < b$ and let $\int_a^b f(x)\,dx$ exist, so that*

$$\int_a^x f(y)\,dy = \mathrm{F}(x)$$

exists on $[a, b]$. Then $\mathrm{F}(x)$ is continuous on $[a, b]$.

(The same wording as in Theorem 393.)

Preliminary Remark: We arranged our definitions the way we did in order for this to hold for improper integrals also.

Proof: 1) If ξ is on $[a, b]$ and is not a γ, then

$$\mathrm{F}(x) = \mathrm{a} \text{ constant} + \text{proper} \int_\xi^x f(y)\,dy$$

in a neighborhood of ξ, and Theorem 393 proves our assertion at ξ.

2) If ξ is a γ, then in case $\xi < b$ we have for suitable $\varepsilon > 0$ and for $\xi < x \leqq \xi + \varepsilon$ that

$$\mathrm{F}(x) = \mathrm{a} \text{ constant} - \text{proper} \int_x^{\xi+\varepsilon} f(y)\,dy\,,$$

and Definition 90 shows the continuity on the right; in case $\xi > a$ we have for suitable $\varepsilon > 0$ and for $\xi - \varepsilon \leqq x < \xi$ that

$$\mathrm{F}(x) = \mathrm{a} \text{ constant} + \text{proper} \int_{\xi-\varepsilon}^x f(y)\,dy\,,$$

and Definition 90 shows the continuity on the left.

Theorem 435: *Let $a < b$ and let $\int_a^b f(x)\,dx$ exist, so that*

$$\int_x^b f(y)\,dy = \mathrm{G}(x)$$

exists on $[a, b]$. Then $\mathrm{G}(x)$ is continuous on $[a, b]$.

(The same wording as in Theorem 394.)

Proof: $$\mathrm{G}(x) = \int_a^b f(y)\,dy - \mathrm{F}(x)$$

and Theorem 434.

Theorem 436: *Let $a < b$, let $\int_a^b f(x)\,dx$ exist, let $g(x)$ be continuous on $[a, b]$, and let*

$$g'(x) = f(x) \text{ for } a < x < b \text{ except at the } \gamma\text{'s.}$$

Then we have

$$\int_a^b f(x)\,dx = g(b) - g(a)\,.$$

(Almost the same wording as in Theorem 399.)

Proof: Because of the "additivity" of both sides of our equality (the reader will understand what is meant), let $k = 1$ w.l.g. For $a < \alpha < \beta < b$, we have by Theorem 399 that

$$\int_\alpha^\beta f(x)\, dx = g(\beta) - g(\alpha)\,.$$

Since $g(x)$ is continuous on the left at b and on the right at a, $\lim\limits_{\substack{\beta = b \\ \rightarrow}}$ followed by $\lim\limits_{\substack{\alpha = a \\ \leftarrow}}$ gives the conclusion, by Theorems 434 and 435.

Theorem 437: *If $a < b$ and if $\int_a^b f(x)\, dx$ and $\int_a^b |f(x)|\, dx$ exist, then*

$$\left| \int_a^b f(x)\, dx \right| \leq \int_a^b |f(x)|\, dx\,.$$

Preliminary Remark: The wording is almost the same as that of Theorem 400; however the existence of $\int_a^b |f(x)|\, dx$ must be explicitly assumed; it does not follow from that of $\int_a^b f(x)\, dx$. **Counter-example:**

$$a = 0, \quad b = 1, \quad f(x) = \frac{1}{x} \sin \frac{1}{x}\,.$$

For $0 < \alpha < 1$ we have

$$\int_\alpha^1 \frac{1}{x} \sin \frac{1}{x}\, dx = \int_\alpha^1 x \frac{1}{x^2} \sin \frac{1}{x}\, dx = \int_\alpha^1 x \left(\cos \frac{1}{x} \right)' dx$$

$$= \left\{ x \cos \frac{1}{x} \right\}_\alpha^1 - \int_\alpha^1 \cos \frac{1}{x}\, dx = \cos 1 - \alpha \cos \frac{1}{\alpha} - \int_\alpha^1 \cos \frac{1}{x}\, dx\,.$$

$$\lim_{\substack{\alpha = 0 \\ \leftarrow}} \int_\alpha^1 \cos \frac{1}{x}\, dx$$

exists by Theorem 418 since $\cos \dfrac{1}{x}$ is bounded for $0 < x \leq 1$. For the same reason, we have

$$\lim_{\substack{\alpha = 0 \\ \leftarrow}} \alpha \cos \frac{1}{\alpha} = 0\,.$$

$$\int_0^1 \frac{1}{x} \sin \frac{1}{x}\, dx$$

therefore exists.

However,

(1)
$$\int_0^1 \left| \frac{1}{x} \sin \frac{1}{x} \right| dx$$

is meaningless. For, by Theorems 278, 275, and 265, we have for integral $m > 0$ and

$$2m\pi + \frac{\pi}{4} \leqq \frac{1}{x} \leqq 2m\pi + \frac{\pi}{2}$$

that

$$\sin \frac{1}{x} \geqq \sin \frac{\pi}{4} = \frac{1}{\sqrt{2}} \, ;$$

hence we have for integral $m > \dfrac{1}{2\pi}$ that

$$\int_{\frac{1}{2m\pi + \frac{\pi}{2}}}^{\frac{1}{2m\pi + \frac{\pi}{4}}} \left| \frac{1}{x} \sin \frac{1}{x} \right| dx \geqq \frac{1}{\sqrt{2}} \int_{\frac{1}{2m\pi + \frac{\pi}{2}}}^{\frac{1}{2m\pi + \frac{\pi}{4}}} \frac{dx}{x}$$

$$= \frac{1}{\sqrt{2}} \log \left(1 + \frac{1}{8m + 1} \right) \geqq \frac{1}{\sqrt{2}} \log \left(1 + \frac{1}{9m} \right) > \frac{p}{m} \, ,$$

where p is > 0 and is independent of m. Therefore (since the harmonic series diverges), for every $\omega > 0$ we have for suitable α with $0 < \alpha < 1$ that

$$\int_\alpha^1 \left| \frac{1}{x} \sin \frac{1}{x} \right| dx > \omega \, ,$$

so that (1) cannot exist.

Proof: Since

$$- |f(x)| \leqq f(x) \leqq |f(x)| \quad \text{on } [a, b] \text{ except at the } \gamma\text{'s}$$

(which may be taken to be the same for both integrals), we have by Theorem 431 that

$$- \int_a^b |f(x)| \, dx \leqq \int_a^b f(x) \, dx \leqq \int_a^b |f(x)| \, dx \, .$$

Theorem 438: *Let* $a < b$ *and let* $\int_a^b f(x) \, dx$ *exist. Then*

$$\int_a^b f(x) \, dx = \int_{a-c}^{b-c} f(y + c) \, dy \, .$$

(The same wording as in Theorem 406.)

Theorem 439: *Let $a < b$ and let $\int_a^b f(x)\, dx$ exist. Then*

$$\int_a^b f(x)\, dx = \int_{-b}^{-a} f(-y)\, dy\,.$$

(The same wording as in Theorem 407.)

Theorem 440: *Let $a < b$, let $\int_a^b f(x)\, dx$ exist, and let $\mu > 0$. Then*

$$\int_a^b f(x)\, dx = \mu \int_{\frac{a}{\mu}}^{\frac{b}{\mu}} f(\mu y)\, dy\,.$$

(The same wording as in Theorem 408.)

Simultaneous proof of Theorems 438-440: Follows from Theorems 406-408 by applying them to α, β with $\gamma_{\nu-1} < \alpha < \beta < \gamma_\nu$.

CHAPTER 29

THE INTEGRAL WITH INFINITE LIMITS

If

$$f(x) = \frac{1}{x}, \quad \omega > 0,$$

then

$$\int_1^\omega f(x)\, dx = \log \omega,$$

which has no $\lim_{\omega=\infty}$. We shall not define

$$\int_1^\infty \frac{dx}{x}.$$

If

$$f(x) = \frac{1}{x^2}, \quad \omega > 0$$

then

$$\int_1^\omega f(x)\, dx = 1 - \frac{1}{\omega}$$

has the limit 1 as $\omega = \infty$. We shall define

$$\int_1^\infty \frac{dx}{x^2} = 1.$$

Definition 94: $\qquad \displaystyle\int_a^\infty f(x)\, dx = \lim_{\omega=\infty} \int_a^\omega f(x)\, dx,$

i. r. h. s. i. m.

Definition 95: $\qquad \displaystyle\int_{-\infty}^b f(x)\, dx = \lim_{\omega=-\infty} \int_\omega^b f(x)\, dx,$

i. r. h. s. i. m.

Definition 96: $\int_{-\infty}^{\infty} f(x)\, dx = \int_{-\infty}^{0} f(x)\, dx + \int_{0}^{\infty} f(x)\, dx\,,$

i. r. h. s. i. m.

Example: $\int_{-\infty}^{\infty} \dfrac{dx}{1 + x^2} = \lim_{\omega=-\infty} \int_{\omega}^{0} \dfrac{dx}{1 + x^2} + \lim_{\omega=\infty} \int_{0}^{\omega} \dfrac{dx}{1 + x^2}$

$= \lim_{\omega=-\infty} (-\arctan \omega) + \lim_{\omega=\infty} \arctan \omega = -\left(-\dfrac{\pi}{2}\right) + \dfrac{\pi}{2} = \pi\,.$

Definition 97: $\int_{\infty}^{a} f(x)\, dx = -\int_{a}^{\infty} f(x)\, dx\,,$

i. r. h. s. i. m.

Definition 98: $\int_{b}^{-\infty} f(x)\, dx = -\int_{-\infty}^{b} f(x)\, dx\,,$

i. r. h. s. i. m.

Definition 99: $\int_{\infty}^{-\infty} f(x)\, dx = -\int_{-\infty}^{\infty} f(x)\, dx\,,$

i. r. h. s. i. m.

Theorem 441: *If the integrals*

$$\int_{-\infty}^{c} f(x)\, dx,\quad \int_{c}^{\infty} f(x)\, dx$$

exist for some c, then

$$\int_{-\infty}^{\infty} f(x)\, dx$$

exists, and

$$\int_{-\infty}^{\infty} f(x)\, dx = \int_{-\infty}^{c} f(x)\, dx + \int_{c}^{\infty} f(x)\, dx\,.$$

Proof: $\int_{\omega}^{0} = \int_{\omega}^{c} + \int_{c}^{0};$

$\omega \to -\infty$ yields

$$\int_{-\infty}^{0} = \int_{-\infty}^{c} + \int_{c}^{0}.$$

$$\int_{0}^{\omega} = \int_{c}^{\omega} + \int_{0}^{c};$$

$\omega \to \infty$ yields

$$\int_{0}^{\infty} = \int_{c}^{\infty} + \int_{0}^{c}.$$

Therefore, we have

$$\int_{-\infty}^{0} + \int_{0}^{\infty} = \int_{-\infty}^{c} + \int_{c}^{\infty}.$$

For the remainder of this chapter, each of the limits of integration a, b will stand either for a number, or for ∞, or for $-\infty$.

Theorem 442: $\displaystyle\int_a^b \big(f(x) + g(x)\big)\, dx = \int_a^b f(x)\, dx + \int_a^b g(x)\, dx,$

i. r. h. s. i. m.

(The same wording as in Theorem 423.)
Proof: Obvious by Theorem 423.

Theorem 443: $\displaystyle\int_a^b C f(x)\, dx = C\int_a^b f(x)\, dx,$

i. r. h. s. i. m.

(The same wording as in Theorem 424.)
Proof: Obvious by Theorem 424.

Theorem 444: $\displaystyle\int_a^b \big(f(x) - g(x)\big)\, dx = \int_a^b f(x)\, dx - \int_a^b g(x)\, dx,$

i. r. h. s. i. m.

(The same wording as in Theorem 425.)
Proof: Obvious by Theorem 425.

For the remainder of this chapter, we write $a < b$ or $a \leqq b$ also in the case that a stands for $-\infty$ while b is a number or ∞; as well as the case that a is a number while b stands for ∞. Furthermore, $a < x < b$ ($a \leqq x \leqq b$) means, for a "$=$" $-\infty$ and for every number b, that x is a number $< b$ ($\leqq b$); for b "$=$" ∞ and for every number a, that x is a number $> a$ ($\geqq a$); for a "$=$" $-\infty$, b "$=$" ∞, that x is a number (in both cases).

Let a be a number and let $\displaystyle\int_a^\infty f(x)\, dx$ exist. For every $\omega > a$ we have that

$\displaystyle\int_a^\omega$ is an improper integral in the sense of Definition 91 with a finite number of γ's. In every case we have

$$\int_a^\infty = \sum_{\nu=0}^\infty \int_{\gamma_\nu}^{\gamma_{\nu+1}},$$

where all of the integrals on the right are meant in the sense of Definition 90,

$$\gamma_0 = a, \quad \gamma_\nu < \gamma_{\nu+1},$$

and γ_ν increases with ν beyond all bounds.

The same holds mutatis mutandis for $\displaystyle\int_{-\infty}^b$, where b is a number (with a decreasing γ-sequence).

For $\displaystyle\int_{-\infty}^\infty$, we therefore have to deal with two γ-sequences, one of each kind.

Theorem 445: *Let $a < b$, let $\int_a^b f(x)\,dx$ exist, and let*

$$f(x) \geqq 0 \text{ for } a \leqq x \leqq b \text{ except at the } \gamma\text{'s.}$$

Then we have

$$\int_a^b f(x)\,dx \geqq 0 \,.$$

(Almost the same wording as in Theorem 429.)

Proof: Obvious by Theorem 429.

Theorem 446: *Let $a < b$, let $\int_a^b f(x)\,dx$ exist, and let*

$$f(x) > 0 \text{ for } a \leqq x \leqq b \text{ except at the } \gamma\text{'s.}$$

Then we have

$$\int_a^b f(x)\,dx > 0 \,.$$

(Almost the same wording as in Theorem 430.)

Proof: Since $f(x)$ is improperly integrable over some interval, the proof proceeds like that of Theorem 430.

Theorem 447: *If $a < b$, if $\int_a^b f(x)\,dx$ and $\int_a^b g(x)\,dx$ exist* (w.l.g. with the same γ's), *and if*

$$f(x) \leqq g(x) \text{ for } a \leqq x \leqq b \text{ except at the } \gamma\text{'s,}$$

then

$$\int_a^b f(x)\,dx \leqq \int_a^b g(x)\,dx \,.$$

(Almost the same wording as in Theorem 431.)

Proof: Obvious by Theorem 431.

Theorem 448: *Let $a < b$, let $\int_a^b g(x)\,dx$ and $\int_a^b f(x)\,g(x)\,dx$ exist* (w.l.g. with the same γ's), *and let*

$$g(x) \geqq 0 \text{ for } a \leqq x \leqq b \text{ except at the } \gamma\text{'s.}$$

Let $f(x)$ be bounded from above for $a \leqq x \leqq b$ except at the γ's, and let l be the l.u.b. of $f(x)$ thereon. Then

$$\int_a^b f(x)\,g(x)\,dx \leqq l \int_a^b g(x)\,dx \,.$$

(Almost the same wording as in Theorem 432.)

Preliminary Remark: If we assume that $f(x)$ is bounded from below for $a \leq x \leq b$ (instead of from above) except at the γ's, and that its g.l.b. is λ, then by applying this theorem to $-f(x)$ we obtain

$$\int_a^b f(x)\, g(x)\, dx \geq \lambda \int_a^b g(x)\, dx\,.$$

Proof: Obvious by Theorem 432.

Theorem 449: *Let $a < b$, and let $f(x)$ be continuous on every closed interval belonging to $a \leq x \leq b$ and bounded for $a \leq x \leq b$. Let $\int_a^b g(x)\, dx$ and $\int_a^b f(x)\, g(x)\, dx$ exist (w.l.g. with the same γ's) and let*

$$g(x) \geq 0 \ \text{for}\ a \leq x \leq b\ \text{except at the}\ \gamma\text{'s}.$$

Then there exists a ξ on $a \leq x \leq b$ such that

$$\int_a^b f(x)\, g(x)\, dx = f(\xi) \int_a^b g(x)\, dx\,.$$

(Almost the same wording as in Theorem 433.)

Proof: If l is the l.u.b. and λ the g.l.b. of $f(x)$ for $a \leq x \leq b$, then we have by Theorem 448 and its preliminary remark that

$$\lambda \int_a^b g(x)\, dx \leq \int_a^b f(x)\, g(x)\, dx = t \leq l \int_a^b g(x)\, dx\,.$$

W.l.g., let

$$\int_a^b g(x)\, dx > 0\,;$$

for otherwise any ξ on $a \leq x \leq b$ would be of the required kind.

1) If

$$\lambda \int_a^b g(x)\, dx < t < l \int_a^b g(x)\, dx\,,$$

then somewhere on $a \leq x \leq b$ we have

$$f(\xi) \int_a^b g(x)\, dx < t\,,$$

and somewhere

$$f(\xi) \int_a^b g(x)\, dx > t\,,$$

so that somewhere

$$f(\xi) \int_a^b g(x)\, dx = t\,.$$

2) Let

$$t = \lambda \int_a^b g(x)\, dx \quad \text{or} \quad t = l \int_a^b g(x)\, dx\,.$$

W.l.g., the latter; for otherwise we would consider $-f(x)$ instead of $f(x)$. It suffices to show that for some ξ we have

$$f(\xi) = l\,.$$

Assume that we always had

$$f(\xi) < l.$$

For a suitable $[\alpha, \beta]$ belonging to $a \leq x \leq b$ on which $g(x)$ is properly integrable, we have

$$\int_\alpha^\beta g(x)\,dx > 0.$$

$l - f(x)$ is continuous on that interval and so is $\geq p > 0$, so that

$$\int_\alpha^\beta (l - f(x))\, g(x)\,dx \geq p \int_\alpha^\beta g(x)\,dx.$$

Therefore we would have

$$\int_a^b (l - f(x))\, g(x)\,dx \geq p \int_\alpha^\beta g(x)\,dx > 0,$$

$$0 = l \int_a^b g(x)\,dx - t = l \int_a^b g(x)\,dx - \int_a^b f(x)\, g(x)\,dx > 0.$$

Theorem 450: *Let $a < b$, let $\int_a^b f(x)\,dx$ exist, and let $g(x)$ be continuous on every closed interval belonging to $a \leq x \leq b$. If $a = -\infty$, then let*

$$\lim_{x=-\infty} g(x) = \text{``} g(-\infty) \text{''} \ exist;$$

if $b = \infty$, then let

$$\lim_{x=\infty} g(x) = \text{``} g(\infty) \text{''} \ exist.$$

Furthermore, let

$$g'(x) = f(x) \ for \ a < x < b \ except \ at \ the \ \gamma's.$$

Then we have

$$\int_a^b f(x)\,dx = g(b) - g(a).$$

(Almost the same wording as in Theorem 436.)

Proof: Obvious by Theorem 436.

Theorem 451: *If $a < b$ and if $\int_a^b f(x)\,dx$ and $\int_a^b |f(x)|\,dx$ exist, then*

$$\left| \int_a^b f(x)\,dx \right| \leq \int_a^b |f(x)|\,dx.$$

(The same wording as in Theorem 437.)

Proof: Obvious by Theorem 437.

Theorem 452: *Let* $a < b$, *and let* $\int_a^b f(x)\,dx$ *exist. Then we have*

$$\int_a^b f(x)\,dx = \int_{a-c}^{b-c} f(y+c)\,dy,$$

where (*just for the moment*) *we let* $a - c$ *mean* $-\infty$ *for* $a = -\infty$, *and* $b - c$ *mean* ∞ *for* $b = \infty$.

(Almost the same wording as in Theorem 438.)

Proof: Obvious by Theorem 438.

Theorem 453: *Let* $a < b$, *and let* $\int_a^b f(x)\,dx$ *exist. Then we have*

$$\int_a^b f(x)\,dx = \int_{-b}^{-a} f(-y)\,dy,$$

where (*just for the moment*) *we let* $-a$ *mean* ∞ *for* $a = -\infty$.

(Almost the same wording as in Theorem 439.)

Preliminary Remark: We need not mention explicitly that (just for the moment) $-b$ has the meaning $-\infty$ if $b = \infty$; for what is $-\infty$ to stand for if not for $-\infty$?

Proof: Obvious by Theorem 439.

Theorem 454: *Let* $a < b$, *let* $\int_a^b f(x)\,dx$ *exist, and let* $\mu > 0$. *Then we have*

$$\int_a^b f(x)\,dx = \mu \int_{\frac{a}{\mu}}^{\frac{b}{\mu}} f(\mu y)\,dy,$$

where (*just for the moment*) *we let* $\dfrac{a}{\mu}$ *mean* $-\infty$ *for* $a = -\infty$, *and* $\dfrac{b}{\mu}$ *mean* ∞ *for* $b = \infty$.

(Almost the same wording as in Theorem 440.)

Proof: Obvious by Theorem 440.

Theorem 455:
$$\lim_{x=\infty} g(x)$$

exists if and only if for every $\delta > 0$ *there exist a* ξ *such that*

(1) $$\left| g(x_2) - g(x_1) \right| < \delta \quad \text{for } x_2 > x_1 \geqq \xi.$$

Proof: 1) If

$$\lim_{x=\infty} g(x) = c$$

then we have for every $\delta > 0$ and for a suitable ξ that

$$\left| g(x) - c \right| < \frac{\delta}{2} \quad \text{for } x \geqq \xi,$$

then

$$\int_{a}^{\infty} f(x)\, dx$$

so that, for $x_2 > x_1 \geqq \xi$,

$$| g(x_2) - g(x_1) | = | (g(x_2) - c) - (g(x_1) - c) | < \frac{\delta}{2} + \frac{\delta}{2} = \delta.$$

2) For every $\delta > 0$ let there exist a ξ with (1). $g(x)$ is then defined for $x \geqq p$ for a suitable p. By Theorem 206,

$$\sum_{n=0}^{\infty} (g(p + n + 1) - g(p + n))$$

converges; hence

$$\lim_{n=\infty} g(p + n) = c.$$

exists. By hypothesis, we further have

$$\lim_{x=\infty} (g(x) - g(p + [x - p])) = 0;$$

hence we have

$$\lim_{x=\infty} g(x) = c.$$

Theorem 456: *Let a be a number. If*

$$\int_a^\omega f(x)\, dx$$

exists for all $\omega > a$, then

$$\int_a^\infty f(x)\, dx$$

exists if and only if for every $\delta > 0$ there exists a ξ such that

$$\left| \int_{x_1}^{x_2} f(x)\, dx \right| < \delta \quad \text{for } x_2 > x_1 \geqq \xi.$$

Proof: Theorem 455 with

$$g(x) = \int_a^x f(y)\, dy.$$

Example: $a = 0,\ f(x) = \dfrac{\sin x}{x}.$

$$\int_0^\omega \frac{\sin x}{x}\, dx,\ \omega > 0,$$

exists, since $\dfrac{\sin x}{x}$ is continuous for $x > 0$ and is bounded for $0 < x \leqq \omega$.
Let $\delta > 0$. For $x_2 > x_1 \geqq \dfrac{3}{\delta}$ we have by the first example to Theorem 404
that

$$\left| \int_{x_1}^{x_2} \frac{\sin x}{x}\, dx \right| \leqq \frac{2}{x_1} < \delta .$$

Theorem 457: *If*

$$g(x_2) \geqq g(x_1) \ \ for \ \ x_2 \geqq x_1 \geqq p ,$$

$$g(x) \ is \ bounded \ for \ x \geqq p ,$$

then

$$\lim_{x=\infty} g(x)$$

exists.

Preliminary Remark: $\qquad x = \dfrac{1}{y}$

gives the following result: If $q > 0$ and if $G(y)$ is bounded for $0 < y \leqq q$ and

$$G(y_2) \geqq G(y_1) \ \ for \ 0 < y_2 \leqq y_1 \leqq q ,$$

then

$$\lim_{\underleftarrow{y=0}} G(y) .$$

exists.

Proof: By Theorem 27,

$$\lim_{n=\infty} g(n) = c$$

exists. Since

$$g([x]) \leqq g(x) \leqq g([x] + 1) \ \ for \ \ x \geqq p + 1,$$

we therefore have

$$\lim_{x=\infty} g(x) = c .$$

Theorem 458: *Let a be a number. If*

$$\int_a^\omega f(x)\, dx$$

exists and is bounded for all $\omega \geqq a$, and if

$$f(x) \geqq 0 \ \ for \ \ x \geqq a \ except \ at \ the \ \gamma\text{'s},$$

then

$$\int_a^\infty f(x)\, dx$$

exists.

Proof: Theorem 457 with

$$g(x) = \int_a^x f(y)\,dy\,.$$

Theorem 459: *Let* N *be an integer, and let*

$$f(x) \geqq 0 \quad for \ x \geqq N\,,$$

(1)
$$f(x_2) \leqq f(x_1) \quad for \ x_2 \geqq x_1 \geqq N\,.$$

Then if the series

$$\sum_{n=N}^{\infty} f(n)$$

converges, the integral

$$\int_N^{\infty} f(x)\,dx$$

exists, and conversely.

Preliminary Remark: By (1), $\int_N^{\omega} f(x)\,dx$ exists as a proper integral for $\omega > N$.

Proof: 1) If

$$\sum_{n=N}^{\infty} f(n) = c$$

then we have for integral $m > N$ that

$$\int_N^m f(x)\,dx = \sum_{n=N}^{m-1} \int_n^{n+1} f(x)\,dx \leqq \sum_{n=N}^{m-1} f(n) \leqq c\,,$$

so that for $\omega \geqq N$,

$$\int_N^{\omega} f(x)\,dx \leqq \int_N^{[\omega]+1} f(x)\,dx \leqq c\,;$$

hence,

$$\int_N^{\infty} f(x)\,dx$$

exists by Theorem 458.

2) If

$$\int_N^{\infty} f(x)\,dx = C$$

then we have for integral $m > N$ that

$$\sum_{n=N+1}^m f(n) \leqq \sum_{n=N+1}^m \int_{n-1}^n f(x)\,dx = \int_N^m f(x)\,dx \leqq C\,;$$

and hence the convergence of

$$\sum_{n=N}^{\infty} f(n)\,.$$

Examples: 1) Let

$$f(x) = \frac{1}{x^s}, \quad s > 1$$

for $x \geq 1$. Then we have for $\omega > 1$ that

$$\int_1^\omega f(x)\,dx = \left\{ -\frac{1}{s-1}\frac{1}{x^{s-1}} \right\}_1^\omega = \frac{1}{s-1} - \frac{1}{s-1}\frac{1}{\omega^{s-1}}.$$

Thus,

$$\int_1^\infty \frac{dx}{x^s}$$

exists, and therefore by Theorem 459

$$\sum_{n=1}^\infty \frac{1}{n^s}.$$

converges.

2) Let

$$f(x) = \frac{1}{x \log x}$$

for $x \geq 2$. Then we have for $\omega > 2$ that

$$\int_2^\omega f(x)\,dx = \{\log \log x\}_2^\omega = \log \log \omega - \log \log 2.$$

Since this has no limit as $\omega \to \infty$

$$\sum_{n=2}^\infty \frac{1}{n \log n}$$

diverges.

Theorem 460: *Let a be a number. If*

$$\int_a^\infty f(x)\,dx$$

exists, and if

$$\lim_{x=\infty} f(x) = C,$$

then

$$C = 0.$$

Proof: Otherwise let, w.l.g., $C > 0$. There would exist a $\xi > a$ such that

$$f(x) > \frac{C}{2} \quad \text{for } x \geq \xi.$$

For $\omega > \xi$, we would have

$$\int_a^\omega f(x)\,dx = \int_a^\xi f(x)\,dx + \int_\xi^\omega f(x)\,dx \geq \int_a^\xi f(x)\,dx + \frac{C}{2}(\omega - \xi);$$

and hence

$$\int_a^\infty f(x)\,dx$$

would not exist.

Theorem 461: *Let a be a number. If*

$$\int_a^\infty f(x)\,dx$$

exists, and if $f(x)$ is continuous for $x \geq a$, then

$$\lim_{x=\infty} f(x)$$

need not exist; $f(x)$ need not even be bounded.

Proofs: 1) $$f(x) = \sqrt{x} \cos (x^2)$$

is not bounded for $x \geq 1$. By Theorem 404 we have for $\delta > 0,\, x_2 > x_1 > \dfrac{1}{\delta^2}$ that

$$\left| \int_{x_1}^{x_2} \sqrt{x} \cos (x^2)\,dx \right| = \left| \int_{x_1}^{x_2} \frac{1}{2\sqrt{x}} 2x \cos (x^2)\,dx \right| = \left| \int_{x_1}^{x_2} \frac{1}{2\sqrt{x}} (\sin (x^2))'\,dx \right|$$

$$\leq \frac{1}{\sqrt{x_1}} < \delta ,$$

so that, by Theorem 456,

$$\int_1^\infty f(x)\,dx$$

exists.

2) According to a widespread superstition, what makes this theorem work is the existence of positive and negative values of $f(x)$. To eradicate this superstition, let

$$f(x) = \begin{cases} n^4 \left(x - n + \dfrac{1}{n^3} \right) & \text{for } n - \dfrac{1}{n^3} \leq x \leq n , \\ n^4 \left(-x + n + \dfrac{1}{n^3} \right) & \text{for } n \leq x \leq n + \dfrac{1}{n^3} , \\ 0 & \text{otherwise.} \end{cases} \quad \left. \right\} \; n \text{ an integer} \geq 2,$$

Thus $f(x)$ is uniquely defined, continuous, and ≥ 0. Since

$$\int_{n-\frac{1}{n^3}}^{n+\frac{1}{n^3}} f(x)\,dx = n^4 \int_{n-\frac{1}{n^3}}^{n} \left(x - n + \frac{1}{n^3} \right) dx - n^4 \int_{n}^{n+\frac{1}{n^3}} \left(x - n - \frac{1}{n^3} \right) dx$$

$$= n^4 \int_0^{\frac{1}{n^3}} z\,dz - n^4 \int_{-\frac{1}{n^3}}^{0} z\,dz = \frac{1}{n^2} ,$$

we have for every $\omega > 0$ that

$$\int\limits_0^\omega f(x)\,dx \leqq \sum_{n=2}^\infty \frac{1}{n^2}\;;$$

$$\int\limits_0^\infty f(x)\,dx$$

therefore exists, by Theorem 458. However, since

$$f(n) = n \text{ for } n \text{ an integer } \geqq 2,$$

$f(x)$ is not bounded for $x \geqq 0$.

3) If we want an example with $f(x) > 0$ for $x \geqq a$, then we need only add e^{-x} to the function of example 2).

Theorem 462: *Let a be a number. Let*

$$\int\limits_a^\omega f(x)\,dx$$

exist for every $\omega > a$. Let

$$\left| f(x) \right| \leqq g(x) \text{ for } x \geqq a$$

(say, $g(x) = |f(x)|$). Let

$$\int\limits_a^\infty g(x)\,dx$$

exist. Then

$$\int\limits_a^\infty f(x)\,dx$$

exists.

Proof: $$0 \leqq g(x) - f(x) \leqq 2g(x).$$

We have for $\omega \geqq a$ that

$$\int\limits_a^\omega \big(g(x) - f(x)\big)\,dx \leqq 2\int\limits_a^\omega g(x)\,dx \leqq 2\int\limits_a^\infty g(x)\,dx.$$

Therefore, by Theorem 458,

$$\int\limits_a^\infty \big(g(x) - f(x)\big)\,dx \text{ exists,}$$

so that, by Theorem 444,

$$\int\limits_a^\infty f(x)\,dx = \int\limits_a^\infty \Big(g(x) - \big(g(x) - f(x)\big)\Big)\,dx.$$

Theorem 463: *Let* $a > 0$ *and let* $\int_a^\omega f(x)\,dx$ *exist for* $\omega > a$. *For suitable* $P > 1$ *and suitable* p, *let*

$$|f(x)| \leq \frac{p}{x^P} \quad for \ x \geq a.$$

Then

$$\int_a^\infty f(x)\,dx$$

exists.

Proof: $\displaystyle \int_a^\omega \frac{p}{x^P}\,dx = \frac{p}{P-1}\left(\frac{1}{a^{P-1}} - \frac{1}{\omega^{P-1}}\right) \to \frac{p}{(P-1)a^{P-1}},$

and Theorem 462.

CHAPTER 30

THE GAMMA FUNCTION

This chapter applies the theory of integrals with infinite limits, in that it develops the main properties of an especially important function of analysis.

Theorem 464; $$\int_0^\infty e^{-t}\,t^{x-1}\,dt$$

is meaningful for $x > 0$ (and so, by Theorem 446, is positive).

Proof: $$\int_0^1 e^{-t}\,t^{x-1}\,dt$$

exists. For, we have for $0 < \alpha < 1$ that

$$\int_\alpha^1 e^{-t}\,t^{x-1}\,dt \leqq \int_\alpha^1 t^{x-1}\,dt = \frac{1-\alpha^x}{x} < \frac{1}{x}\,,$$

and so is bounded, and the left-hand side increases with decreasing α so that it has a $\lim\limits_{\underset{\leftarrow}{\alpha=0}}$ by the preliminary remark to Theorem 457.

Furthermore, we have for fixed x and large t that

$$e^{-t}\,t^{x-1} < \frac{1}{t^2}\,,$$

so that

$$\int_1^\infty e^{-t}\,t^{x-1}\,dt$$

exists by Theorem 463.

Definition 100: $\Gamma(x) = \int_0^\infty e^{-t}\,t^{x-1}\,dt$ *for* $x > 0$.

Nota bene: The integral is meaningless for $x \leqq 0$, since we have for $0 < \alpha < 1$ that

$$\int_\alpha^1 e^{-t}t^{x-1}\,dt \geqq e^{-1}\int_\alpha^1 t^{-1}\,dt = -e^{-1}\log\alpha\,,$$

so that no $\lim\limits_{\underset{\leftarrow}{\alpha=0}}$ exists.

Theorem 465: $\Gamma(x+1) = x\,\Gamma(x)$ *for* $x > 0$.

Proof: We have for $0 < a < \omega$ that

$$\int_\alpha^\omega e^{-t}\, t^x\, dt = \left\{ -e^{-t}\, t^x \right\}_\alpha^\omega + \int_\alpha^\omega e^{-t}x\, t^{x-1}\, dt$$

$$= -e^{-\omega}\,\omega^x + e^{-\alpha}\,\alpha^x + \int_\alpha^\omega e^{-t}x\, t^{x-1}\, dt;$$

$\lim\limits_{\substack{\alpha = 0 \\ \longleftarrow}}$ yields

$$\int_0^\omega e^{-t}\, t^x\, dt = -e^{-\omega}\,\omega^x + \int_0^\omega e^{-t}x\, t^{x-1}\, dt;$$

$\lim\limits_{\omega = \infty}$ yields

$$\Gamma(x+1) = \int_0^\infty e^{-t}\, t^x dt = \int_0^\infty e^{-t}x\, t^{x-1}\, dt = x\,\Gamma(x).$$

Theorem 466: $\Gamma(x+n) = \Gamma(x) \prod\limits_{v=0}^{n-1} (x+v)$ *for integral* $n > 0$ *and* $x > 0$.

Proof: $n = 1$ is Theorem 465. $n+1$ follows from n since, by Theorem 465,

$$\Gamma(x+n+1) = (x+n)\,\Gamma(x+n) = (x+n)\,\Gamma(x) \prod_{v=0}^{n-1} (x+v) = \Gamma(x) \prod_{v=0}^{n} (x+v).$$

Theorem 467: $\Gamma(x+1) = x!$ *for integral* $x \geq 0$.

Proof: $$\Gamma(1) = \int_0^\infty e^{-t} dt = 1,$$

so that by Theorem 466 (with 1 in place of x, x in place of n), we have for $x > 0$ that

$$\Gamma(1+x) = \Gamma(1) \prod_{v=0}^{x-1} (1+v) = x!.$$

Theorem 468: *We have for* $0 < x < 1$ *that*

$$\lim_{n = \infty} \frac{\Gamma(x+n)}{n!\, n^{x-1}} = 1.$$

Preliminary Remark: The assertion may be written

$$\frac{\Gamma(x+n)}{\Gamma(n)\, n^x} \to 1,$$

by Theorem 467.

Proof: For integral $n > 0$, we set

$$\int_0^n e^{-t} t^{x+n-1} dt = I_1,$$

$$\int_n^\infty e^{-t} t^{x+n-1} dt = I_2.$$

For $0 < t \leqq n$, we have

$$t^x \leqq n^x,$$

$$t^{x-1} \geqq n^{x-1};$$

therefore we have

$$n^{x-1} \int_0^n e^{-t} t^n dt \leqq I_1 \leqq n^x \int_0^n e^{-t} t^{n-1} dt.$$

For $t \geqq n$, we have

$$t^x \geqq n^x,$$

$$t^{x-1} \leqq n^{x-1};$$

therefore we have

$$n^x \int_n^\infty e^{-t} t^{n-1} dt \leqq I_2 \leqq n^{x-1} \int_n^\infty e^{-t} t^n dt.$$

Now we have

$$\int_0^n e^{-t} t^n dt = \left\{ -e^{-t} t^n \right\}_0^n + \int_0^n e^{-t} n t^{n-1} dt = -e^{-n} n^n + n \int_0^n e^{-t} t^{n-1} dt,$$

so that

$$n^x \int_0^n e^{-t} t^{n-1} dt - e^{-n} n^{x+n-1} \leqq I_1 \leqq n^{x-1} \int_0^n e^{-t} t^n dt + e^{-n} n^{x+n-1},$$

$$n^x \int_0^\infty e^{-t} t^{n-1} dt - e^{-n} n^{x+n-1} \leqq I_1 + I_2 \leqq n^{x-1} \int_0^\infty e^{-t} t^n dt + e^{-n} n^{x+n-1},$$

$$n^x \Gamma(n) - e^{-n} n^{x+n-1} \leqq \Gamma(x+n) \leqq n^{x-1} \Gamma(n+1) + e^{-n} n^{x+n-1},$$

$$1 - \frac{e^{-n} n^{n-1}}{\Gamma(n)} \leqq \frac{\Gamma(x+n)}{\Gamma(n) n^x} \leqq 1 + \frac{e^{-n} n^{n-1}}{\Gamma(n)},$$

$$\left| \frac{\Gamma(x+n)}{\Gamma(n) n^x} - 1 \right| \leqq \frac{e^{-n} n^{n-1}}{\Gamma(n)} = \frac{n^n}{e^n n!}.$$

But the right-hand side approaches 0 as $n \to \infty$, since for every integer $m > 0$ we have

$$\frac{e^n n!}{n^n} \geqq \frac{n!}{n^n} \sum_{j=0}^m \frac{n^{n+j}}{(n+j)!} = 1 + \sum_{j=1}^m \frac{n^j}{\prod\limits_{k=1}^j (n+k)} = 1 + \sum_{j=1}^m \prod_{k=1}^j \frac{n}{n+k},$$

where on the right, each of the $m + 1$ summands $\to 1$ as $n \to \infty$, so that we have, ultimately,

$$\frac{e^n n!}{n^n} > m .$$

Theorem 469: *For $x > 0$, we have*

$$\lim_{n = \infty} \frac{\Gamma(x + n)}{n! \; n^{x-1}} = 1.$$

Proof: This is trivial for $x = 1$, since

$$\frac{\Gamma(1 + n)}{n!} = 1;$$

we had this in Theorem 468 for $0 < x < 1$. Hence it suffices to proceed from x to $x + 1$. Indeed, we have

$$\frac{\Gamma(x + 1 + n)}{n! \; n^x} = \frac{\Gamma(x + n)}{n! \; n^{x-1}} \frac{x + n}{n} \to 1 \cdot 1 = 1.$$

Theorem 470: *For $x > 0$, we have*

$$\Gamma(x) = \lim_{n = \infty} \frac{n! \, n^x}{\prod\limits_{\nu=0}^{n} (x + \nu)} .$$

Proof: By Theorems 469 and 466, we have

$$1 = \lim_{n = \infty} \frac{\Gamma(x + n)}{n! \; n^{x-1}} = \Gamma(x) \lim_{n = \infty} \frac{\prod\limits_{\nu=0}^{n-1} (x + \nu)}{n! \; n^{x-1}} = \Gamma(x) \lim_{n = \infty} \frac{\prod\limits_{\nu=0}^{n} (x + \nu)}{n! \; n^x} .$$

Theorem 471:
$$\lim_{m = \infty} \left(\sum_{n=1}^{m} \frac{1}{n} - \log m \right) = C$$

exists, is > 0, and is < 1.

Proof: For integral $n > 0$, we set

$$g(n) = \frac{1}{n} - \int_{n}^{n+1} \frac{dt}{t} ;$$

then we have

$$0 = \frac{1}{n} - \frac{1}{n} < g(n) < \frac{1}{n} - \frac{1}{n + 1} ,$$

so that

$$\sum_{n=1}^{\infty} g(n)$$

converges and the value of this series, which we call C, is > 0 and

$$< \sum_{n=1}^{\infty} \left(\frac{1}{n} - \frac{1}{n+1} \right) = 1 .$$

For integral $m > 1$, we now have

$$\sum_{n=1}^{m-1} g(n) = \sum_{n=1}^{m-1} \frac{1}{n} - \int_1^m \frac{dt}{t} = \sum_{n=1}^{m} \frac{1}{n} - \frac{1}{m} - \log m ;$$

hence we have

$$\sum_{n=1}^{m} \frac{1}{n} - \frac{1}{m} - \log m \to C ,$$

$$\sum_{n=1}^{m} \frac{1}{n} - \log m \to C .$$

Definition 101: C *is called Euler's constant.*
I do not know whether it is rational or irrational.
Theorem 472: *For $x > 0$, we have*

$$\frac{1}{\Gamma(x)} = e^{Cx} \, x \prod_{\nu=1}^{\infty} \left(\left(1 + \frac{x}{\nu} \right) e^{-\frac{x}{\nu}} \right).$$

Proof: For

$$f_n(x) = \frac{\prod_{\nu=0}^{n} (x+\nu)}{n! \, n^x}$$

we know from Theorem 470 that

(1) $$\lim_{n=\infty} f_n(x) = \frac{1}{\Gamma(x)} .$$

Now for $n > 0$, we have

$$f_n(x) = \frac{x}{n^x} \prod_{\nu=1}^{n} \frac{x+\nu}{\nu} = \frac{x}{n^x} \prod_{\nu=1}^{n} \left(1 + \frac{x}{\nu} \right)$$

$$= e^{-x \log n + \sum_{\nu=1}^{n} \frac{x}{\nu}} \, x \prod_{\nu=1}^{n} \left(\left(1 + \frac{x}{\nu} \right) e^{-\frac{x}{\nu}} \right).$$

From (1) and

$$\lim_{n=\infty} e^{-x \log n + x \sum_{\nu=1}^{n} \frac{1}{\nu}} = e^{x \lim_{n=\infty} \left(\sum_{\nu=1}^{n} \frac{1}{\nu} - \log n \right)} = e^{Cx}$$

the conclusion, together with the convergence of the infinite product, follows.

Theorem 473: *For $x > 0$, we have*

(1)
$$\frac{\Gamma'(x)}{\Gamma(x)} = -C - \frac{1}{x} - \sum_{\nu=1}^{\infty} \left(\frac{1}{x+\nu} - \frac{1}{\nu}\right)$$

and for integral $n \geq 1$, we have

(2)
$$\frac{d^n\left(\dfrac{\Gamma'(x)}{\Gamma(x)}\right)}{dx^n} = (-1)^{n-1} n! \sum_{\nu=0}^{\infty} \frac{1}{(x+\nu)^{n+1}}.$$

Proof: By Theorems 472 and 282,

(3)
$$\log \Gamma(x) = -Cx - \log x - \sum_{\nu=1}^{\infty} \left(\log\left(1 + \frac{x}{\nu}\right) - \frac{x}{\nu}\right).$$

$$\left(\log\left(1 + \frac{x}{\nu}\right) - \frac{x}{\nu}\right)' = \frac{1}{1 + \dfrac{x}{\nu}} \cdot \frac{1}{\nu} - \frac{1}{\nu} = \frac{1}{x+\nu} - \frac{1}{\nu} = -\frac{x}{(x+\nu)\nu}.$$

$$\sum_{\nu=1}^{\infty} \frac{x}{(x+\nu)\nu}$$

converges uniformly for $0 < x < \omega$ for every $\omega > 0$, since

$$\frac{x}{(x+\nu)\nu} < \frac{\omega}{\nu^2};$$

therefore (3) may be differentiated term by term, giving (1); for if

$$\log \Gamma(x) = G(x),$$

then $G'(x)$ exists, so that

$$\Gamma'(x) = (e^{G(x)})' = G'(x) e^{G(x)} = G'(x) \Gamma(x).$$

Now, we have

$$\left(\frac{1}{x+\nu} - \frac{1}{\nu}\right)' = -\frac{1}{(x+\nu)^2};$$

$$\sum_{\nu=1}^{\infty} \frac{1}{(x+\nu)^2}$$

converges uniformly for $x > 0$ since

$$\frac{1}{(x+\nu)^2} < \frac{1}{\nu^2}$$

for all $x > 0$. Hence from (1) we obtain

$$\left(\frac{\Gamma'(x)}{\Gamma(x)}\right)' = \frac{1}{x^2} + \sum_{\nu=1}^{\infty} \frac{1}{(x+\nu)^2} = \sum_{\nu=0}^{n} \frac{1}{(x+\nu)^2},$$

which is (2) with $n = 1$.

(2) with $n + 1$ follows from (2) with n, since

$$(- 1)^{n-1} n! \left(\frac{1}{(x + v)^{n+1}}\right)' = (- 1)^{n-1} n! \frac{- (n + 1)}{(x + v)^{n+2}}$$

$$= (-\cdot 1)^n (n + 1)! \frac{1}{(x + v)^{n+2}}$$

and the fact that

$$\frac{1}{(x + v)^{n+2}} < \frac{1}{v^{n+2}} \text{ for } v \geqq 1$$

implies the uniform convergence of

$$\sum_{v=0}^{\infty} \frac{1}{(x + v)^{n+2}}$$

for $x > 0$.

Theorem 474: $\Gamma(x) \Gamma(1 - x) = \dfrac{\pi}{\sin \pi x}$ *for* $0 < x < 1$.

Preliminary Remark: In particular, for $x = \frac{1}{2}$ we obtain

$$\Gamma^2(\tfrac{1}{2}) = \pi,$$

$$\Gamma(\tfrac{1}{2}) = \sqrt{\pi}.$$

Proof: By Theorem 470, we have

$$\frac{n! \, n^x}{\prod\limits_{v=0}^{n} (x + v)} \to \Gamma(x),$$

so that

$$\frac{n! \, n^x}{\prod\limits_{v=1}^{n} (x + v)} \to x \, \Gamma(x) \, ;$$

furthermore,

$$\frac{n! \, n^{1-x}}{\prod\limits_{v=0}^{n} (1 - x + v)} \to \Gamma(1 - x),$$

and because

$$\frac{n}{1 - x + n} \to 1$$

we have, therefore,

$$\frac{n! \, n^{-x}}{\prod\limits_{v=0}^{n-1} (1 - x + v)} = \frac{n! \, n^{-x}}{\prod\limits_{v=1}^{n} (- x + v)} \to \Gamma(1 - x).$$

Hence we have

$$\frac{(n!)^2}{\prod\limits_{\nu=1}^{n} (\nu^2 - x^2)} \to x\,\Gamma(x)\,\Gamma(1-x),$$

$$\prod_{\nu=1}^{n} \left(1 - \frac{x^2}{\nu^2}\right) = \frac{\prod\limits_{\nu=1}^{n} (\nu^2 - x^2)}{(n!)^2} \to \frac{1}{x\,\Gamma(x)\,\Gamma(1-x)}.$$

Therefore, we have by Theorem 283 that

$$\frac{\sin \pi x}{\pi x} = \frac{1}{x\,\Gamma(x)\,\Gamma(1-x)},$$

$$\Gamma(x)\,\Gamma(1-x) = \frac{\pi}{\sin \pi x}.$$

Theorem 475: *If $x > 0$ and if k is an integer $\geqq 1$, then*

$$\prod_{\nu=0}^{k-1} \Gamma\left(x + \frac{\nu}{k}\right) = (2\pi)^{\frac{k-1}{2}}\, k^{-kx+\frac{1}{2}}\, \Gamma(kx).$$

Proof: By Theorem 470, we have for $0 \leqq \nu \leqq k-1$, ν an integer, that

$$\Gamma\left(x + \frac{\nu}{k}\right) = \lim_{n=\infty} \frac{n!\, n^{x+\frac{\nu}{k}}}{\prod\limits_{\mu=0}^{n} \left(x + \frac{\nu}{k} + \mu\right)} = \lim_{n=\infty} \frac{n!\, n^{x+\frac{\nu}{k}-1}}{\prod\limits_{\mu=0}^{n-1} \left(x + \frac{\nu}{k} + \mu\right)}$$

$$= \lim_{n=\infty} \frac{n!\, n^{x-1}\, n^{\frac{\nu}{k}}\, k^n}{\prod\limits_{\mu=0}^{n-1} (kx + \nu + k\mu)}.$$

Since

$$2\sum_{\nu=0}^{k-1} \nu = \sum_{\nu=0}^{k-1} \nu + \sum_{\nu=0}^{k-1} (k-1-\nu) = \sum_{\nu=0}^{k-1} (k-1) = k(k-1),$$

we therefore have that

$$\prod_{\nu=0}^{k-1} \Gamma\left(x + \frac{\nu}{k}\right) = \lim_{n=\infty} \frac{(n!)^k\, n^{k(x-1)}\, n^{\frac{k-1}{2}}\, k^{nk}}{\prod\limits_{j=0}^{kn-1} (kx + j)}.$$

On the other hand, we have by Theorem 470 that

$$\Gamma(kx) = \lim_{n=\infty} \frac{n!\, n^{kx-1}}{\prod\limits_{j=0}^{n-1} (kx + j)},$$

so that, replacing n by kn,

$$\Gamma(kx) = \lim_{n=\infty} \frac{(kn)!\, k^{kx-1}\, n^{kx-1}}{\prod\limits_{j=0}^{kn-1} (kx+j)}.$$

From this it follows that

$$p_k(x) = \frac{\prod\limits_{\nu=0}^{k-1} \Gamma\left(x + \frac{\nu}{k}\right)}{\Gamma(kx)\, k^{-kx+\frac{1}{2}}} = \lim_{n=\infty} \frac{(n!)^k\, n^{k(x-1)}\, n^{\frac{k-1}{2}}\, k^{nk}}{(kn)!\, k^{kx-1}\, n^{kx-1}\, k^{-kx+\frac{1}{2}}}$$

$$= \lim_{n=\infty} \frac{(n!)^k\, k^{nk+\frac{1}{2}}}{(kn)!\, n^{\frac{k-1}{2}}}$$

is independent of x, and is $= p_k$.

First we determine

$$p_2 = p_2(\tfrac{1}{2}) = \frac{\Gamma(\tfrac{1}{2})\, \Gamma(1)}{\Gamma(1)\, 2^{-\frac{1}{2}}} = \Gamma(\tfrac{1}{2})\, 2^{\frac{1}{2}} = \sqrt{2\pi}.$$

Therefore we have

$$\Gamma(x)\, \Gamma(x + \tfrac{1}{2}) = \sqrt{2\pi}\, 2^{-2x+\frac{1}{2}} \Gamma(2x).$$

From this, it follows more generally that

$$p_k{}^2 = p_k\left(\frac{1}{2k}\right) p_k\left(\frac{1}{k}\right) = \frac{\prod\limits_{\nu=0}^{k-1} \Gamma\left(\frac{2\nu+1}{2k}\right)}{\sqrt{\pi}}\, \frac{\prod\limits_{\nu=0}^{k-1} \Gamma\left(\frac{2\nu+2}{2k}\right)}{k^{-\frac{1}{2}}}$$

$$= \frac{\prod\limits_{\lambda=1}^{2k} \Gamma\left(\frac{\lambda}{2k}\right)}{\sqrt{\pi}\, k^{-\frac{1}{2}}} = \frac{\prod\limits_{\lambda=1}^{k} \left(\Gamma\left(\frac{\lambda}{2k}\right) \Gamma\left(\frac{\lambda}{2k} + \frac{1}{2}\right)\right)}{\sqrt{\pi}\, k^{-\frac{1}{2}}}$$

$$= \frac{\prod\limits_{\lambda=1}^{k} \left(\sqrt{2\pi}\, 2^{-\frac{\lambda}{k}+\frac{1}{2}} \Gamma\left(\frac{\lambda}{k}\right)\right)}{\sqrt{\pi}\, k^{-\frac{1}{2}}} = \frac{(2\pi)^{\frac{k}{2}}\, 2^{-\frac{k+1}{2}+\frac{k}{2}} \prod\limits_{\lambda=1}^{k} \Gamma\left(\frac{\lambda}{k}\right)}{\sqrt{\pi}\, k^{-\frac{1}{2}}}$$

$$= (2\pi)^{\frac{k-1}{2}}\, p_k\left(\frac{1}{k}\right) = (2\pi)^{\frac{k-1}{2}}\, p_k,$$

$$p_k = (2\pi)^{\frac{k-1}{2}}.$$

CHAPTER 31

FOURIER SERIES

Introduction

Our main goal will be to prove, among other things, the following:

1) If $f(x)$ is continuous everywhere, and if $f(x)$ is of period 2π; if $f(x)$ is piecewise monotonic on $[-\pi, \pi]$, i.e. if there exist numbers x_ν, $0 \leq \nu \leq m$ with

$$x_{\nu-1} < x_\nu \ \text{ for } 1 \leq \nu \leq m \, ,$$

$$x_0 = -\pi, \quad x_m = \pi \, ,$$

such that $f(x)$ is monotonic on every $[x_{\nu-1}, x_\nu]$; then there exist numbers a_n, b_n independent of x such that for all x we have

$$f(x) = \tfrac{1}{2}a_0 + \sum_{n=1}^{\infty} (a_n \cos nx + b_n \sin nx).$$

And in fact, this is accomplished by

$$(1) \qquad \begin{cases} a_n = \dfrac{1}{\pi} \displaystyle\int_{-\pi}^{\pi} f(x) \cos nx \, dx \, , \\[4mm] b_n = \dfrac{1}{\pi} \displaystyle\int_{-\pi}^{\pi} f(x) \sin nx \, dx \, . \end{cases}$$

(This is the so-called **Fourier series** of $f(x)$.)

2) If we remove the hypothesis of piecewise monotonicity, then the conclusion does not hold.

Theorem 476: *If $a < b$ and if $f(x)$ is properly integrable from a to b, then*

$$\lim_{\omega = \infty} \int_a^b f(x) \sin \omega x \, dx = 0.$$

Proof: Let $\delta > 0$ be given. With the usual notation (with respect to $f(x)$), we subdivide the interval $[a, b]$ in such a way that

$$\sum_{\nu=1}^n e_\nu s_\nu < \frac{\delta}{2}.$$

For every

$$\omega > \frac{4}{\delta} \sum_{\nu=1}^n |f(a_\nu)|$$

we have

$$\left| \int_a^b f(x) \sin \omega x \, dx \right| = \left| \sum_{\nu=1}^n \int_{a_{\nu-1}}^{a_\nu} f(x) \sin \omega x \, dx \right|$$

$$= \left| \sum_{\nu=1}^n \int_{a_{\nu-1}}^{a_\nu} (f(x) - f(a_\nu)) \sin \omega x \, dx + \sum_{\nu=1}^n f(a_\nu) \int_{a_{\nu-1}}^{a_\nu} \sin \omega x \, dx \right|$$

$$\leq \sum_{\nu=1}^n e_\nu s_\nu + \sum_{\nu=1}^n |f(a_\nu)| \frac{2}{\omega} < \frac{\delta}{2} + \frac{\delta}{2} = \delta.$$

Notations:

$$f_+(\xi) = \lim_{\substack{x = \xi \\ \leftarrow}} f(x), \quad \text{if it exists,}$$

$$f_-(\xi) = \lim_{\substack{x = \xi \\ \rightarrow}} f(x), \quad \text{if it exists.}$$

By the preliminary remark to Theorem 457, $f_+(\xi)$ surely exists if for some $c > 0$, $f(x)$ is bounded and monotonic for $\xi < x \leq \xi + c$ (i.e. $f(x_2) \geq f(x_1)$ for $\xi < x_2 \leq x_1 \leq \xi + c$ or $f(x_2) \leq f(x_1)$ for $\xi < x_2 \leq x_1 \leq \xi + c$); and $f_-(\xi)$ surely exists if for some $c > 0$, $f(x)$ is bounded and monotonic for $\xi - c \leq x < \xi$.

Theorem 477: *Let $f(x)$ be properly integrable from 0 to π, let $0 < c \leq \pi$, and let $f(x)$ be monotonic for $0 < x \leq c$. Then we have*

$$\lim_{m=\infty} \int_0^\pi f(x) \frac{\sin (m + \tfrac{1}{2})x}{\dfrac{x}{2}} dx = 2f_+(0) \int_0^\infty \frac{\sin y}{y} dy .$$

Preliminary Remarks: By the example to Theorem 456 we know that the integral on the right exists. The integral on the left exists since

$$G(x) = \begin{cases} \dfrac{\sin (m + \tfrac{1}{2})x}{\dfrac{x}{2}} & \text{for } 0 < x \leqq \pi, \\[2em] 2m + 1 & \text{for } x = 0 \end{cases}$$

is continuous on $[0, \pi]$, and so is properly integrable from 0 to π.

Proof: 1) Let

$$f_+(0) = 0.$$

W.l.g., let $f(x)$ be monotonically non-decreasing for $0 < x \leqq c$ (otherwise we consider $- f(x)$). W.l.g., let

$$f(0) = 0 ;$$

for otherwise we change the definition of $f(x)$ at 0 (which does not affect the hypothesis or the conclusion).

Let $\delta > 0$ be given. Choose an ε such that

$$0 < \varepsilon < c, \quad 0 \leqq f(\varepsilon) < \delta.$$

By Theorem 405, there exists for every $m > 0$ an η (depending on δ and m) such that

$$0 \leqq \eta \leqq \varepsilon,$$

$$\int_0^\varepsilon f(x) \frac{\sin (m + \tfrac{1}{2})x}{\dfrac{x}{2}} dx = \int_0^\varepsilon f(x) \, G(x) \, dx = f(\varepsilon) \int_\eta^\varepsilon G(x) \, dx$$

$$= f(\varepsilon) \int_\eta^\varepsilon \frac{\sin (m + \tfrac{1}{2})x}{\dfrac{x}{2}} dx = 2f(\varepsilon) \int_{\eta(m+\tfrac{1}{2})}^{\varepsilon(m+\tfrac{1}{2})} \frac{\sin y}{y} dy .$$

Since

$$\int_0^\infty \frac{\sin y}{y} dy$$

converges, we have for a suitable universal constant p that

$$\left| \int_0^\omega \frac{\sin y}{y} dy \right| < p \quad \text{for } \omega \geqq 0,$$

so that for $0 \leqq a \leqq b$,

$$\left| \int_a^b \frac{\sin y}{y} \, dy \right| = \left| \int_0^b \frac{\sin y}{y} \, dy - \int_0^a \frac{\sin y}{y} \, dy \right| < 2p \, ,$$

so that

$$\left| \int_0^\varepsilon f(x) \frac{\sin\left(m + \tfrac{1}{2}\right)x}{\dfrac{x}{2}} \, dx \right| \leqq 2 f(\varepsilon) \cdot 2p < 4p\delta .$$

Since $\dfrac{f(x)}{\dfrac{x}{2}}$ is properly integrable on $[\varepsilon, \pi]$, we have by Theorem 476 that

for a suitable m_0 (depending on ε, and so on δ) and for $m \geqq m_0$,

$$\left| \int_\varepsilon^\pi f(x) \frac{\sin\left(m + \tfrac{1}{2}\right)x}{\dfrac{x}{2}} \, dx \right| < \delta \, ,$$

so that

$$\left| \int_0^\pi f(x) \frac{\sin\left(m + \tfrac{1}{2}\right)x}{\dfrac{x}{2}} \, dx \right| < (4p + 1)\,\delta \, .$$

Therefore, as asserted, we have

$$\lim_{m = \infty} \int_0^\pi f(x) \frac{\sin\left(m + \tfrac{1}{2}\right)x}{\dfrac{x}{2}} \, dx = 0 \, .$$

2) In the general case it follows from 1), applied to $f(x) - f_+(0)$ instead of to $f(x)$, that

$$\int_0^\pi \left(f(x) - f_+(0)\right) \frac{\sin\left(m + \tfrac{1}{2}\right)x}{\dfrac{x}{2}} \, dx \to 0 \, ;$$

but we have

$$\int_0^\pi f_+(0) \frac{\sin\left(m + \tfrac{1}{2}\right)x}{\dfrac{x}{2}} \, dx = 2 f_+(0) \int_0^{\pi\left(m + \frac{1}{2}\right)} \frac{\sin y}{y} \, dy$$

$$\to 2 f_+(0) \int_0^\infty \frac{\sin y}{y} \, dy \, ,$$

so that

$$\int_0^\pi f(x) \frac{\sin (m + \frac{1}{2})x}{\frac{x}{2}} dx \to 2f_+(0) \int_0^\infty \frac{\sin y}{y} dy.$$

Theorem 478: *Let* $f(x)$ *be properly integrable from* $-\pi$ *to* π, *let* $0 < c \leq \pi$, *and let* $f(x)$ *be monotonic for* $-c \leq x < 0$ *and for* $0 < x \leq c$ (not necessarily in the same sense for both cases). *Let* a_n *be defined by* (1). *Then we have*

$$\tfrac{1}{2}a_0 + \sum_{n=1}^\infty a_n = \frac{f_-(0) + f_+(0)}{2}.$$

Proof: For integral $m > 0$, we have

$$\sin \frac{x}{2} \left(1 + 2 \sum_{n=1}^m \cos nx\right) = \sin \frac{x}{2} + \sum_{n=1}^m \left(-\sin (n - \tfrac{1}{2})x + \sin (n + \tfrac{1}{2})x\right)$$

$$= \sin (m + \tfrac{1}{2}) x,$$

and hence for $0 < |x| < 2\pi$ we have

$$1 + 2 \sum_{n=1}^m \cos nx = \frac{\sin (m + \frac{1}{2})x}{\sin \frac{x}{2}}.$$

Therefore we have

$$\tfrac{1}{2}a_0 + \sum_{n=1}^m a_n = \frac{1}{2\pi} \int_{-\pi}^\pi f(x) \left(1 + 2 \sum_{n=1}^m \cos nx\right) dx$$

$$= \frac{1}{2\pi} \int_{-\pi}^\pi f(x) \frac{\sin (m + \frac{1}{2}) x}{\sin \frac{x}{2}} dx$$

$$= \frac{1}{2\pi} \int_0^\pi f(x) \frac{\sin (m + \frac{1}{2})x}{\sin \frac{x}{2}} dx + \frac{1}{2\pi} \int_0^\pi f(-x) \frac{\sin (m + \frac{1}{2})x}{\sin \frac{x}{2}} dx.$$

Setting

$$h(x) = \begin{cases} \dfrac{1}{\dfrac{x}{2}} - \dfrac{1}{\sin \dfrac{x}{2}} & \text{for } 0 < x \leq \pi, \\[3mm] 0 & \text{for } x = 0, \end{cases}$$

we have that $h(x)$ is continuous on $[0, \pi]$ since

$$\lim_{\substack{x=0 \\ \leftarrow}} h(x) = \lim_{\substack{x=0 \\ \leftarrow}} \left(\frac{\sin \dfrac{x}{2} - \dfrac{x}{2}}{\left(\dfrac{x}{2} \right)^2} \cdot \frac{\dfrac{x}{2}}{\sin \dfrac{x}{2}} \right) = 0 \cdot 1 = 0.$$

Therefore, by Theorem 476, we have

$$\int_0^\pi f(x)\, h(x) \sin (m + \tfrac{1}{2})x \, dx \to 0$$

and

$$\int_0^\pi f(-x)\, h(x) \sin (m + \tfrac{1}{2})x \, dx \to 0\;;$$

hence by Theorem 477, we have

$$\int_0^\pi f(x)\, \frac{\sin (m + \tfrac{1}{2})x}{\sin \dfrac{x}{2}}\, dx \to 2 f_+(0) \int_0^\infty \frac{\sin y}{y}\, dy$$

and

$$\int_0^\pi f(-x)\, \frac{\sin (m + \tfrac{1}{2})x}{\sin \dfrac{x}{2}}\, dx \to 2 f_-(0) \int_0^\infty \frac{\sin y}{y}\, dy\,.$$

Consequently,

$$\tfrac{1}{2} a_0 + \sum_{n=1}^\infty a_n = \frac{f_-(0) + f_+(0)}{\pi} \int_0^\infty \frac{\sin y}{y}\, dy\,.$$

This last integral can be obtained by setting

$$f(x) = 1.$$

Then we have

$$\tfrac{1}{2} a_0 = \frac{1}{2\pi} \int_{-\pi}^\pi dx = 1\,,$$

$$a_n = \frac{1}{\pi} \int_{-\pi}^\pi \cos nx \, dx = \frac{1}{\pi} \left\{ \frac{\sin nx}{n} \right\}_{-\pi}^\pi = 0 \quad \text{for } n > 0.$$

Therefore we have

$$1 = \frac{2}{\pi} \int_0^\infty \frac{\sin y}{y}\, dy\,,$$

$$\int_0^\infty \frac{\sin y}{y}\, dy = \frac{\pi}{2}\,.$$

Theorem 479: *Let* $f(x)$ *be properly integrable from* $-\pi$ *to* π *and let* $c > 0$. *Either let* $-\pi < \xi < \pi$ *and let* $f(x)$ *be monotonic on* $\xi - c \leqq x < \xi$ *and on* $\xi < x \leqq \xi + c$, *or let* $\xi = -\pi$ *and let* $f(x)$ *be monotonic on* $\pi - c \leqq x < \pi$ *and on* $-\pi < x \leqq -\pi + c$. *Let* a_n, b_n *be defined by* (1). *Then we have*

$$\tfrac{1}{2} a_0 + \sum_{n=1}^{\infty} (a_n \cos n\xi + b_n \sin n\xi) = \begin{cases} \dfrac{f_-(\xi) + f_+(\xi)}{2} & \text{for } -\pi < \xi < \pi, \\[2mm] \dfrac{f_-(\pi) + f_+(-\pi)}{2} & \text{for } \xi = -\pi. \end{cases}$$

Proof: W.l.g., let c be $< \pi$ and be so small that the two intervals of monotonicity are in $-\pi < x < \pi$.

W.l.g., let $f(x)$ have the period 2π; for otherwise we change the definition, and always define $f(x)$ in such a way that it is of period 2π, keeping the old definition in $-\pi \leqq x < \pi$. This does not affect either the hypothesis or the conclusion. The latter then reads simply

$$\tfrac{1}{2} a_0 + \sum_{n=1}^{\infty} (a_n \cos n\xi + b_n \sin n\xi) = \frac{f_-(\xi) + f_+(\xi)}{2}.$$

Now

$$F(x) = f(x + \xi)$$

(in place of $f(x)$) satisfies the hypotheses of Theorem 478 concerning $f(x)$. In place of πa_n, we obtain

$$\int_{-\pi}^{\pi} f(y + \xi) \cos ny \, dy = \int_{-\pi+\xi}^{\pi+\xi} f(x) \cos n(x - \xi) \, dx = \int_{-\pi+\xi}^{\pi} + \int_{\pi}^{\pi+\xi}$$

$$= \int_{-\pi+\xi}^{\pi} f(x) \cos n(x - \xi) \, dx + \int_{-\pi}^{-\pi+\xi} f(y + 2\pi) \cos n(y + 2\pi - \xi) \, dy$$

$$= \int_{-\pi+\xi}^{\pi} f(x) \cos n(x - \xi) \, dx + \int_{-\pi}^{-\pi+\xi} f(y) \cos n(y - \xi) \, dy$$

$$= \int_{-\pi}^{\pi} f(x) \cos n(x - \xi) \, dx = \cos n\xi \int_{-\pi}^{\pi} f(x) \cos nx \, dx + \sin n\xi \int_{-\pi}^{\pi} f(x) \sin nx \, dx$$

$$= \pi(a_n \cos n\xi + b_n \sin n\xi).$$

Therefore we have by Theorem 478 that

$$\frac{f_-(\xi) + f_+(\xi)}{2} = \frac{F_-(0) + F_+(0)}{2} = \tfrac{1}{2} a_0 + \sum_{n=1}^{\infty} (a_n \cos n\xi + b_n \sin n\xi).$$

Example: $f(x) = x$ on $[-\pi, \pi]$.

We have

$$\pi a_n = \int_{-\pi}^{\pi} x \cos nx \, dx = \int_{0}^{\pi} x \cos nx \, dx + \int_{-\pi}^{0} x \cos nx \, dx$$

$$= \int_{0}^{\pi} x \cos nx \, dx - \int_{0}^{\pi} y \cos ny \, dy = 0,$$

$$\pi b_n = \int_{-\pi}^{\pi} x \sin nx \, dx = \left\{ - x \frac{\cos nx}{n} \right\}_{-\pi}^{\pi} + \frac{1}{n} \int_{-\pi}^{\pi} \cos nx \, dx$$

$$= - \frac{2\pi (-1)^n}{n}.$$

Hence we have for $-\pi < x < \pi$ that

$$x = - 2 \sum_{n=1}^{\infty} \frac{(-1)^n \sin nx}{n} = - 2 \sum_{n=1}^{\infty} \frac{\sin n(x + \pi)}{n} ;$$

for $x = -\pi$ every term on the right-hand side is 0, which is in agreement with Theorem 479, which states that the value of the right-hand side is

$$\frac{f_-(\pi) + f_+(-\pi)}{2} = \frac{\pi + (-\pi)}{2} = 0.$$

If x is replaced by $x - \pi$, we obtain

$$\sum_{n=1}^{\infty} \frac{\sin nx}{n} = \begin{cases} 0 & \text{for } x = 0, \\[2mm] \dfrac{\pi}{2} - \dfrac{x}{2} & \text{for } 0 < x < 2\pi. \end{cases}$$

The assertion 1) of the introduction is contained in Theorem 479 as a very special case, since $-\pi \leqq \xi < \pi$ suffices because of periodicity, since for every such ξ there exists a c in the sense of Theorem 479 and since the right-hand side of the equality of Theorem 479 is $f(\xi)$ because of continuity.

And finally, the second assertion of the introduction!

Theorem 480: *We do not have*

$$f(x) = \tfrac{1}{2} a_0 + \sum_{n=1}^{\infty} (a_n \cos nx + b_n \sin nx)$$

for every continuous function $f(x)$ having period 2π, where a_n, b_n are determined by (1).

Proof: If n and ν are integers $\geqq 0$, we set

$$A_{\nu, n} = \int_{0}^{\pi} 2 \sin (\nu + \tfrac{1}{2}) x \cos nx \, dx.$$

Then we have

$$A_{\nu,\,n} = \int_0^\pi \left(\sin \left(\nu + \tfrac{1}{2} + n \right)x + \sin \left(\nu + \tfrac{1}{2} - n \right)x \right) dx$$

(2)
$$= \frac{1}{\nu + \tfrac{1}{2} + n} + \frac{1}{\nu + \tfrac{1}{2} - n} = 2 \frac{\nu + \tfrac{1}{2}}{(\nu + \tfrac{1}{2})^2 - n^2} \begin{cases} > 0 \text{ for } n \leq \nu, \\ < 0 \text{ for } n > \nu. \end{cases}$$

Therefore we have for integral $m > 0$ that

$$\frac{1}{2} A_{\nu,\,0} + \sum_{n=1}^{m} A_{\nu,\,n} = \sum_{n=-m}^{m} \frac{1}{\nu + \tfrac{1}{2} + n} = \sum_{n=m-2\nu}^{m} \frac{1}{\nu + \tfrac{1}{2} + n} \to 0 \text{ as } m \to \infty,$$

hence

$$\frac{1}{2} A_{\nu,\,0} + \sum_{n=1}^{\infty} A_{\nu,\,n} = 0,$$

so that, by (2), we have for every integral $m > 0$ that

$$S_{\nu,\,m} = \frac{1}{2} A_{\nu,\,0} + \sum_{n=1}^{m} A_{\nu,\,n} > 0.$$

In particular, we have for $\nu \geq 1$ that

$$S_{\nu,\,\nu} = \frac{1}{2} A_{\nu,\,0} + \sum_{n=1}^{\nu} A_{\nu,\,n} > \sum_{n=1}^{\nu} \frac{1}{\nu + \tfrac{1}{2} - n} > \sum_{n=1}^{\nu} \frac{1}{\nu + 1 - n}$$

$$= \sum_{k=1}^{\nu} \frac{1}{k} > \int_1^\nu \frac{dy}{y} = \log \nu.$$

Now we set

$$f(x) = \sum_{h=1}^{\infty} \frac{\sin\left((2^{h^3} + 1) \dfrac{|x|}{2} \right)}{h^2} \quad \text{for } -\pi \leq x \leq \pi.$$

The series converges uniformly, since

$$|\sin| \leq 1;$$

hence it represents a continuous function on $[-\pi, \pi]$. We have

$$f(-\pi) = f(\pi).$$

If we extend the definition of $f(x)$ everywhere by making it periodic with period 2π, then $f(x)$ is continuous everywhere.

$$\sum_{h=1}^{\infty} \frac{\sin\left((2^{h^3} + 1)\frac{x}{2}\right)\cos nx}{h^2} \qquad (= f(x)\cos nx)$$

converges uniformly on $[0, \pi]$ for every $n \geqq 0$, since

$$|\sin \cdot \cos| \leqq 1.$$

Therefore, we have

$$\pi a_n = \int_{-\pi}^{\pi} f(x)\cos nx\, dx = 2\int_{0}^{\pi} f(x)\cos nx\, dx$$

$$= \sum_{h=1}^{\infty} \frac{1}{h^2}\int_{0}^{\pi} 2\sin\left((2^{h^3} + 1)\frac{x}{2}\right)\cos nx\, dx = \sum_{h=1}^{\infty} \frac{1}{h^2} A_{2^{h^3}-1,\, n};$$

hence for integral $m > 0$ and integral $k > 0$,

$$s_m = \frac{1}{2} a_0 + \sum_{n=1}^{m} a_n = \frac{1}{\pi}\sum_{h=1}^{\infty} \frac{1}{h^2} S_{2^{h^3}-1,\, m} > \frac{1}{\pi}\, \frac{1}{k^2} S_{2^{k^3}-1,\, m},$$

so that, for every integral $k > 0$,

$$s_{2^{k^3}-1} > \frac{1}{\pi}\, \frac{1}{k^2} S_{2^{k^3}-1,\, 2^{k^3}-1} > \frac{1}{\pi}\, \frac{1}{k^2}\log\left(2^{k^3-1}\right) = \frac{k^3 - 1}{k^2}\, \frac{\log 2}{\pi}$$

Therefore, s_m is not bounded. Hence

$$\sum_{n=1}^{\infty} \left(a_n\cos\left(n\cdot 0\right) + b_n\sin\left(n\cdot 0\right)\right)$$

diverges.

INDEX OF DEFINITIONS

STRING FIGURES, and other monographs
By BALL, CAJORI, CARSLAW, and PETERSEN

FOUR VOLUMES IN ONE:
String Figures, *by W. W. Rouse Ball;*
The Elements of Non-Euclidean Plane Geometry, *by H. S. Carslaw;*
A History of the Logarithmic Slide Rule, *by F. Cajori;*
Methods and Theories for the Solution of Problems of Geometrical Construction, *by J. Petersen*

—528 pp. 5¼x8. [130] Four vols. in one. **$3.95**

THÉORIE DES OPÉRATIONS LINÉAIRES
By S. BANACH

—1933. xii + 250 pp. 5¼x8¼. [110] **$3.95**

THEORIE DER FUNKTIONEN MEHRERER KOMPLEXER VERÄNDERLICHEN
By H. BEHNKE and P. THULLEN

—(Ergeb. der Math.) 1934. vii+115 pp. 5½x8½. [68] **$3.25**

LEHRBUCH DER FUNKTIONENTHEORIE
By L. BIEBERBACH

"One of the best introductions to the theory of functions of a complex variable. . . . scores of new problems, methods and results. **Indispensable for anyone interested in modern developments.**"
—*Bulletin of the A. M. S.*
OUT OF PRINT

CONFORMAL MAPPING
By L. BIEBERBACH

"The first book in English to give an elementary, readable account of the Riemann Mapping Theorem and the distortion theorems and uniformisation problem with which it is connected. . . . The fourth presented in very attractive and readable form."
—*Math. Gazette.*

". . . thorough and painstaking . . . lucid and clear and well arranged . . . an excellent text."
—*Bulletin of the A. M. S.*

Engineers will profitably use this book for its accurate exposition."—*Appl. Mechanics Reviews.*
—1952. vi + 234 pp. 4½x6½. [90] **$2.50**

BASIC GEOMETRY
By G. D. BIRKHOFF and R. BEATLEY

A highly recommended high-school text by two eminent scholars.
—Third edition. 1959. 294 pp. 5¼x8. [120] **$3.95**

KREIS UND KUGEL
By W. BLASCHKE

Isoperimetric properties of the circle and sphere, the (Brunn-Minkowski) theory of convex bodies, and differential-geometric properties (in the large) of convex bodies. A standard work.

—x + 169 pp. 5½x8½. [59] Cloth **$3.50**
[115] Paper **$1.50**

VORLESUNGEN ÜBER INTEGRAL-GEOMETRIE. Vols. I and II
By W. BLASCHKE
AND
EINFÜHRUNG IN DIE THEORIE DER SYSTEME VON DIFFERENTIALGLEI-CHUNGEN
By E. KÄHLER

—222 pp. 5½x8½. [64] Three Vols. in One **$4.50**

VORLESUNGEN ÜBER FOURIERSCHE INTEGRALE
By S. BOCHNER

"A readable account of those parts of the subject useful for applications to problems of mathematical physics or pure analysis."
—*Bulletin of the A. M. S.*

—1932. 237 pp. 5½x8½. Orig. publ. at $6.40. [42] **$4.50**

ALMOST PERIODIC FUNCTIONS
By H. BOHR

Translated by H. COHN. From the famous series *Ergebnisse der Mathematik und ihrer Grenzgebiete*, a beautiful exposition of the theory of Almost Periodic Functions written by the creator of that theory.

—1951. 120 pp. 6x9. Lithotyped. German edition was $4.50.
[27] **$2.50**

THEORIE DER KONVEXEN KÖRPER
By T. BONNESEN and W. FENCHEL

"Remarkable monograph."
—*J. D. Tamarkin, Bulletin of the A. M. S.*
—1934. 171 pp. 5½x8½. Orig. publ. at $7.50 [54] **$3.95**

A TREATISE ON DIFFERENTIAL EQUATIONS
By G. BOOLE

Including the Supplementary Volume.

—Fifth edition. 1959. xxiv + 735 pp. 5¼x8. [128] **$6.00**

THE CALCULUS OF FINITE DIFFERENCES
By G. BOOLE

A standard work on the subject of finite differences and difference equations by one of the seminal minds in the field of finite mathematics.

Some of the topics covered are: *Interpolation, Finite Integration, Summation of Series, General Theory of Difference and Differential Equations of First Order, Linear DEqns with Variable Coefficients, Linear DEqns, Geometrical Applications.*

Numerous exercises with answers.

—Fourth edition. 1958. xii+336 pp. 5x8.   [121]   **$4.95**

MEASURE AND INTEGRAL
By C. CARATHÉODORY

—About 360 pp. Translated from the German.   **In prep.**

THEORY OF FUNCTIONS
By C. CARATHÉODORY

Translated by F. STEINHARDT. The recent, and already famous textbook, *Funktionentheorie.*

Partial Contents: **Part One.** Chap. I. Algebra of Complex Numbers II. Geometry of Complex Numbers. III. Euclidean, Spherical, and Non-Euclidean Geometry. **Part Two.** Theorems from Point Set Theory and Topology. Chap. I. Sequences and Continuous Complex Functions. II. Curves and Regions. III. Line Integrals. **Part Three.** Analytic Functions. Chap. I. Foundations. II. The Maximum-modulus principle. III. Poisson Integral and Harmonic Functions. IV. Meromorphic Functions. **Part Four.** Generation of Analytic Functions by Limiting Processes. Chap. I. Uniform Convergence. II. Normal Families of Meromorphic Functions. III. Power Series. IV. Partial Fraction Decomposition and the Calculus of Residues. **Part Five.** Special Functions. Chap. I. The Exponential Function and the Trigonometric Functions. II. Logarithmic Function. III. Bernoulli Numbers and the Gamma Function.

Vol. II.: **Part Six.** Foundations of Geometric Function Theory. Chap. I. Bounded Functions. II. Conformal Mapping. III. The Mapping of the Boundary. **Part Seven.** The Triangle Function and Picard's Theorem. Chap. I. Functions of Several Complex Variables. II. Conformal Mapping of Circular-Arc Triangles. III. The Schwarz Triangle Functions and the Modular Function. IV. Essential Singularities and Picard's Theorems.

"A book by a master . . . Carathéodory himself regarded [it] as his finest achievement . . . written from a catholic point of view."—*Bulletin of A.M.S.*

—Vol. I. Second edition. 1958. 310 pp. 6x9.   [97]   **$4.95**
—Vol. II. 1954. 220 pp. 6x9.   [106]   **$4.95**

VORLESUNGEN ÜBER REELLE FUNKTIONEN
By C. CARATHÉODORY

This great classic is at once a book for the beginner, a reference work for the advanced scholar and
a source of inspiration for the research worker.

—2nd, latest complete, ed. 728 pp. 5½x8½. Orig. publ. at
$11.60. [38] **$8.00**

ELECTRIC CIRCUIT THEORY and the OPERATIONAL CALCULUS
By J. R. CARSON

"A rigorous and logical exposition and treatment
of the Heaviside operational calculus and its applications to electrical problems . . . will be enjoyed
and studied by mathematicians, engineers and
scientists."—*Electrical World.*

—2nd ed. 206 pp. 5¼x8. [92] Cloth **$3.95**
[114] Paper **$1.88**

TEXTBOOK OF ALGEBRA
By G. CHRYSTAL

The usefulness, both as a textbook and as a work
of reference, of this charming classic is attested
to by the number of editions it has run through—
the present being the sixth. Its richness of content
can be only appreciated by an examination of the
twelve-hundred-page book itself. **Thousands of
valuable exercises (with solutions).**

6th ed. 2 Vols. 1235 pages. 5⅜x8. [84] Two vol. set **$8.00**

EIGENWERTPROBLEME UND IHRE NUMERISCHE BEHANDLUNG
By L. COLLATZ

"**Part I** presents an interesting and valuable col-
lection of PRACTICAL APPLICATIONS.
"**Part II** deals with the MATHEMATICAL
THEORY.
"**Part III** takes up various methods of NUMER-
ICAL SOLUTION of boundary value problems.
These include step-by-step approximations, graph-
ical integration, the Rayleigh-Ritz method and
methods depending on finite differences. Here, as
throughout the book, the theory is kept in close
touch with practice by numerous specific examples."
—*Mathematical Reviews.*

—1945. 350 pp. 5½x8½. Orig. pub. at $8.80. [41] **$4.95**

ALGEBREN
By M. DEURING

—(Ergeb. der Math.) 1935. v+143 pp. 5½x8½. Orig. pub.
at $6.60. [50] **$3.95**

HISTORY OF THE THEORY OF NUMBERS
By L. E. DICKSON

"A monumental work . . . Dickson always has in mind the needs of the investigator . . . The author has [often] expressed in a nut-shell the main results of a long and involved paper *in a much clearer way than the writer of the article did himself*. The ability to reduce complicated mathematical arguments to simple and elementary terms is highly developed in Dickson."—*Bulletin of A. M. S.*

—Vol. I (Divisibility and Primality) xii+486 pp. Vol. II (Diophantine Analysis) xxv+803 pp. Vol. III (Quadratic and Higher Forms) v+313 pp. [86] Three vol. set **$23.50**

THE INTEGRAL CALCULUS
By J. W. EDWARDS

A leisurely, immensely detailed, textbook of over 1,900 pages, rich in illustrative examples and manipulative techniques and containing much interesting material that must of necessity be omitted from less comprehensive works.

There are forty large chapters in all. The earlier cover a leisurely and a more-than-usually-detailed treatment of all the elementary standard topics. Later chapters include: Jacobian Elliptic Functions, Weierstrassian Elliptic Functions, Evaluation of Definite Integrals, Harmonic Analysis, Calculus of Variations, etc. Every chapter contains many exercises (with solutions).

—2 vols. 1,922 pp. 5x8. Originally published at $31.50 the set. [102], [105] Each volume **$7.50**

AUTOMORPHIC FUNCTIONS
By L. R. FORD

"Comprehensive . . . remarkably clear and explicit."—*Bulletin of the A. M. S.*
—2nd ed. (Cor. repr.) x+333 pp. 5⅜x8. [85] **$4.95**

THE CALCULUS OF EXTENSION
By H. G. FORDER

Partial Contents: I. Plane Geometry. II. Geometry in Space. III. Applications to Projective Geometry. ... VIII. Applications to Systems of Linear Equations and Determinants. XII. Oriented Circle and Systems of Circles. XIII. The General Theory of Matrices ... XV. Algebraic Products..

—1941-60. xvi + 490 pp. 5⅜x8. [135] Summer, 1960. Probably **$4.95**

RUSSIAN MATHEMATICAL BIBLIOGRAPHY
By G. E. FORSYTHE

A bibliography of Russian Mathematics Books for the past quarter century. Supplements may be issued. Added subject index.
—1956. 106 pp. 5x8. [111] **$3.95**

THE THEORY OF MATRICES
By F. R. GANTMACHER

Translated from the Russian, with further revisions by the Author.

This treatise by one of Russia's leading mathematicians gives, in easily accessible form, a coherent account of matrix theory with a view to applications in mathematics, theoretical physics, statistics, electrical engineering, etc. The individual chapters have been kept as far as possble independent of each other, so that the reader acquainted with the contents of Chapter I can proceed immediately to the chapters that especially interest him. Much of the material has been available until now only in the periodical literature.

Partial Contents. VOL ONE. I. Matrices and Matrix Operations. II. The Algorithm of Gauss and Applications. III. Linear Operators in an n-Dimensional Vector Space. IV. Characteristic Polynomial and Minimal Polynomial of a Matrix (Generalized Bézout Theorem, Method of Faddeev for Simultaneous Computation of Coefficients of Characteristic Polynomial and Adjoint Matrix, ...). V. Functions of Matrices (Various Forms of the Definition, Components, Application to Integration of System of Linear Differential Eqns, Stability of Motion, ...). VI. Equivalent Transformations of Polynomial Matrices; Analytic Theory of Elementary Divisors. VII. The Structure of a Linear Operator in an n-Dimensional Space (Minimal Polynomial, Congruence, Factor Space, Jordan Form, Krylov's Method of Transforming Secular Eqn, ...). VIII. Matrix Equations (Matrix Polynomial Eqns, Roots and Logarithm of Matrices, ...). IX. Linear Operators in a Unitary Space. X. Quadratic and Hermitian Forms.

VOLUME TWO. XI. Complex Symmetric, Skew-symmetric, and Orthogonal Matrices. XII. Singular Pencils of Matrices. XIII. Matrices with Non-Negative Elements (General Properties, Spectral Properties, Reducible Matrices, Primitive and Imprimitive Matrices, Stochastic Matrices, Limiting Probabilities for Homogeneous Markov Chain, Totally Non-Negative Matrices, Oscillatory Matrices...). XIV. Applications of the Theory of Matrices to the Investigation of Systems of Linear Differential Equations (Systems with Variable Coefficients, Lyapunov Transformations, Reducible Systems, Erugin's Theorem, Multiplicative Integral, Volterra's Calculus, Differential Systems in Complex Domain, Analytic Functions of Several Matrices, The Research of Lappo-Danilevskii, ...). XV. The Problem of Routh-Hurwitz and Related Questions (Routh's Algorithm, Lyapunov's Theorem, Method of Quadratic Forms, Infinite Hankel Matrices of Finite Rank, Supplements to Routh-Hurwitz Theorem, Stability Criterion of Liénard and Chipart, Properties of Hurwitz Polynomials, Stieltjes' Theorem, Representation by Continued Fractions, Domain of Stability, Markov Parameters, Problem of Moments. Theorems of Markov and Chebyshev. Generalized Routh-Hurwitz Problem, ...). Bibliography.

—Vol. I. 1959. x + 374 pp. 6x9.   [131]   **$6.00**
—Vol. II. 1959. x + 277 pp. 6x9.   [133]   **$6.00**

LES INTÉGRALES DE STIELTJES et leurs Applications aux Problèmes de la Physique Mathématique

By N. GUNTHER

—1932. 498 pp. 5½x8 in. [63] **$5.95**

LEÇONS SUR LA PROPAGATION DES ONDES ET LES ÉQUATIONS DE L'HYDRODYNAMIQUE

By J. HADAMARD

"[Hadamard's] unusual analytic proficiency enables him to connect in a wonderful manner the physical problem of propagation of waves and the mathematical problem of Cauchy concerning the characteristics of partial differential equations of the second order."—*Bulletin of the A. M. S.*

—viii+375 pp. 5½x8½. [58] **$4.95**

REELLE FUNKTIONEN. Punktfunktionen

By H. HAHN

—426 pp. 5½x8½. Orig. pub. at $12.80. [52] **$5.50**

INTRODUCTION TO HILBERT SPACE AND THE THEORY OF SPECTRAL MULTIPLICITY

By P. R. HALMOS

Prof. Halmos' latest book gives a clear, readable introductory treatment of Hilbert Space. The multiplicity theory of continuous spectra is treated, for the first time in English, in full generality.

—1957. 2nd. ed. (c. repr. of 1st ed.). 120 pp. 6x9. [82] **$3.25**

RAMANUJAN:
Twelve Lectures on His Life and Works.

By G. H. HARDY

— viii + 236 pp. 6x9 [136] **$3.95**

GRUNDZÜGE DER MENGENLEHRE

By F. HAUSDORFF

Some of the topics in the Grundzüge omitted from later editions:

Symmetric Sets—Principle of Duality—most of the "Algebra" of Sets—most of the "Ordered Sets"—Partially Ordered Sets—Arbitrary Sets of Complexes—Normal Types—Initial and Final Ordering—Complexes of Real Numbers—General Topological Spaces—Euclidean Spaces—the Special Methods Applicable in the Euclidean plane—Jordan's separation Theorem—The Theory of Content and Measure—The Theory of the Lebesgue Integral.

—First edition. 484 pp. 5½x8¼. [61] **$4.95**